SCIENCE
ANNUAL

A Modern Science Anthology for the Family

1989

ACKNOWLEDGMENTS

Sources of articles appear below, including those reprinted with the kind permission of publications and organizations.

GUEST STARS ALWAYS WELCOME, Page 8: Reprinted with permission from NATURAL HISTORY, Vol. 96, No. 9; Copyright The American Museum of Natural History, 1987.

EXPLOSIONS IN THE SOLAR ATMOSPHERE, Page 14: Reprinted with permission from *Astronomy* magazine.

ROBOTS IN SPACE, Page 29: Reprinted with permission from THE FUTURIST, published by the World Future Society, 4916 Saint Elmo Avenue, Bethesda, MD 20814.

LEARNING TO LOVE GYM, Page 40: Copyright © 1987 by The New York Times Company. Reprinted by permission.

THE HYPNOTIC TRANCE, Page 47: Reprinted by permission from the March/April 1987 issue of *The Sciences*, published by the New York Academy of Sciences, 2 East 63rd St., New York, NY 10021.

MIXED MESSAGES FROM THE MEDIA, p. 54: Reprinted by permission of PREVENTION. Copyright 1987, Rodale Press, Inc. All rights reserved.

BORN TO BE SHY?, Page 58: Reprinted with permission from PSYCHOLOGY TODAY magazine. Copyright © 1987 American Psychological Association.

A SENSE OF SCENTS, Page 70: Article first appeared in the July/August 1987 issue of THE CONSERVATIONIST.

THE LORDS OF THE FLIES, Page 75: Shannon Brownlee/DISCOVER © 1987, Family Media, Inc.

DRUGS FROM THE SEA, Page 82: Reprinted from *Pacific Discovery,* the quarterly science magazine of the California Academy of Sciences.

THE DEADLY GAME OF STEROIDS, Page 89: Reprinted from *FDA Consumer,* November 1987, U.S. Food and Drug Administration.

BIG BROTHER MAY BE WATCHING, Page 100: Reprinted from February 9, 1987, issue of *Business Week* by special permission, copyright © 1987 by McGraw-Hill, Inc.

SOFTWARE CATCHES THE TEAM SPIRIT, Page 106: Reprinted with permission, FORTUNE, © 1987 Time Inc. All rights reserved.

COMPUTERS IN THE CLASSROOM, Page 112: Reprinted with permission from *Technology Review,* copyright 1987.

BATS AND STATS, Page 119: Babe Cipher/*Discover* magazine © 1987 Discover Publications Inc.

AVERTING AVALANCHES, Page 130: Reprinted through the courtesy of Halsey Publishing Co., publishers of *Echelon* magazine.

MASTERING THE MICROBURST, Page 136: Reprinted with permission from SCIENCE NEWS, the weekly newsmagazine of science, copyright 1987 by Science Service, Inc.

UNDERWATER CANYONS, Page 142: Reprinted from *Popular Science* with permission © 1987 Times Mirror Magazines, Inc.

PIONEERING MIDDLE EARTH, Page 148: Copyright 1987 by Bill Lawren and reprinted with permission of Omni Publications International Ltd.

COPING WITH BLACKOUTS, Page 165: Reprinted with permission of the author; article first appeared in SMITHSONIAN, February 1987.

TRANSFORMING THE SEA WIND, Page 179: Reprinted with permission of the author; article first appeared in the October 1987 issue of *Oceans.*

ECOLOGY OF THE CANOPY, Page 190: Copyright © 1988 by The New York Times Company. Reprinted by permission.

A DEAD CHIEF'S REVENGE?, Page 198: Reprinted with permission from NATURAL HISTORY, Vol. 96, No. 8; Copyright The American Museum of Natural History, 1987.

HAZARDS OF THE GAME, Page 206: Reprinted with permission of the author; article first appeared in *Audubon,* the magazine of the National Audubon Society.

FOREST IN THE DUNES, Page 214: Reprinted by permission from *Sea Frontiers,* © 1987 by the International Oceanographic Foundation, 3979 Rickenbacker Causeway, Virginia Key, Miami, FL 33149.

MEDICINE'S NEW SUPERSLEUTHS, Page 224: Reprinted through the courtesy of Halsey Publishing Co., publishers of SKY magazine.

ANATOMY OF A HEADACHE, Page 232: Reprinted with permission of the author; article first appeared in SMITHSONIAN, December 1987.

A CURE FOR MYOPIA?, Page 245: Reprinted, with permission, from *Consumers' Research* magazine, Washington, D.C.

REAPPRAISING THE DINOSAURS, Page 256: Copyright 1987 by the National Wildlife Federation. Reprinted from the December–January 1987 issue of NATIONAL WILDLIFE magazine.

STAFF

EDITORIAL

Editorial Director
Bernard S. Cayne

Executive Editor
Joseph M. Castagno

Managing Editor
Doris E. Lechner

Copy Editors
David M. Buskus
Ronald B. Roth

Proofreaders
Stephan Romanoff
Meghan O'Reilly

Chief Indexer
Jill Schuler

Manuscript Typist
Jeannette Piastuch

Art Assistant
Elizabeth Farrington

Art Director
Eric E. Akerman

Production Editor
Diane L. George

Staff Assistant
Jennifer Pickett Vogt

Manager, Picture Library
Jane H. Carruth

Chief, Photo Research
Ann Eriksen

Photo Researcher
Paula J. Kobylarz

Photo Assistant
Renee L. Sturges

MANUFACTURING

Director of Manufacturing
Joseph J. Corlett

Production Manager
Teresa Kluk

Production Assistant
Barbara L. Persan

CONTRIBUTORS

KATHERINE AMBRUS, Contributing editor, *The Conservationist*
A SENSE OF SCENTS

JULES ASHER, Free-lance science writer
BORN TO BE SHY?

JOHN BARBER, Senior writer, *Maclean's*
RELAUNCHING THE AIRSHIP

ALISON B. BASS, Senior editor, *Technology Review*
COMPUTERS IN THE CLASSROOM

BRUCE BOWER, Staff writer, *Science News*
REVIEW OF THE YEAR: BEHAVIORAL SCIENCES

SHANNON BROWNLEE, Staff writer, *Discover*
THE LORDS OF THE FLIES

TOM CALLAHAN, Free-lance writer, skier, and former Outward Bound instructor
AVERTING AVALANCHES

ANTHONY J. CASTAGNO, Energy consultant; manager, nuclear information, Northeast Utilities, Hartford, CT
REVIEW OF THE YEAR: ENERGY

JAMES R. CHILES, Free-lance writer specializing in technology
THE CABLE UNDER THE SEA
TITANIUM THE MAGNIFICENT

ERIK ECKHOLM, Deputy science and health editor, *The New York Times*
ECOLOGY OF THE CANOPY

JOLEE EDMONDSON, Free lance journalist; award-winning author of two golf books; contributor to *Golf Digest* and other national magazines
HAZARDS OF THE GAME

DIANE D. EDWARDS, Life sciences/biomedicine editor, *Science News*
RECALL OF THE WILD WOLF

A. GORDON EMSLIE, Associate professor of physics, University of Alabama, Huntsville
EXPLOSIONS IN THE SOLAR ATMOSPHERE

ANNE R. FIELD, Staff editor, *Business Week*
BIG BROTHER MAY BE WATCHING

ARTHUR FISHER, Science and technology editor, *Popular Science*
THE WORLD'S BIGGEST MACHINE

JOHN FREE, Senior editor, *Popular Science*
Coauthor, ELECTRONIC ESPIONAGE

NAOMI FREUNDLICH, Associate editor, *Popular Science*
Coauthor, ELECTRONIC ESPIONAGE

ROBERT GANNON, Consulting science editor, *Popular Science*
UNDERWATER CANYONS

C. P. GILMORE, Editor-in-chief, *Popular Science*
Coauthor, ELECTRONIC ESPIONAGE

JEFFREY H. HACKER, Free-lance writer
RUNNING ON SUNSHINE
GARBAGE IN, ENERGY OUT

KATHERINE HARAMUNDANIS, Free-lance writer formerly with Smithsonian Astrophysical Laboratory, Cambridge, MA; coauthor, *An Introduction to Astronomy*
REVIEW OF THE YEAR: ASTRONOMY

GLADWIN HILL, National environmental correspondent—retired, *The New York Times*
REVIEW OF THE YEAR: THE ENVIRONMENT

JOHN HOLMES, Writer, *Insight* magazine
A MOST ENLIGHTENING EXPERIMENT

ROBERT J. HUTCHINSON, Free-lance writer; currently an editor, *Hawaii* magazine
TRANSFORMING THE SEA WIND

EMILY GREENSPAN KELTING, Author, *Little Winners: Inside the World of the Child Sports Star*
LEARNING TO LOVE GYM

EDWIN KIESTER, JR., Free-lance writer specializing in medicine and science
ANATOMY OF A HEADACHE

MARC KUSINITZ, Free-lance science writer
REVIEW OF THE YEAR: PHYSICAL SCIENCES

BILL LAWREN, Contributing editor, *Omni*
PIONEERING MIDDLE EARTH

HARVEY B. LILLYWHITE, Professor of zoology, University of Florida, Gainesville
SNAKES UNDER PRESSURE

DENNIS L. MAMMANA, Free-lance science writer; director of production and resident astronomer, Reuben H. Fleet Space Theater & Science Center, San Diego, CA
REVIEW OF THE YEAR: SPACE SCIENCE
BIOSPHERE II

DOWNS MATTHEWS, Contributing editor, *The Lamp*
A PLETHORA OF PINNIPEDS

WILLIAM H. MATTHEWS III, Regents' professor of geology emeritus, Lamar University, Beaumont, TX
REVIEW OF THE YEAR: EARTH SCIENCES

ADRIENNE MAYOR, Free-lance writer, editor, and artist
MARINE MIRAGES

MARTIN M. McLAUGHLIN, Free-lance consultant; former vice president for education, Overseas Development Council, Washington, DC
Coauthor, REVIEW OF THE YEAR: PAST, PRESENT, AND FUTURE

ROGER W. MILLER, Director, communications staff, U.S. Food and Drug Administration
THE DEADLY GAME OF STEROIDS

RICHARD MONASTERSKY, Earth sciences editor, *Science News*
MASTERING THE MICROBURST

MICHAEL J. MOONEY, Free-lance writer/photographer specializing in the environment, oceanography, and meteorology
FOREST IN THE DUNES

VIRGINIA MORELL, Contributor, *National Wildlife* magazine
REAPPRAISING THE DINOSAURS

JOHN NIELSEN, Free-lance writer; science and technology reporter, *The Orange County Register,* California
LAST CHANCE FOR THE CONDOR

JANA PACE, Free-lance writer
A CURE FOR MYOPIA?

MICHAEL PARFIT, Writer; author of *South Light: A Journey to the Last Continent* and *The Boys behind the Bombs*
COPING WITH BLACKOUTS

ELAINE PASCOE, Free-lance writer
THE 1987 NOBEL PRIZE FOR PHYSIOLOGY OR MEDICINE
THE 1987 NOBEL PRIZES FOR PHYSICS AND CHEMISTRY
REVIEW OF THE YEAR: TECHNOLOGY
IN MEMORIAM

CATHY PERLMUTTER, Contributor, *Prevention*
MIXED MESSAGES FROM THE MEDIA

JIM PETTIGREW, JR., Movie buff; writer on new technology and entertainment
BEYOND THE BIJOU

ANTHONY RAMIREZ, Associate editor, *Fortune*
SUPERCONDUCTORS GET DOWN TO BUSINESS

LOUIS S. RICHMAN, Associate editor, *Fortune*
SOFTWARE CATCHES THE TEAM SPIRIT

JAMES L. SCHEFTER, West Coast editor, *Popular Science*
REVIEW OF THE YEAR: COMPUTERS AND MATHEMATICS

ROBERT L. SCHEINA, Historian, U.S. Coast Guard
THE *TITANIC*'S LEGACY TO SAFETY

HARALDUR SIGURDSSON, Professor of oceanography, University of Rhode Island, Narragansett Bay
A DEAD CHIEF'S REVENGE?

JOANNE SILBERNER, Associate editor, health, *U.S. News & World Report*
REVIEW OF THE YEAR: BIOLOGY

ELEANOR SMITH, Free-lance writer specializing in health and science
DRUGS FROM THE SEA

DAVID SPIEGEL, Associate professor of psychiatry and director of the adult psychiatric outpatient clinic, Stanford University Medical Center, California
THE HYPNOTIC TRANCE

F. RICHARD STEPHENSON, Astronomer and senior research fellow, Department of Physics, University of Durham, Durham, England
GUEST STARS ALWAYS WELCOME

BOB STROHM, Executive editor, *National Wildlife* magazine
REVIEW OF THE YEAR: WILDLIFE

JENNY ELIZABETH TESAR, Free-lance science and medical writer; author, *Parents as Teachers, Introduction to Animals, Preparing for the SAT and Other Aptitude Tests*
REVIEW OF THE YEAR: HEALTH AND DISEASE
LYME DISEASE

TERRI THOMPSON, Department editor, energy, *Business Week*
THE MUSIC OF HIGH TECH

GARY TURBAK, Contributor, *National Wildlife* magazine
THE SHY BOBCAT SURVIVES

BERNIE WARD, Professional writer; author or coauthor of six books on sports and organized crime
MEDICINE'S NEW SUPERSLEUTHS

LELLAND A. C. WEAVER, Director of industrial research and development programs, Westinghouse R&D Center, Pittsburgh, PA
ROBOTS IN SPACE

PETER S. WELLS, Director, Center for Ancient Studies, University of Minnesota, Minneapolis
Coauthor, REVIEW OF THE YEAR: PAST, PRESENT, AND FUTURE

CONTENTS

ASTRONOMY
AND
SPACE SCIENCE

The orbiter Atlantis, *the latest addition to NASA's fleet of space shuttles, emerges from the Vehicle Assembly Building at Kennedy Space Center. NASA plans to resume an ambitious schedule of shuttle flights later this year.*

AP/Wide World

REVIEW
OF THE
YEAR

ASTRONOMY AND SPACE SCIENCE

Repercussions from the 1986 *Challenger* space shuttle disaster continued to be felt by astronomers and space explorers. Analyses of astronomical phenomena were severely hampered by a lack of appropriate space observation platforms and repeated launch failures. This problem was particularly evident when the sudden appearance of a supernova early in 1987 set off a worldwide scramble for observing time on telescopes, airborne observation platforms, and orbiting satellites to study the critical phases of supernova development before they had past.

THE SUPERNOVA

Supernova 1987A (or SN 1987A) was undoubtedly the most talked-about astronomical event of 1987. The supernova was discovered accidently by Ian K. Shelton of the University of Toronto while he was photographing the Large Magellanic Cloud from Las Campanas Observatory in Chile. SN 1987A is the first supernova visible to the naked eye since 1604.

Supernovas—stars that explode with exceptional brilliance—represent a special case of star growth and provide unique opportunities for astronomers to understand many aspects of stellar evolution and structure. Prior to its

collapse, the supernova had been a B3 Ia star with a temperature as high as 29,325° F (16,000° Kelvin) and a mass 15 to 19 times that of the Sun. SN 1987A did not behave as expected: it brightened rapidly, dimmed quickly, and then brightened again. At its second brightening, a mysterious object redder than the supernova— perhaps a new star created by the explosion— was observed. Much material has been detected flying out from the supernova; once this material thins out, the pulsar expected to be seen at the center should become visible. (See also page 8.)

THE SOLAR SYSTEM

New observations of Pluto and its companion Charon have helped to redefine their sizes and determine the compositions of their atmospheres. Pluto measures about 1,425 miles (2,300 kilometers) in diameter, has an atmosphere of methane, polar caps of methane ice, and a temperature of about 50° K (−369° F or −223° C); Charon is smaller, with a diameter of 800 miles (1,280 kilometers), an atmosphere of water ice, and a temperature of about 58° K (−355° F or −215° C). Pluto's polar caps appear to undergo seasonal changes; the Pluto/Charon system is about one-fifth the mass of the Moon, much smaller than previously thought. ■ Search continues for Planet X, a supposed undiscovered tenth planet some astronomers believe is responsible for unexplained discrepancies in the orbits of Uranus, Neptune, and Pluto. The search progressed this year using analyses of the paths of Pioneers 10 and 11, which are now leaving the solar system in opposite directions; so far no evidence of the supposed planet has been found. The proposed Planet X would be 5 times more massive than Earth and take almost 1,000 years to orbit the solar system, traveling a highly elliptical orbit inclined at least 30 degrees from the plane in which the planets move. Some suggest Planet X must be an interloper from outside the solar system. ■ Skyflux observations made by IRAS (InfraRed Astronomical Satellite) found many moving objects at high galactic latitudes that are neither known comets nor asteroids. The observed dust trails tend to lie in the ecliptic, the plane in which the planets move. These numerous trails are likely created by undiscovered short-period comets or asteroids. ■ Evidence of the role of impact cratering in many solar system phenomena continues to grow. Impacts have caused some aspects of mass extinction, generated fragments of matter that are exchanged between the bodies of the solar system, and may have plausibly created objects such as the Moon. New craters formed by impacts continue to be identified on Earth, at least one on the continental shelf.

THE MILKY WAY GALAXY

Numerous observations continue to confirm the presence of protoplanetary disks surrounding stars in our galaxy. In one case a star may have a companion "brown dwarf." The stars Beta Pictoris, HL Tauri, and T Tauri, all classic variable stars of known type, each appear to be surrounded by a disk of matter. Some observations suggest Beta Pictoris has a dark companion rather than a disk. Vega is also known to have such a disk, as are 20 young stars in Taurus; researchers now estimate that about 15 percent of young stars in our galaxy are surrounded by such disks. A brown dwarf may be the companion of Giclas 29–38, a star located in the constellation Pisces. The infrared observations indicate that while Giclas 29–38, a white dwarf, has a temperature of 1,628° F (877° C), its "brown" companion is only 1,700° F (927° C). The object is probably about 40 to 80 times the mass of Jupiter, or about 15 percent of the Sun's diameter. Brown dwarfs are believed to comprise the bulk of "cold dark matter," which is said to make up 80 to 90 percent of the matter in the universe. What we see when we observe the stars and galaxies is only 10 to 20 percent of the mass; thus, finding any direct evidence of cold dark matter is critical to our understanding of the universe. Brown dwarfs are thought to be objects with a mass so small they do not become stars. They are nonetheless more massive than typical planets, and perhaps were formed by fragmentation and condensation in interstellar clouds. Unlike red dwarfs, the lowest-mass "true" stars, brown dwarfs cannot sustain steady nuclear burning of hydrogen. Planets are thought to form in accretion disks around stars and generate no energy by fusion. Hypothetical brown dwarfs have masses 10 to 80 times that of Jupiter. Earlier optical observations of stars such as Barnard's star and VanBiesbroeck 8 appeared to detect wobbles indicating dark, planetlike companions, although these findings have not been confirmed independently. Very low-mass companions are suggested for Gamma Cephei, a binary star with a planet in a 2.7-year orbit; Epsilon Eridani, the red dwarf Gliese 623 with a companion about 90 times the mass of Jupiter; and Gliese 569, a relatively young star. ■ PSR 1821–24, a unique pulsar, is believed to have no companion as required by theory. Embedded in globular cluster Messier 28/NGC 6628, the pulsar may feed on energy from the globular cluster itself. ■ The extended Lick Northern Proper Motion program, which began in 1947 and is now 97 percent complete, has analyzed the data of 60,000 of 300,000 stars using a background reference frame of external galaxies. The program discovered a third major component in the structure of our galaxy. Earlier theory described our galaxy as a central sphere with a flat outer disk surrounding it; stars in the central sphere are old and do not rotate around the core of the galaxy, while those in the disk rotate in streams on roughly circular tracks. The new third component appears to be made of blue stars that participate in galactic rotation but move much more slowly than the disk population. Within our own galaxy, the best-known candidate for a black hole, Cygnus X-1, emitted massive bursts of gamma rays. The observations confirm the model of a dense black hole surrounded by a disk of matter sucked out of its companion supergiant. As material falls in toward the black hole, it is heated to 1 billion degrees F (5 billion degrees Kelvin), and gives off bursts of energy. Cygnus X-1, at 40 solar masses, provides insight into the million-solar-mass black hole at the center of our galaxy, and the billion-solar-mass black holes that power quasars. ■ Compact dark structures never seen before have been found in a program observing 36 quasars; the objects are elongated, 500 to 1,000 times more numerous than stars, and may represent further examples of cold dark matter in our galaxy.

THE UNIVERSE

Quasars with greater redshifts than earlier seen have been found. Two quasars, with redshifts of 4.07 and 4.43, respectively, near the South Galactic Pole may be orbiting each other, while a third (redshift 4.4) was accidentally discovered during observations of a radio galaxy. So far, over 20 quasars with these higher redshifts have been found; an object with a redshift over 4 is moving at greater than 90 percent the speed of light. ■ A protogalaxy may have been observed for the first time. Dubbed 3C 326.1, it may be two-thirds of the way back to time zero and just beginning to form. We see it today as it looked 12 billion years ago; it is creating up to 5,000 new stars per year (about 1,000 times faster than a mature galaxy

Cosmonaut Yuri Romanenko (above) returned to Earth after a record 326 days in space. On a separate mission, Soviet space monkey Yerosha (Russian for "troublemaker") created havoc when, after freeing a paw, it played with anything it could touch.

such as our own), has a mass of about 100 billion suns, and is 100 billion times more luminous than the Sun. This galaxy is about three times bigger than our own. While previously it was thought that most galaxies formed in the first 100 million years of the universe, this case shows that galaxies continued to form even 12 billion years after the "Big Bang." ■ Markarian 348, an odd-shaped spiral galaxy perhaps 13 times the size of the Milky Way, may be the largest galaxy known, with a diameter of 1.3 million light-years (our own galaxy, by comparison, is only 100,000 light-years across). ■ Large-scale structures of the universe have begun to be found. Rich clusters of galaxies appear to be embedded in structures of much larger scale, such as shell surfaces, while galaxies appear to be distributed on thin sheets surrounding voids.

KATHERINE HARAMUNDANIS

A CHANGE IN MOMENTUM

The year was characterized by a continued shift in momentum between the two traditional space superpowers.

The National Aeronautics and Space Administration's (NASA's) annual budget was less than 1 percent of the U.S. federal budget, compared with nearly 4 percent two decades ago. During 1987 NASA scheduled only six launchings—half of which were completed, but only two of which were successful.

By contrast, the Soviet Union flew 80 missions during the year. The Soviets have a space station in orbit, are developing a reuseable shuttle, and

launch four to five times more payloads each year than the U.S., with a far greater lift capacity. In 1988 they will embark on the first of a series of Mars missions, with the goal of launching a sample-return flight before the end of the century.

U.S. SPACE PROGRAM

The U.S. took a positive step, however, when nearly two years of back-to-back Titan rocket failures ended with the successful February launch of a Titan 3B, followed by a Titan 34D nine months later. But the news was dominated by shuttle modification and testing. During the year, scientists chose the final design for the new booster rockets and O-ring seals that caused the *Challenger* accident in 1986. In February, shuttle astronauts began their first training since the accident. Another milestone was reached when the shuttle *Discovery* was powered up for testing. These events provided a spark of life in an otherwise comatose space program.

NASA officials remained optimistic, however, and announced an ambitious schedule of flights for upcoming years. These include the launching of the Hubble Space Telescope, the Galileo mission to Jupiter, the Ulysses solar observatory, the Mars Observer, the Magellan radar-mapping of Venus, and the Tracking and Data Relay Satellite.

SOVIET UNION PROGRAM

On October 4, 1987, the Space Age was 30 years old. On that day three decades earlier, the Russian craft Sputnik I became the first artificial satellite to orbit Earth. In celebration of this historic event, and in its new spirit of *glasnost* (openness), the U.S.S.R. hosted the Space Future Forum, a three-day extravaganza of seminars and speeches, attended by several hundred invited scientists, journalists, and space artists from around the world. The February launch of Colonel Yuri V. Romanenko to the U.S.S.R.'s Mir station on a new Soyuz TM-2 craft was carried live on Soviet television—only the second time in history the U.S.S.R. televised such an event.

In December, Romanenko returned from the station in which he had lived and worked for a record 326 days. The fatigue, homesickness, and muscle deterioration experienced by the 43-year-old cosmonaut suggest that the upper limit to safe spaceflight in weightlessness may be two years. But all was not positive in the Soviet space program. Their highly successful Proton booster program suffered major setbacks on January 30 and April 24, when the fourth and uppermost stages malfunctioned and stranded their communication-satellite payloads in low and useless orbits. And Energia, a booster as powerful as the U.S.'s Saturn V, failed during its first field test in May, when its dummy payload plunged into the Pacific Ocean.

NO LONGER A MONOPOLY

The "superpowers" no longer have the last word in space technology, as programs are appearing on nearly every continent.

The active European Space Agency (ESA), with an annual budget of over $1 billion, is developing the Hermes spaceplane and the Columbus space station, along with the free-flying platform Eureca B. In June, Japan announced plans to develop a futuristic shuttle/spaceplane that will take off and land on a conventional runway. Also on the Japanese drawing boards are a small colony of space platforms and a space station and orbiting factory for developing such products as ultrafast semiconductors and pure drugs that can be produced only in low-gravity environments. China has created an active manned-spaceflight program, and is studying ways it might use the U.S./international space station once it is operational in the next decade. Also entering the space arena is South America. Brazil is assisting the U.S., France, Canada, West Germany, and the ESA in a number of projects, but has built an active program of its own, including plans to construct and launch four satellites over the next six years. Chile, meanwhile, has contributed to the U.S. space program by completing in February a contingency runway on Easter Island to handle aborted U.S. shuttle launches from Vandenberg Air Force Base in California.

SYGMA

The U.S. successfully launched two Titan rockets in 1987, ending a two-year series of back-to-back rocket failures.

MARKETING SPACE

With the U.S. space program temporarily grounded, government-backed projects in both Western Europe and Asia are rushing into the commercial space market. China is marketing its new Long March boosters. Comparable in power to the U.S. Saturn 1B, these rockets can deploy a 20-ton payload into low-Earth orbit. They will be launched from a pad now being constructed in southwestern China. The commercial launchers of the ESA are back on track after a major failure in 1986 caused a 15½-month grounding of the Ariane rockets. On September 15, 1987, an Ariane 3 rocket rose from Earth and launched the ESA back into the lucrative commercial-satellite business by successfully deploying two Australian communications satellites. The Soviets, meanwhile, are selling everything from satellites to rides on rockets to rockets themselves, and are providing a low-cost alternative to those of the U.S., ESA, and China. They are marketing seven different rockets, for half to a quarter of the price of other nations. They also are making available high-resolution satellite photos of the Earth for $500 to $800. For the first time, private industry is getting heavily into the act. American Rocket Developments (AMROC) has emerged as one of only two start-up companies in the U.S. that have a chance to launch a payload into orbit within the next year or so. They promise a relatively inexpensive service—$8 million per launching, compared with an estimated $50 million by competitors. Even the conservative Japanese construction industry has entered the market. Shimizu Construction Company has formed a space-development project team to study building techniques for use in space.

DENNIS L. MAMMANA

7

GUEST STARS *Always Welcome*

by F. Richard Stephenson

The recent explosion of a star in the Large Magellanic Cloud, a satellite galaxy of our Milky Way, is a reminder that the seemingly orderly universe can at times be very violent. So far from Earth that the light from the explosion took about 170,000 years to reach us, the star became clearly visible to the unaided eye in the Southern Hemisphere for several weeks following its discovery February 23, 1987. At maximum brilliance, it was radiating 100 million times as much energy as the Sun.

Stellar explosions on a scale this great are known as supernovas. They have catastrophic consequences for the star involved. In what is known as a Type I explosion, the entire star is blown apart. The current supernova is a Type II—the spontaneous collapse of a fairly massive star at the end of its active life, when all the hydrogen in its core has been transformed into helium and heavier elements and the nuclear reactions in its core have ceased. The outer layers of the star are then blown off into space, and the core collapses into a superdense neutron star, composed primarily of neutrons—atomic particles that have no charge.

Supernovas are rare. The Milky Way contains about 100,000 million stars, yet one of these huge stellar explosions typically occurs only three or four times a century in our galaxy. They are observed even less frequently, because

Astronomers and stargazers alike rejoiced when the star-like glow of a supernova blazed into view over the southern sky in February 1987. The supernova—the first such occurrence since 1604—gives scientists a once-in-a-lifetime opportunity to study the composition of stars.

clouds of galactic dust tend to obscure them. Thus, we usually don't notice a supernova unless it is relatively near Earth. Although the supernova in the Large Magellanic Cloud is outside of our galaxy, it was readily seen, since its light path avoided much of the obscuring dust in the Milky Way.

Historical Detective Work

As the result of careful telescopic searches, several new supernovas are detected every year in distant galaxies. But the last such event known to have been seen in our galaxy occurred in 1604, five years before the advent of telescopic astronomy. For descriptions of supernovas that occurred in our neighborhood, we therefore have to rely on observations made with the unaided eye. Nevertheless, the remnants of those explosions can now be detected with radio telescopes and X-ray satellites hundreds or even thousands of years after the original outburst. Historical detective work, especially in Oriental chronicles, can confirm the original appearance of supernovas whose aftereffects are now detectable with modern instruments.

From at least as early as 200 B.C., Chinese emperors employed official astronomers to keep a regular watch of the sky, both night and day, and to interpret any unusual celestial omens. Although the main motive for observation was astrological, the stargazers of ancient and medieval China have left many useful records of comets, supernovas, and other rare phenomena. Summaries of the reports of the Chinese astronomers are readily available today in the officially compiled dynastic histories that cover the entire period between 200 B.C. and the 17th century A.D. By about A.D. 1000, Korean and Japanese astronomers maintained a watch of the sky following the pattern adopted in China. From then on, it is not unusual to find several independent descriptions of the same phenomenon.

Chinese astronomers had a special term for comets with evident tails, *hui-hsing* (broom star). A comet with a less obvious tail was usually described as a *po-hsing* (bushy star), while an unusual starlike object was customarily termed a *k'o-hsing* (guest star). The modern astronomer-detective cannot assume, however, that all guest stars were supernovas. The term guest star was usually applied to stellar explosions, but comets and supernovas were sometimes mistaken for each other, although comets move across the sky.

Novas versus Supernovas

Even if we can be sure that a guest star did not move, it might have been a "mere" nova—that is, the sudden, irregular brightening of a binary star. Although not in the same league as a supernova, a nova explosion is still on a vast scale compared with the light output of a normal star. At peak brilliance the output may exceed 100,000 suns for several days.

A major difference between the two types of exploding stars lies in the intensity of the radiation emitted by their remnants after the outburst itself has subsided. The remains of supernovas are among the most powerful sources of radio waves and X rays in the sky and remain active for many thousands of years. By comparison, the remains of novas are very feeble radiation emitters and are barely detectable even with modern instruments.

About 150 supernova remnants in our galaxy have been discovered by radio and X-ray astronomers. The true nature of a supernova can be readily recognized by the type of radiation it emits. The remnants have very strong magnetic fields and behave like giant particle accelerators, producing nonthermal radiation.

Potential supernovas can usually be identified in early records by how long they were visible. Modern observations of supernovas appearing in galaxies outside the Milky Way show that they fade very slowly after attaining peak brightness. This was an obvious characteristic of the recent outburst in the Large Magellanic Cloud. Hence we would expect a supernova in our own galaxy that was bright enough to be seen by the unaided eye to remain visible for many months or even years. Ordinary novas, on the other hand, tend to wane rapidly after maximum, and furthermore, the greater the real brightness of the star, the faster it declines. For these reasons, studies of historical supernovas are best restricted to those guest stars that remained visible for more than about six months.

Sightings from the Orient

Historical records, mainly from the Orient, reveal that over the past 2,000 years, as many as eight stellar outbursts have remained visible to

Ian K. Shelton of the University of Toronto accidentally discovered Supernova 1987A while he was photographing the Large Magellanic Cloud from Las Campanas Observatory in Chile.

© Vera A. Lentz/Visions

the unaided eye for at least six months. Seven of these appeared either within or close to the track of the Milky Way and thus rate as good supernova candidates. They appeared in A.D. 185 (in Centaurus), 393 (in Scorpius), 1006 (in Lupus), 1054 (in Taurus), 1181 (in Cassiopeia), 1572 (also in Cassiopeia), and 1604 (in Ophiuchus). In the case of the two earliest guest stars, only a single report of each is available, and celestial locations are rather vague. For the five stars seen since A.D. 1000, however, several independent records still survive. These give sufficiently precise positions to enable us to establish a link with a present-day supernova remnant in every case.

On the evening of April 30, 1006 (on the Julian calendar), the brightest supernova on record shone forth. Discovered by astronomers in Egypt, the star was detected the following night in both China and Japan and was also seen in various parts of Europe. One of the most careful Chinese accounts is contained in the astronomical treatise of the official history of the Sun dynasty (960–1279).

Arab and European records testify to the extreme brilliance of the star. A Baghdad observer wrote that "its rays on the earth were like the rays of the moon," while in Egypt it was said that "the sky was shining because of its light; the intensity was a little more than a quarter of that of moonlight." Lupus is a southern constellation, and the star would not have been visible in the more northerly parts of Europe. Yet in Switzerland, where the supernova barely skimmed the southern horizon, it was described by one stargazer as "glittering in aspect and dazzling the eyes." From these various descriptions, it would seem that at maximum brilliance, the star was about as bright as the half-moon. It was thus vastly more luminous than Venus, which often dominates the evening or morning sky.

Combining individual estimates of position gives a location for the supernova near the star Beta in Lupus. Only two known supernova remnants lie anywhere near this site. One of these is the Lupus Loop, a very old remnant that must have been expanding for up to about 100,000 years to reach its present extensive size. The other remnant is much more compact and about 1,000 years old. It was discovered in 1965 with the 210-foot (64-meter)-diameter radio telescope at Parkes in New South Wales. That remnant, known as PKS 1459–41, has since been detected in both X rays and visible light. Its distance from us is estimated at only about 3,000 light-years, and there is little absorption of light by galactic dust clouds in its direction. This same condition would account for the great brilliance of the supernova of 1006.

The Supernova of 1054

A guest star that appeared in 1054 must surely be known to everyone with an interest in astronomy. Although much fainter than its predecessor in 1006, its remnant—the Crab nebula—is one of the strongest sources of radio waves and X rays in the sky. The original outburst was noticed in Constantinople (Istanbul), but the only useful observations were made by the astronomers of China and Japan. The following three extracts from Chinese histories during the Sung dynasty contain the main details (I have converted the dates to the Julian calendar):

July 4, 1054: "A guest star appeared approximately several inches [a fraction of a degree] to the southeast of T'ien-kuan. After more than a year it gradually vanished."

August 27, 1054: "Earlier, in July, the guest star appeared in the morning at the east, guarding T'ien-kuan. It was visible in the day, like Venus. It had pointed rays on all sides and its color was pink. Altogether it was visible [in daylight] for 23 days."

April 6, 1056: "The Director of the Astronomical Bureau reported that since July 1054 a guest star had appeared in the morning at the east, guarding T'ien-kuan and now vanished."

In order to be visible in daylight, the guest star must have been about as bright as Venus—as the second text states. There are, however, no indications of extreme brilliance, unlike the outburst in 1006. The position of the guest star is carefully described, for T'ien-kuan was equivalent to the rather isolated star Zeta in Taurus. Japanese observers also stated that the guest star "flared up at T'ien-kuan." There is nothing to suggest any movement of the star during the 21 months of visibility, so a comet can be ruled out. Likewise, such a long duration is much more characteristic of a supernova than a nova.

Nebular Remnants

The Crab nebula is the only supernova remnant found in the vicinity of Zeta Tauri. A faint patch of light a little to the northwest (not southeast) of Zeta Tauri, the Crab nebula was discovered by the English astronomer William Bevis in 1731. But it was not until 1928 that Edwin Hubble, the American astronomer, first linked that object with the stellar outburst of 1054. Interest in the Crab nebula (so named by the 19-century British observer Lord Rosse) was heightened by the discovery of radio emission from it in 1948. It is now known to contain a pulsar (a rapidly rotating neutron star that emits flashes of radiation), the product of a Type II supernova, and to emit vast quantities of radiation to all wavelengths, from short gamma rays to longer radio waves. Its total power output, about 100,000 times that of the Sun, is mostly produced by the pulsar, which rotates 30 times every second (a normal star rotates once every few days).

Photographs taken a few decades apart reveal the rapid expansion of the Crab nebula and indicate that the initial explosion occurred about 900 years ago. The only evidence that seems to contradict the identification of the nebula as the remnant of the supernova of 1054 is its location, about one degree northwest of Zeta Tauri. This conflicts with the most careful Chinese description of the position of the guest star. Possibly an error in direction was made when the original reports of the imperial astronomers were condensed for inclusion in the official history of the time. Certainly, Oriental records give no reason for suspecting there was another supernova in this vicinity during the past two millennia.

A third medieval supernova was observed by Chinese and Japanese astronomers in 1181. This was visible for only six months and may have been considerably fainter than its two predecessors. The star appeared in the constellation Cassiopeia, and independent descriptions of its position by astronomers in South China, North China, and Japan all agree on a location near Epsilon in Cassiopeia.

In order to deduce the most accurate position from the various texts, which mention several star groups in Cassiopeia, I undertook careful studies of medieval Chinese star maps. Only a single supernova remnant lies near the site of the outburst, and this fits the observed location very well. The remnant is known as 3C 58 (number 58 in the third Cambridge catalog of cosmic radio sources). Although a much feebler emitter of both radio waves and X rays than the Crab nebula, 3C 58 bears many similarities to the nebula, suggesting that 3C 58 was probably produced by a supernova of Type II. The remnant may thus contain a pulsar that has not yet been discovered.

The Rise of European Astronomy

After 1181, nearly four centuries elapsed before the appearance of the next supernova—in 1572. In the interim the traditional astronomy of China was surpassed by the new astronomy of Renaissance Europe. Without doubt the best observations of the 1572 supernova, which was as bright as Venus and remained visible for 15 months, were made by European astronomers—notably the Danish astronomer Tycho Brahe. The position of the star, measured to within a small fraction of a degree, was very close to Kappa in Cassiopeia. Careful notes were kept of its changing brightness by comparing it with the other stars. The position as measured by Brahe was so accurate that it actually lies inside the compact radio and X-ray source that is now recognized as the remnant of the supernova. Further, Brahe's brightness estimates show that the supernova was of Type I. The star is thus the earliest supernova whose type can be established from the historical data alone. The type is in fact confirmed by modern observations of the remnant, which does not contain a pulsar.

The most detailed Chinese description is worth quoting for its historical interest, but it will be seen that this is far from precise. It is contained in a detailed chronicle of the Ming dynasty (1368–1644), dated November 8, 1572: ''At night a guest star was seen at the northeast; it was like a crossbow pellet. It appeared beside Ko-tao (in Cassiopeia) in the degrees of Tung-pi lunar mansion. It gradually became fainter. It emitted light in the form of pointed rays. After November 24 at night the same star was orange in color. It was as large as a lamp and the pointed rays of light came out in all directions. It was seen before sunset. At the time, the Emperor noticed it from his palace. He

was alarmed and at night he prayed in the open air on the Vermillion Steps.''

Finally, only 32 years later, in 1604, we come to the most recent galactic supernova on record. Once again, European astronomers supplied most of the scientific data regarding an accurate position (in the constellation Ophiuchus) and the changing brightness of the star. At peak brightness, this supernova was probably not as bright as Venus, and the duration of its visibility—12 months—was shorter than that of the supernova in 1572. The position measured by the German astronomer Johannes Kepler and other Europeans was even more accurate than that of Tycho Brahe, and long before radio waves from it were detected, the faint optical remnant was discovered. The changing pattern of brightness deduced from the estimates of Kepler resembles a Type I supernova, although the rate of decline was unusually rapid. The remnant, which is similar to that of the 1572 supernova, reveals no trace of a pulsar.

Chinese observations of the supernova in 1604 were very poor, but the Korean astronomers made a remarkable series of observations of it—although these were rather crude by the European standards. On almost every clear night for nearly six months, the Koreans measured the guest star's position to the nearest degree and reported on its brightness. The Koreans also regularly recorded when thick clouds

In medieval Europe, studies of the heavens were heavily influenced by astrology. China, Korea, and Japan, however, maintained strong astronomical traditions.

The Granger Collection

Giraudon/Art Resource

During the Renaissance, Danish astronomer Tycho Brahe (left) made detailed observations of the supernova that occurred in 1572. Some astronomers speculate that the fabled Star of Bethlehem (right) may have been a supernova.

blanketed the sky or if bright moonlight made observation difficult. The brightness comparisons, first with the planets Venus and Jupiter and later with Antares (the very red star in Scorpius) and other fainter stars, accord well with European estimates. The late 16th century was a time of remarkable achievement by the official astronomers of Korea, as demonstrated in 1592, when they made careful observations of a nova in Cetus over a 15-month period. This star was not noticed in China or even in Europe.

Why Study Supernovas?

Supernovas are of special interest in astronomy today. They are recognized as intense sources of cosmic rays—high-energy subatomic particles that continually enter the earth's atmosphere and can penetrate far below ground level. A relatively close supernova—say within about 50 light-years of the Solar System—would have serious consequences for life on Earth. The Earth would be showered with cosmic rays and very shortwave radiation such as gamma rays and X rays. One of the effects would be to destroy the upper atmosphere's ozone layer, which protects us from incoming solar ultraviolet radiation; another effect would be the production of genetic mutations.

The occurrence of five bright supernovas in the past thousand years leads us to speculate about future events. Almost certainly, the light from other nearby supernovas is on its way to us, but because of the vast distances involved, it may take many hundreds of years to reach Earth. What is sure is that we are better able today to study a supernova outburst than ever before. Nothing, however, can diminish the importance of the contribution made by our stargazing predecessors—especially the sky watchers of the Orient. Without their efforts, we would have no direct knowledge of the occurrence of any supernova in our galaxy. Present-day astronomers have good reason to be grateful to them.

Big Bear Solar Observatory, photo courtesy R.L. Moore

EXPLOSIONS in the SOLAR ATMOSPHERE

by A. Gordon Emslie

To a casual observer the Sun is constant. But the atmosphere of our star is often wracked by tremendous explosions—called solar flares—that release prodigious amounts of energy and accelerate billions of tons of material at speeds up to 1 million miles

A seahorse-shaped flare, covering 4 billion square miles, represents an outburst of energy from the Sun's surface.

(1.6 million kilometers) per hour. Astronomers are now studying these complex explosions with instruments ranging from radio-telescope arrays to gamma-ray spectrometers to learn exactly how solar flares work.

The first recorded solar flare occurred on September 1, 1859. English astronomers Richard C. Carrington and R. Hodgson were observing sunspots that day when they independently witnessed the event. The flare lasted only a few tens of seconds and, as the astronomers described in back-to-back papers in the *Monthly Notices* of the Royal Astronomical Society, appeared as "two patches of intensely bright and white light" among an unusually large group of sunspots. Carrington concluded that "the phenomenon took place at an elevation considerably above the general surface of the Sun."

A few minutes after the flare, there was an intense disturbance in Earth's magnetic field, and early the next morning, many observers reported a brilliant auroral display. Carrington noted the coincidence between these events and the flare, but was reluctant to associate them, noting that "one swallow does not a summer make." Today we know that terrestrial magnetic disturbances are intimately related to solar flares, and that flares affect Earth by, among other things, causing the auroras, or northern lights, disrupting radio communications, and corroding long pipelines by inducing large electrical currents.

What Carrington and Hodgson saw was an extremely rare occurrence known as a white-light flare—so named because the flare enhances the Sun's emission throughout the visible spectrum. In general, flares are best seen from Earth by observing the Sun through a filter transparent only to light from the hydrogen-alpha (Hα) spectral line located in the red-orange region of the spectrum.

Activity on the Sun

Like most stars and even planets, the Sun has a magnetic field. The average strength of this magnetic field is comparable to that of Earth's field. Unlike that of Earth, however, the Sun's magnetic field is continuously changing: the strength of the field rises and falls with a period of approximately eleven years. As the field grows stronger, the Sun enters a phase of heightened activity that culminates once each cycle. The last period of peak activity, or solar maximum, occurred in 1980–81; the next is predicted for sometime during 1991 or 1992.

During periods of high solar activity, the size and number of active regions—areas on the Sun's surface where the magnetic field strength is enhanced—increase greatly. Frequently, sunspots are embedded in these active regions, so the number of sunspots on the face of the Sun also increases during phases of high activity. These sunspots, which possess magnetic fields up to a thousand times stronger than normal, appear darker than the surrounding surface because they are 1,800 to 3,600° F (1,000 to 2,000° C) cooler. (The German apothecary Heinrich Schwabe discovered the eleven-year solar-activity cycle in 1843 by observing the variation in sunspot numbers over time.)

The driving force behind all solar activity is the outflow of energy from the Sun's interior. Every second the Sun converts 4 million tons (3.6 million metric tons) of hydrogen into helium in nuclear reactions deep within its interior. The energy created in these reactions takes about a million years to make its way to the surface, where it is radiated into space.

Solar activity manifests itself in many ways. This periodic activity, however, is confined mostly to the outer layers of the Sun; the nuclear furnaces in the Sun's core continue to produce power at a steady rate. The Sun is surrounded by a "skin" of million-degree gas called the corona. This tenuous gas can be seen in white light only during a total solar eclipse, when the Moon's disk obscures the blinding disk of the Sun. But X-ray telescopes in Earth orbit can view the corona at all times, and show the corona as a bright shell surrounding a relatively cool, dim central star.

When solar activity is near minimum, dark gaps called coronal holes appear in the corona. Hot gases escaping from these regions constitute the solar wind, a stream of charged particles that flows throughout the solar system. When solar activity is near maximum, coronal holes are nearly absent, and instead we see prominences (relatively cool, dense regions of gas high above the solar limb [the outer edge of the apparent disk of the Sun]), a large number of active regions and sunspots, and a dramatic rise in the number and size of solar flares. At peak solar activity the Sun can produce many flares each day. Although the energy released in a single flare is negligible compared to the total energy output of the Sun, flares are sufficiently localized that they show up as very bright regions in H-alpha, in ultraviolet light and X rays, and even occasionally in white light.

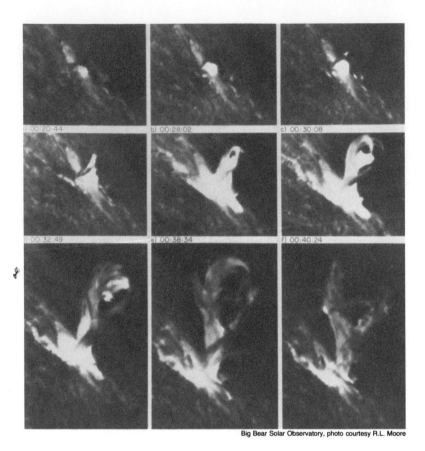

a) 00:20:44 b) 00:28:02 c) 00:30:08

d) 00:32:49 e) 00:38:34 f) 00:40:24

Solar flares grow rapidly. In this sequence covering less than 35 minutes, the flare begins as a sudden brightening on the Sun's surface (upper left), usually in the neighborhood of sunspots. Within minutes, the flare increases to maximum brightness. During this time, billions of tons of material are ejected from the Sun at speeds approaching a million miles per hour. When the cast-off material reaches the earth, it produces dramatic aurora displays and widespread radio interference. Large, bright flares often last an hour or longer; smaller ones may disappear in minutes.

Big Bear Solar Observatory, photo courtesy R.L. Moore

Solar Magnetism

The only energy source capable of producing the violent outbursts observed in solar flares is magnetic in nature, which ties in well with the increased frequency of flares during times of enhanced magnetic activity. As more and more regions of strong magnetic fields appear on the Sun, they are pressed together, building up magnetic energy in much the same way that pressing two magnets together requires a greater energy input as they get closer to each other. At some point the system becomes unstable, and, in the same way as the two pressed-together magnets will fly apart when suddenly released, all the stored energy is given off in a blinding flash of X rays and ultraviolet radiation and in a burst of energetic electrons and protons. Solar astronomers do not yet understand the details of this process, but there is ample evidence supporting the basic scenario.

One popular model for explaining solar flares requires the released magnetic energy to accelerate huge numbers of particles. The thousands and sometimes millions of volts necessary to do this are believed to be produced by changes in the magnetic field strengths caused by interacting magnetic structures. (Although the ability of magnetic field changes to accelerate particles is a fundamental principle of the theory of electromagnetism developed by Scottish physicist James Clerk Maxwell in the 19th century, solar scientists do not fully understand how magnetic energy is converted to the energy of fast particles in solar flares.) Accelerated electrons stream through the solar atmosphere, heating the atmosphere through friction and producing X rays by a process known as bremsstrahlung (from the German words *bremsen*, meaning "to brake," and *Strahlung*, meaning "radiation"). Accelerated protons collide with other nuclei, giving off gamma radiation when the excited nuclei decay radioactively.

The Observational Jackpot

Unfortunately, most of the radiation produced during a solar flare never reaches Earth's surface. Our atmosphere effectively blocks all the high-energy radiation—ultraviolet, X rays, and gamma rays—and lets pass only visible light, including H-alpha, as well as radio waves. To better understand the physical processes taking place within solar flares, astronomers need to study all the radiation that flares emit.

One of the major steps in this direction was the observations made from the manned U.S. space station Skylab. During 1973 and 1974, three crews used Skylab's telescopes to observe ultraviolet and X-radiation emanating from flares. But it was the Solar Maximum Mission (or Solar Max) satellite that revolutionized our knowledge of solar flares.

Launched into Earth orbit on February 14, 1980, Solar Max carried an array of seven instruments, six of which were designed specifically to study solar flares. Among these instruments was the first telescope designed to take pictures in high-energy X rays, and a gamma-ray spectrometer to measure the high-energy gamma radiation from nuclear reactions in flares. Also on board were telescopes to produce simultaneous images and spectra of low-energy X rays and of ultraviolet radiation, a high-energy X-ray spectrometer, and a coronagraph to study the ejection of material into space. As part of an unprecedented international effort known as the Solar Maximum Year, several ground-based optical and radio telescopes made observations in coordination with Solar Max to provide relatively uninterrupted, around-the-clock observations of the Sun.

In November 1980, the guidance and pointing system of Solar Max failed. Unable to maintain an accurate fix on the Sun, the spacecraft remained in orbit with only the high-energy X-ray and gamma-ray spectrometers functioning (which did not require accurate pointing) until early 1984, when the spacecraft was repaired in orbit during a pioneering space shuttle mission. In the period between the failure of the pointing system and its subsequent repair, solar scientists began analyzing the enormous quantity of data Solar Max gathered.

Simultaneous Acceleration

One of the more startling findings was that the highest-energy X rays, called hard X rays (produced by electrons accelerated by tens of thousands of volts), are generated at the same time as the gamma rays (produced by nuclear reactions involving protons accelerated by many millions of volts). Until Solar Max, solar astronomers thought the protons were accelerated in a separate, second stage of the flare. But the close timing of the X-ray and gamma-ray bursts proved this wrong: the electrons and protons are accelerated simultaneously within seconds after the start of the flare. Solar physicists, who had struggled for years with the problem of how the electrons are rapidly accelerated, were now faced with twice the problem they had before.

Magnetic loops (below left) form the structures within which solar flares occur. In a computer-enhanced photograph of the same loops (below right), the red regions indicate matter moving toward the Sun, the blue regions away.

Courtesy A. Gordon Emslie

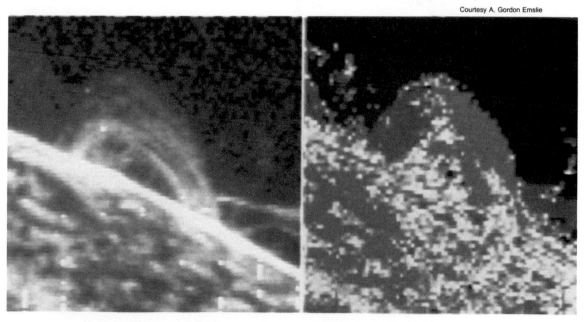

Observations of high-energy neutrons compounded the problem. The gamma-ray spectrometer on Solar Max, which was also sensitive to high-energy neutrons, started detecting solar flare neutrons only about 100 seconds after the hard X rays arrived at the spacecraft. Because X rays travel the 93 million miles (150 million kilometers) from the Sun to Earth at the speed of light, these observations implied that the neutrons had a velocity not much slower than light—about eight-tenths of light speed, in fact. A neutron with this velocity has a huge kinetic energy and can be produced only in nuclear reactions occurring between protons accelerated by up to a billion volts and atoms in the solar atmosphere.

Based on these unprecedented observations, solar scientists have concluded that flares act as colossal particle accelerators. These accelerated particles strike atoms in the solar

atmosphere along the particles' path, producing the X-ray and gamma-ray emissions, while the ultraviolet and optical radiation comes from the hot gases created by the particle bombardment.

This picture of energetic particles bombarding the solar atmosphere is supported further by results from the hard-X-ray imaging telescope on Solar Max. Early in the development of a flare, just as the hard-X-ray flux starts to rise, the radiation appears to come from two distinct regions separated typically by a few tens of thousands of miles. A comparison of this information with data obtained with Earth-based magnetographs, which map the strength and polarity of the Sun's magnetic field, shows that these regions correspond to the ends of a twisted arch of magnetic flux that has its two feet rooted in the surface of the Sun. (These loops were first observed clearly in ultraviolet and low-energy X-ray images obtained with the instrument package on Skylab.) As the flare progresses, the X-ray emission comes from a much broader region of this magnetic loop centered halfway between the original "footpoints."

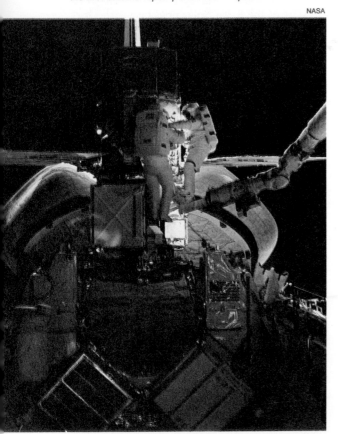

The Solar Max *gave astronomers a means of continuously observing the Sun. Its malfunction and subsequent repair by astronauts on a 1984* Challenger *mission (below) was the first satellite repair performed in space.*

NASA

What Are Flares?

Now that astronomers have had the chance to analyze observations across the electromagnetic spectrum, they have a much better insight into the nature of solar flares. Although the following picture is still controversial to some extent, it is qualitatively consistent with the observational data. In the few days preceding a major flare, motions in the Sun's lower atmosphere twist and massage the magnetic loops protruding from the Sun's surface. At some point the stresses on the loops become too great, and the loops "snap," ejecting material from the Sun and accelerating huge numbers of electrons and protons. These charged particles spiral through the solar atmosphere along magnetic field lines, generating hard X rays and microwaves and heating the lower atmosphere. Driven upward by the strong gas pressures so created, material at temperatures of several million degrees fills the flare loop, causing the loop to glow brightly in X rays. At the same time the lower regions of the loop shine brightly in ultraviolet and optical light. After the particle acceleration ceases, the flare loop relaxes back to its original state, and the high-energy radiation disappears.

This picture is not without problems. Extracting 10 billion billion kilowatt-hours of flare energy from the Sun in as short a time as obser-

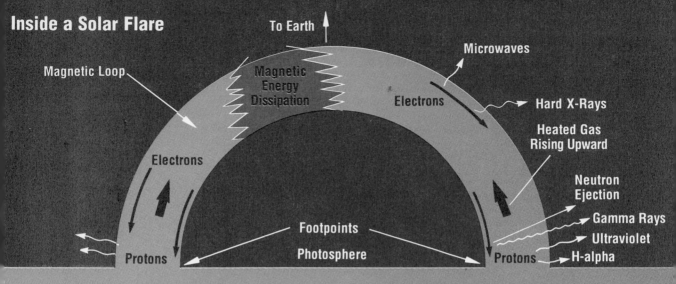

Inside a Solar Flare

To Earth

Magnetic Loop

Magnetic Energy Dissipation

Microwaves

Electrons

Hard X-Rays

Heated Gas Rising Upward

Electrons

Neutron Ejection

Gamma Rays

Ultraviolet

H-alpha

Footpoints

Photosphere

Protons

Protons

Astronomers believe solar flares occur when magnetic loops projecting from the Sun's surface "snap" from the buildup of stresses, accelerating large numbers of electrons and protons. These charged particles spiral along magnetic field lines, emitting electromagnetic radiation and heating the atmosphere at the base of the loop. This heated material then surges up the loop while gas at the "footpoints" emits H-alpha light.

Astronomy Magazine

vations demand is not easy. And it is even more difficult, according to current theories, to produce this energy in the form of accelerated particles. Some solar scientists argue, therefore, that the primary energy release in solar flares may involve the heating of a large volume of gas to temperatures of hundreds of millions of degrees. This hot, dense gas could emit hard X rays and also transport energy to the rest of the atmosphere.

Perhaps a solar flare is really some form of hybrid process that involves both heating and acceleration. If this is so, the same combination of processes may not produce all solar flares. Our theoretical understanding of these enigmatic events is still at a fairly rudimentary level, which should not be surprising because astronomers believe the flare process involves the interaction of magnetic fields on size scales of centimeters to meters, while the best radio and optical telescopes can at best distinguish features about the size of Texas, and the best X-ray telescope can resolve features only about the size of the contiguous United States!

Solar scientists hope to probe solar flares on a finer scale than ever before with new X-ray and gamma-ray imaging telescopes. In a proposal now before the National Aeronautics and Space Administration (NASA), astronomers

recommend that each instrument be carried aloft by a separate balloon. Each balloon would be launched from the Southern Hemisphere and climb to an altitude of about 130,000 feet (40,000 meters), where it will circle the globe for three to four weeks as the instrument observes solar flares. If this proposal comes to fruition, astronomers may finally unravel the mysterious inner workings of flares. By doing this, they will not only gain a better understanding of solar flares, but will be better able to predict solar flares and thereby give advance warning of their harmful effects. The knowledge gained could also be applied to other stars and to the basic physics of high-temperature gases in, for example, laboratory fusion reactors.

In the 130 years since the initial observations by Carrington and Hodgson, we have learned a great deal about solar flares. Despite the many important discoveries made by recent space missions, however, there is still much about flares we do not fully understand. How does the Sun generate such vast amounts of energy in so short a time? What triggers a solar flare in the first place, and are there ways to precisely forecast the occurrence of solar flares? These are just a few of the questions that continue to challenge the astronomers studying these fascinating events.

BIOSPHERE II

by Dennis L. Mammana

N early two centuries ago, Samuel Taylor Coleridge described the "stately pleasure-dome" of Kubla Khan's Xanadu, a man-made world of rivers, caverns, gardens, seas, and hills—a hauntingly beautiful land of which he dreamed during a drug-induced sleep.

Today, scientists are beginning to create Xanadus of their own. It is within such artificial and self-contained worlds that 21st-century humans hope to leave the bonds of Planet Earth and make their homes and workplaces in space.

Unlike our short-term space exploration of recent years, the settlement of our inner solar system will require life-support systems of unprecedented complexity. Many scientists believe that to make such dreams a reality, a totally closed, regenerative ecological life-support system independent of Earth and its resources will almost certainly be required.

Life-Support Systems of Earth

How would such a system work? The answer lies right under our noses—in the fragile sphere of air, water, and life we know as Earth. Our planet is a complex, evolving closed system in which ecosystems of flora and fauna have supported and maintained themselves efficiently for 5 billion years.

Such a regenerating life-support system— a sort of biological perpetual-motion machine— seems a perfect solution to the problem of long-term space missions and settlement. Yet, until recently, it had never even been considered. Even the most farsighted science fiction vision-

© Peter Menzel

Biosphere II (partially represented here by a scale model) will be a closed, self-perpetuating ecosystem independent of Earth and its resources. The complex will simulate the environment in which humans will live on other planets.

teractions—like how the biological system impacts on the physical system.''

And we're learning that we don't live on a passive planet, but rather in an active "biosphere" that supports and nurtures all life within.

Biosphere Beginnings

The concept of a biosphere dates back only a few decades. Perhaps the first to use the word in a scientific sense was the Russian sage, geologist, crystallographer, and cartographer V. I. Vernadsky (1863–1945), who described it as an "envelope of life." More recently, James Lovelock, in his book *Gaia: A New Look at Life on Earth,* described our planet's biology as a dynamic and interrelated system in which life is self-correcting over long time periods.

Experiments to create such a bioregenerative habitat from scratch have been under way for several decades. At the University of Hawaii, materially closed ecosystems on the scale of 1 quart (1 liter) have been studied for some time. In fact, their oldest system is still thriving after 17 years.

The National Aeronautics and Space Administration (NASA) has been developing Controlled Ecology Life Support Systems (CELSS) since 1978. Within, mechanical systems would purify air and water, and each astronaut would have only two or three carbohydrate- and oil-producing plants to supply virtually all food.

More complex has been the work of the Soviet Union. At a research facility at Krasnoyarsk, Siberia, Bios III—a small, artificially lit chamber—produces and recycles half of its own oxygen and water from biological processes. Researchers have lived inside, but their longest stay was only five months. "These guys survived that long," explains Hodges, "because 50 percent of what they survived on they took in with them and stored. When they ate it up, they had to come out. But nevertheless, it was a great experiment, and one of the most important to date.''

Coming of Age

Without a doubt, the most ambitious and unique undertaking of its kind is a $30 million habitat being designed and constructed by Space Bio-

aries were blind to the possibilities offered by such a complex. In the space age, however, the view is changing.

A New View

"One of the biggest changes in the natural paradigm that we operate under occurred when we looked back from space and saw the Earth as a single sphere," recalls Carl N. Hodges, director of the University of Arizona's Environmental Research Lab. "Certainly everybody had seen a globe before, but when we finally saw the real thing, we knew that it was all one system.''

"In addition," says Hodges, "science has gone through a long period of taking everything down to its smallest parts. But now we're moving in the other direction. We're putting it back together, and we're beginning to understand in-

A GLIMPSE INSIDE BIOSPHERE II

Humans as well as plants and animals will thrive under conditions maintained in Biosphere II. The complex will replicate six of the Earth's major biomes: a tropical rain forest; a savanna; a saltwater marsh; a saltwater ocean; a desert; and a small farm. There also will be a human habitat. The artist's view shows how the miniature ecosystems will relate to one another. A glass canopy will maximize sunlight and minimize loss of air and moisture.

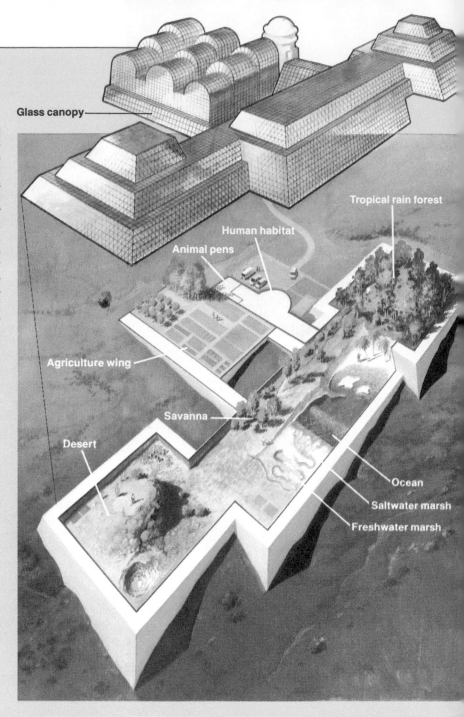

Glass canopy

Tropical rain forest

Human habitat

Animal pens

Agriculture wing

Savanna

Desert

Ocean

Saltwater marsh

Freshwater marsh

sphere Ventures (SBV), in conjunction with the Institute of Ecotechnics, at a 2,500-acre (1,013-hectare) ranch near Tucson, Arizona.

It's called Biosphere II (Biosphere I is the Earth), and is the brainchild of a diverse group of scientists and ecologists—including internationally known engineer and ecological innova-

tor John Allen and Texas multimillionaire Edward Bass.

Biosphere II represents a unique marriage of technology and biology. When completed next year, this 5 million-cubic-foot (140,000-cubic-meter) habitat will be a totally closed and self-supporting environment. It will feature

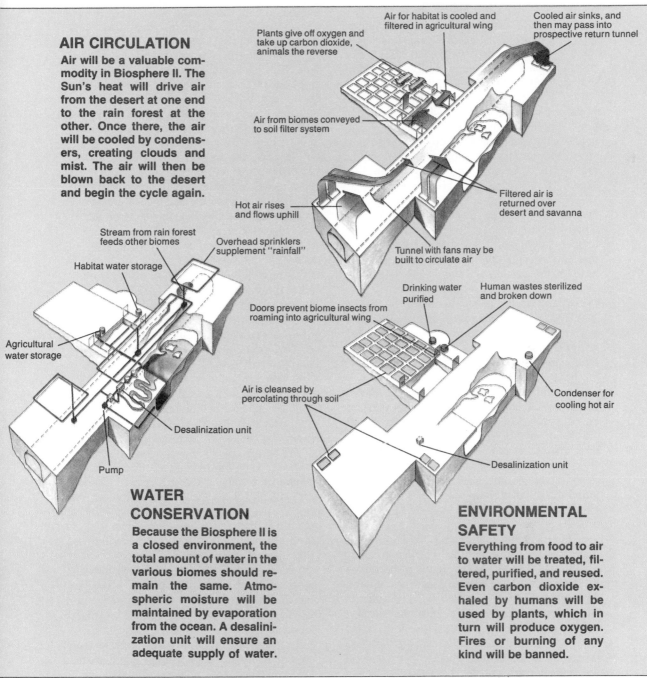

AIR CIRCULATION

Air will be a valuable commodity in Biosphere II. The Sun's heat will drive air from the desert at one end to the rain forest at the other. Once there, the air will be cooled by condensers, creating clouds and mist. The air will then be blown back to the desert and begin the cycle again.

Air for habitat is cooled and filtered in agricultural wing

Cooled air sinks, and then may pass into prospective return tunnel

Plants give off oxygen and take up carbon dioxide, animals the reverse

Air from biomes conveyed to soil filter system

Hot air rises and flows uphill

Filtered air is returned over desert and savanna

Tunnel with fans may be built to circulate air

Stream from rain forest feeds other biomes

Overhead sprinklers supplement "rainfall"

Habitat water storage

Drinking water purified

Human wastes sterilized and broken down

Agricultural water storage

Doors prevent biome insects from roaming into agricultural wing

Desalinization unit

Air is cleansed by percolating through soil

Condenser for cooling hot air

Pump

Desalinization unit

WATER CONSERVATION

Because the Biosphere II is a closed environment, the total amount of water in the various biomes should remain the same. Atmospheric moisture will be maintained by evaporation from the ocean. A desalinization unit will ensure an adequate supply of water.

ENVIRONMENTAL SAFETY

Everything from food to air to water will be treated, filtered, purified, and reused. Even carbon dioxide exhaled by humans will be used by plants, which in turn will produce oxygen. Fires or burning of any kind will be banned.

Illustrations: James Bryant/© DISCOVER 1987, Family Media, Inc.

seven major ecologies, or "biomes": a tropical rain forest; a savanna; a marsh; a saltwater ocean; a desert; a farm; and a human habitat.

The geology, weather, and hydrology of each biome will flow smoothly across well-planned boundaries to help control the system. Computerized louvers will allow in necessary amounts of sunlight within each area and will control the reradiation of energy back into space. Evaporation of water will be used to create clouds, humidity, and a continuous mist, and everything from food to air to water will be recycled by totally natural processes.

But Biosphere II will be more than the

world's most sophisticated greenhouse—it will be a miniature Earth, and a remarkable prototype of a future space habitat. On December 1, 1989, eight scientists will enter the 2-acre (0.81-hectare) biosphere and close the doors behind them for two years. During their stay—about the duration of a manned expedition to Mars—the "biospherians" will perform countless experiments to test the habitat's life-supporting capabilities without outside influence.

Their success will hinge entirely upon the biological regenerative processes within Biosphere II. "That's never been done before," says Hodges, "and it's designed to actually operate forever. The biospherians will make a commitment to stay for two years, but the biological system won't be exhausted at the end of that time. Eight others could walk in, shake hands in the airlock, and stay indefinitely. It's a facility you could set on Mars and expect it to evolve and remain in equilibrium."

Thirteen candidates are currently "in training" for the eight positions. Most of them work as researchers in such places as the tissue culture lab, where disease-resistant plants and others are being cloned for use in the biosphere.

Accompanying the biospherians during their two-year stay will be more than 4,000 species of plants, 200 to 300 species of fish, a wide variety of insects, reptiles, birds, chickens for eggs and meat, and a few goats for milk.

Species selection is now under way, with the various biome teams researching the requirements, adaptability, and uses of various plant and animal species—a long and tedious process at best.

For example, to select the 139 agricultural plants for inclusion requires scientists to study between 3,000 and 4,000 different crops, and to grow each under the precise conditions of light, day length, and temperature it will encounter in Biosphere II. And to help keep the savanna grasses under control, scientists are considering putting termites into the building. But they must be careful to select those species that won't eat the sealants bonding the glass together, or to find sealants termites don't like.

Once Inside

Once sealed inside, the biospherians will receive only sunlight and electronic communications from outside, and will be able to exit only for a medical emergency.

Their quarters will include individual apartments, laboratories, a library and computer, communications and office facilities, and a small amphitheater for meetings and recreational activities.

One thing they won't experience is boredom. The inhabitants will be expected to tend crops and do other maintenance work about four hours each day and spend a similar amount of time on research and observation. Each will work on a wide variety of projects and be ready to cope with potential problems.

But the biospherians won't be without comforts. There will be TVs, stereos, computers, and VCRs inside, and they will electronically receive newspapers and mail. Recreational activities may even include kayaking on the 35-foot (11-meter)-deep "ocean."

And their diet is a far cry from the pills and seaweed one might associate with experiments of this type. It will total 2,364 calories per day, and will include 8 ounces (227 grams) of chicken and fish per week, two eggs and four cups of goat's milk per day, 13 ounces (361 grams) of cereals and legumes (beans and peas) per day, and assorted vegetables and fruits. They also will have 10 coffee trees, enough for about 1 to 2 pounds (0.4 to 0.8 kilograms) of coffee per year, and a small vineyard to produce enough wine "for ceremonial occasions."

Inside the structure, nothing will go to waste. Carbon dioxide exhaled by the researchers will be used by the plants, which will in turn produce oxygen for the humans. The air will be purified by forcing it through packed soil in a new process developed specifically for the project. And human and animal wastes will help to nourish the agricultural crops, as well as algae, bacteria, and water plants that will be fed to the fish and farm animals.

As a prototype for future space habitats, the diversity of life within Biosphere II represents the ultimate in safety "for the same reason that life has survived on Earth," explains Hodges. "It has survived past earthquakes, volcanoes, and other catastrophes because there was a diversity and there were people there that could make decisions and accommodations.

"If you put people in a piece of mechanical equipment with a bad seal, launch them from the surface of the earth, and the craft explodes, there's not a damned thing they can do. But if you put them in a dynamic, evolving system that wants to live, adjustments can be made.

"If the carbon dioxide level gets too high, photosynthesis will increase and the carbon dioxide level will go down. If it drops too low,

In the greenhouse of the University of Arizona's Environmental Research Lab, future biospherians are being trained in intensive-agriculture techniques. Residents of Biosphere II will grow all their own produce.

photosynthesis will decrease and the carbon dioxide level will go up. Or if the rain forest grows too fast and chews up all the carbon, the biospherians can eat more bananas. It's going to be that kind of system."

One feature of the biosphere is that individual parts could actually work alone if necessary. Says Hodges: "You could take an extrapolation from the intensive agriculture section and the habitat, and it would be a perfectly viable life-support system for the Moon or Mars. It would supply all the oxygen, recycle all the water and all of what used to be called 'waste products.' And it would do it in a fashion that would be attractive to the people inside."

Mechanical and Biological Spin-offs

And from Biosphere II, scientists expect that dozens of spin-offs will emerge. "You can imagine all kinds of spin-offs from the actual facility itself," says Hodges. "This will be the world's most sophisticated greenhouse—light control capabilities that have never been in any other building, artificial intelligence controlling shutters that put light where you want it when you want it, an air purification system which takes out the undesirable components from the biological processes themselves—those systems may be used in office buildings one day.

"Until now," says Hodges, "most of the spin-offs from the space program have been hardware—things like Teflon and photovoltaics, and those are nice. But now the spin-offs also are going to be biological, and those may be even nicer." Some are already being produced. Preparatory research for Biosphere II is producing prototype systems for natural recycling and purification of air and water, control of plant pests, and improvements in solar energy and greenhouse systems.

The roots of some crops grown in Biosphere II will dangle into containers of nutrient solution rather than be buried in soil (left). Ladybugs (below) will help control pests in the agricultural biome.

Psychological Spin-offs

Another benefit of the lush and comfortable environment within the biospheres may be purely psychological.

"Unfortunately," says Hodges, "I think the pictures that came back from the Moon and Mars were not terribly exciting in terms of the surfaces themselves. There's something in the reptilian core of our brains that is telling us we're part of the biological system, and that we really don't want to get separated from it. And maybe that's the alert that sounds off when you look at only hardware somewhere. And I think that people are getting excited about what they see in Biosphere II because of the impact it has on the biological system of Biosphere I."

Hodges also believes that biospheres will change the mental image of space life we've grown accustomed to over the years. "The image of going to the Moon and living in army camp housing and mining rocks—that's going to happen anyway," he explains. "But on Mars, for example, there are canyons as wide as the United States and three times as deep as the Grand Canyon, and tall mountains with snow-capped cones. And I think when you put those images together with that of the beautiful and growing habitat you're living in, it's a different

ball game. It's kind of the reverse of us coming to America and clearing the forests. And it's going to be as exciting as can be!

"Then if you add to it the natural biome part, you've got a total dynamic system, including the resources that are in those various biomes—for example, the medicines that come out of the tropics. It can be a dynamic, evolving system just like it is on Earth.

"In fact, if you're somewhere like Mars where you've got carbon dioxide and water, and you begin bringing these into the biosphere, then it becomes a growing dynamic system as you fix carbon and turn it into carbohydrates which can be used for expanding the biosphere itself. So there really is no part which is not relevant for space applications."

As a result, the project has been lauded by the National Commission on Space, a presidential panel appointed to study and make recommendations for U.S. space program goals over the next half century. In their report "Pioneering the Space Frontier: Civilian Space Goals for 21st Century America," the commission states: "Earth supports a biosphere; up to now we know of no other examples. To explore and settle the inner solar system, we must develop biospheres of smaller size, and learn how to build and maintain them."

Environmental Uses

But space exploration is not Biosphere's only application, for the project has captured the interest of environmentalists as well. Within this unique microcosm, scientists hope to learn how biospheres efficiently sustain life on our planet and, possibly, on others. In addition, it may also provide a refuge for, and preservation of, endangered life species on Earth.

"The earth has its problems," says Hodges. "We've got acid rain, dirty air, and we've got carbon dioxide increasing at an alarming rate. Right now we don't have a research tool where we can control the global parameters, like carbon dioxide and the quality of the atmosphere.

"I really believe that one of the problems of Biosphere I [Earth] is that it doesn't have another biosphere to talk to. I see the big payoff of Biosphere II as learning how to do a better job of stewardship of Biosphere I."

Biosphere II also will serve as a valuable tool to study environmental interactions in relatively short times, and correlate the interactions with ecological phenomena that occur on Earth. "You don't have to wait for the president of one country and the prime minister of another country to argue about whether the pollution is real or not," says Hodges. "And one of the neat things about Biosphere II is that it has a much shorter turnaround time than Biosphere I, so you can accelerate the evaluation of effects on ecological systems. In other words, if you do something bad in one of the streams, it'll show up in your coffee cup in a couple of weeks. And you can look at the introduction of medicine to the biospherians and see what its downstream environmental impact will be."

During their two-year stays, biospherians will dine on fresh chicken and produce grown in the agricultural biome.

Below and facing page: © Peter Menzel

Even large-scale global parameters that may affect our future on spaceship Earth can be studied on short order. For example, scientists will be able to run the atmosphere of Biosphere II at the Earth's carbon dioxide levels projected for the year 2038 and see the effect.

A Walking Tour

Once completed, Biosphere II will consist of a series of futuristic glass pyramids and barrel-vaulted structures, as well as a mosquelike building that will ultimately house eight "biospherians."

The four-story white domed building (the human habitat) will include apartments for the eight resident researchers; laboratories, computer, communications, and office facilities; workshops, libraries, and similar facilities.

To the south of the habitat, a series of arched vaults mark the 20,000-square-foot (1,860-square-meter) intensive agricultural biome. Here broad terraces will grow crops for food, fiber, and other human uses, while the terrace sides will house domestic animals.

Immediately adjacent lie the "wilderness" biomes. Here the rain forest towers 80 feet (24 meters) above the floor area. From the forest's central mountain, a stream flows down a waterfall, across the forest floor, and into the next section—the transition biome.

It then flows along a tropical savanna plain (at the top of rock cliffs) and down to a freshwater marsh, into a saltwater marsh, and ultimately into the 35-foot- (11-meter-) deep ocean. Wave action in the ocean will be generated mechanically, and is required for the coral reef ecosystem found at the north end. A thorn scrub forest will complete the savanna biome and will mark the ecotone between the transition and desert biomes.

As in Biosphere I, the "equilibrosphere"—the hydrosphere, atmosphere, and lithosphere—will be one continuous system throughout. The structure is designed to circulate air naturally by convection, but an air tunnel is provided beneath the transition biome for that which must be mechanically driven. And shifts in atmospheric volume and pressure will be accommodated by a 1 million-cubic-foot (28,000-cubic-meter) "lung" structure designed to expand and contract accordingly.

Water circulation will also be partially mechanical and partially "natural." For example, water evaporation from the ocean will be driven by air currents back to the rain forest, where a cooling coil will condense it back into the stream and the rain forest.

Monitoring the system will be no simple task. An extensive computer network will read the more than 5,000 sensors placed in and around the biosphere, gathering data as detailed as the temperature of individual plant leaves.

Future Biospheres on Earth

It may be awhile until biospheres make their way into space, for much work still needs to be done. "It may be 'Biosphere 91' that we set on the surface of Mars," says Hodges. Others will undoubtedly evolve from Biosphere II, and we'll eventually find them everywhere. In fact, SBV hopes to have the capacity to begin production and marketing of biospheres and biospheric systems for use on Earth by 1992.

Potential clients would include space programs, universities, and research institutes, to name a few. Governments would use them to validate questions about the environment. Cities would use their art and architecture for beautifying historic plazas and other urban areas. "I even visualize a time," says Hodges, "when every good high school will want to have its own biosphere—where the outstanding seniors get to go for the last three weeks and skip final exams—and the freshmen aspire to that."

Looking Toward Tomorrow

Upon completion of the two-year experiment, Biosphere II might serve as a safe site for experimenting with genetically engineered microorganisms, for nurturing endangered species, or simply as a showcase to alert the public to the dangers of pollution. (An example of biosphere technologies can be seen today at the "Land" pavilion at the EPCOT [Experimental Prototype Community of Tomorrow] Center near Orlando, Florida.)

And one day, biospheres may provide an extension of life itself beyond the precious and fragile planet of its birth, to the depths of our solar system—someday, perhaps even beyond. Inside, residents will experience sunshine and gravity, a normal day/night cycle, the same area and volume per person that are normal in comfortable urban environments, and plenty of space for growing flowers, grass, and trees—a modern-day Xanadu far beyond the imagination of Coleridge.

In the meantime, researchers continue their work in the desert of Arizona, so that when the 21st century arrives, we'll be ready.

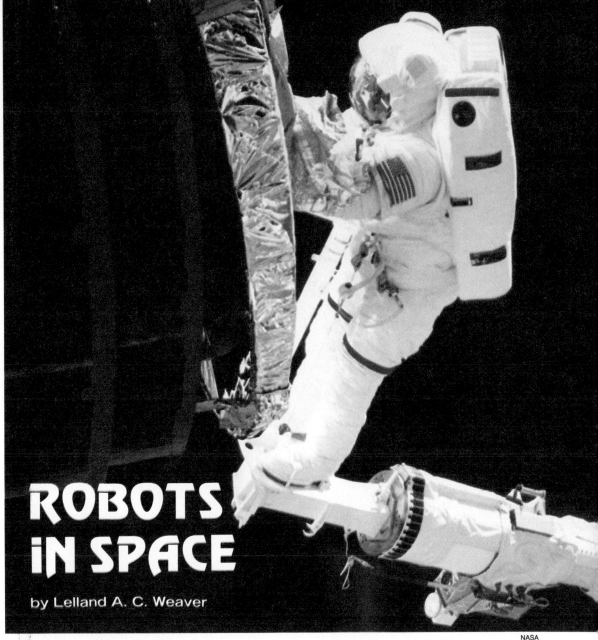

ROBOTS IN SPACE

by Lelland A. C. Weaver

In 1984 a robotic "cherry picker" supported a Discovery *astronaut while he retrieved a satellite astray in space.*

The industrialization of space is imminent. This awesome challenge will make great demands on our talents and technologies, but there will be many tangible rewards we can look forward to in return.

We are privileged to live at a time when the prospect of building factories in space seems neither alien nor fantastic. Rather, it seems a natural extension of the technologies available to us. Moreover, it is a goal that can readily be justified in terms of the many opportunities for development it will make possible in the years and decades to come.

As we continue to gain proficiency in those disciplines that, collectively, have come to define that larger sphere of science known as "space technology," we are reminded again and again of something that is, perhaps, a fundamental characteristic of all progress. Simply stated, it is this: often, those ideas that are initially considered folly will sooner or later become first reasonable, then fashionable, and fi-

Robotic arms will assist in constructing, maintaining, and repairing the proposed space station.

nally practical, and not merely practical, but essential.

We are beginning to unlock the extraordinary potentials of automation. Already, scientists and engineers have learned to create machines that simulate the dexterity, the physical senses, and—in some cases—even the thinking processes of human beings. Mankind has learned to use automation, not simply as a novelty, but as a powerful, practical tool. Automation enhances the productivity of our factories. It dramatically improves the precision and reliability of many types of assembly operations. More important, it allows us to carry out a variety of difficult tasks that we as human beings are simply too clumsy or too fragile to perform effectively.

On Earth, the practical uses of automation already rival even the most exciting fictions. But the greatest challenge for robotics awaits us not here on the ground but in space—and in its application to permanent space stations.

Space Stations and Robots

There is little doubt that robotic systems will be an integral part of any permanent orbiting station. By their very nature, these ''factories in space'' will be required to operate for extended periods of time without the aid of human crews or technicians. Nor will it be feasible to send human troubleshooters into space every time repairs or adjustments are needed. As a result, the space stations now being planned will have to be self-sufficient to a much greater degree than conventional, earthbound facilities.

Manufacturing processes carried out on board the station will need to be automated. But beyond that, robotic devices will be called upon to take the place of human technicians, both in diagnosing equipment malfunctions and in formulating and executing appropriate repair procedures. In addition, automated systems must in many ways exceed the capabilities of human technicians. Space is, after all, a hazardous environment, and many service operations will be either too risky or too difficult for a human operator in a cumbersome pressure suit.

Extensive automation will demand a new generation of extremely sophisticated equipment and systems. In order to meet this requirement, scientists must be able to duplicate to some extent the hands, legs, and eyes of a human technician, as well as a human's capacity to analyze problem situations and generate appropriate responses. Additionally, they must be able to coordinate these functions so that the functions can work together effectively.

Precedents on Earth

Many of the fundamental technologies required already have been created or are currently under development. A wide range of automated systems—incorporating robotics, control systems, and even artificial intelligence—are already in commercial use in applications as diverse as nuclear power generation, advanced production systems, and defense products.

Some of this equipment is exceptionally well suited for work in space. For instance, the containment portion of a nuclear power plant shares many of the features of an orbiting space station. It is a closed environment and, in many ways, is as hazardous and restrictive as space itself. Due to the high levels of radiation inside, the containment area must be totally isolated from the rest of the plant. Access is possible only through special hatchways that are similar to airlocks. And once inside, technicians must wear cumbersome suits complete with breathing equipment—much like an astronaut venturing out into the vacuum of space.

The work is slow, hot, and difficult. Personnel must be continuously rotated to prevent overexposure, sometimes working only a few minutes at a time. Where highly radioactive equipment is involved, technicians must often use long-handled tools in order to maintain a safe distance. At other times, work must be carried out in severely cramped quarters. In the channel head of a nuclear steam generator, for example, there is barely enough room for a single technician to crouch, let alone stand, and access is restricted to a single, narrow passageway. As a result, service operations are often extremely time-consuming. That in turn means increased plant downtime, which, depending on the size of the plant, can result in lost revenues and replacement costs totaling as much as $1 million a day.

The obvious solution to these problems is automation. Robots are impervious to radiation and heat, and they do not suffer from fatigue. Even in the most hostile environments, automated systems can operate virtually round-the-clock with no detectable loss in efficiency or productivity. And, as might be expected, the resulting cost savings can be enormous.

Versatile Automation

The Remotely Operated Service Arm (ROSA), designed specifically for nuclear service operations, is one of the most advanced general-purpose robots in the world. Remotely operated from a computerized control center, ROSA's six independent axes provide freedom of movement in any direction. This excellent articulation, coupled with a variety of tooling attachments, makes it extremely flexible. ROSA is sufficiently mobile to climb unaided into a steam generator channel head. It can lift up to 70 pounds (32 kilograms) at full 7-foot (2-meter) extension, or 450 pounds (200 kilograms) at maximum leverage. As needed, ROSA can be mounted on a self-propelled, wheeled platform that is remotely guided with the aid of miniaturized video cameras.

"Robin," a walking robot, handles radioactive wastes too dangerous for humans to touch. When adapted to function in space, such a robot could perform certain tasks that would expose humans to excessive heat and lethal levels of radiation.

With some fine-tuning, ROSA could go to work on a space station right now. A single ROSA arm could execute the vast majority of service tasks required to maintain equipment inside the facility.

Certainly, this kind of versatility will be essential in space applications, if only because it is impossible to predict all of the contingencies an automated system may be required to cope with. Single-function machines would simply be a waste of time. On the other hand, flexible tools such as ROSA, which actually learn from experience, would become increasingly useful as time goes by.

An even more ambitious example of versatile automation is the Troikabot, a forerunner of the automated manufacturing facilities that will ultimately be used in space applications. As its name suggests, the Troikabot is a permanent, independent work cell utilizing three separate manipulator arms.

Used in combination with an integrated vision system and various manipulator attachments equipped with sensors, the Troikabot incorporates all of the features required for flexible manufacturing operations. The Troikabot has the ability to visually identify the various parts and components of a given assembly. At the same time, it can verify the optical scan using tactile sensors that also properly orient each component for assembly. Alternative sensors can be used to monitor the force and direction of arm movement and verify each step of the assembly process.

Unlike conventional workstations, the Troikabot does not require a stationary work platform designed to accommodate a specific subassembly. Rather, a single arm is used to grasp the subassembly, leaving the other arms free to add components, make the necessary electrical and mechanical connections, and perform whatever other functions may be required.

As designed, the Troikabot is essentially a demonstration system that shows the feasibility of orchestrating several manipulators to perform a single task. As a pilot demonstration, an assembly task involving something called a kumigi was selected. The kumigi is a three-dimensional Chinese wood puzzle with 12 individual parts that can be assembled in a variety of configurations. Each part has a slightly different shape, and each stage of assembly requires a different set of capabilities. For example, some pieces simply join together in the manner of a jigsaw puzzle. Others slide into place. The final piece of the puzzle is the most difficult. As a result of the kumigi's ingenious design, the last piece is slightly larger than the space it must occupy, and the entire puzzle must be manipulated in a very specific way to accommodate it.

The kumigi was found to be an ideal test of the Troikabot's ability. Successful assembly of the puzzle required the ability to discriminate between many similar pieces, to manipulate pieces with precise control of both force and direction, and to verify that the finished configuration is in fact the desired one. These, of course, are exactly the same capabilities that will be expected of an automated manufacturing facility in space.

Expert Systems

Many of the automated systems aboard a space station will require the high degree of flexibility that can be provided only by true artificial intelligence. Impressive progress already has been made in the development of so-called "expert" systems.

One important commercial application of expert systems is currently undergoing pilot testing at the Westinghouse Power Generation Demonstration Center in Orlando, Florida. Here an artificial-intelligence system monitors the operation of turbine generators at several power plants, analyzing performance data to identify potential failures before they happen, and recommending appropriate preventive measures.

Sensors and monitoring equipment installed on generators gather operating data and feed them to a collection center located at the plant site. These data are then relayed to the diagnostic center in Orlando, where they are analyzed using an expert-system program based on the collective knowledge of experienced turbine and generator engineers. Based on that analysis, the system then identifies the specific preventive-maintenance services required to keep the plant on-line. The entire process takes less than a minute!

The obvious value of such systems lies in their ability to speed diagnostics, improve quality, and minimize plant downtime. In space, however, their unique abilities will be potentially more valuable. In that situation, the nearest human troubleshooter will probably be vast distances away; yet, by transmitting operating data directly from a space station to an expert system located on the ground—or even on the

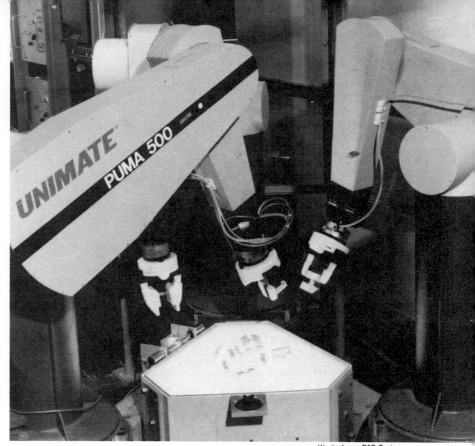

The Troikabot—a forerunner of the automated manufacturing robots that will eventually be used in space—can visually identify the various parts and components of a given assembly. Two of its three manipulator arms successfully complete a kumigi—a three-dimensional Chinese puzzle with 12 individual parts. Engineers use the kumigi to test the Troikabot's ability to discriminate among similar parts and accurately assemble the puzzle. The third arm (not shown) grasps a subassembly for support, eliminating the need for a special work platform.

Westinghouse R&D Center

station itself—the problem could be completely analyzed within minutes. Ideally, the same computer system could then relay maintenance instructions to a ROSA-type on-board service device that could carry out any repairs.

Integration

When we talk about establishing automated factories in space, it is important to remember that what we are proposing is not one single, self-contained system, but many types of equipment working in concert. Certainly, there will be automated workstations incorporating various types of processing and material-handling systems. But chances are, there also will be service robots, like ROSA; sensors and monitors; vision systems; computers and microprocessors. And in order for this space-based factory to function effectively, all of these systems will have to be able to communicate with each other, to work together as a unit.

The problem is that different machines generally have very little in common. They are designed for different purposes, and they are controlled by different devices using different operating systems and different control languages. The solution is an executive system that could act as a universal translator, a master utility that could serve as interpreter, moderator, and commander in chief for all on-board systems and functions.

One such control system—Cell Management Language (CML)—was recently developed by Westinghouse, in conjunction with the Robotics Institute at Carnegie-Mellon University. CML is a powerful, rule-based software language that uses artificial intelligence and advanced database techniques to manage communication and supervision within a single work cell, or among multiple work cells.

CML has the capability not only to accept input from many systems in a variety of languages, but also to translate communications between systems as needed. That makes operations a lot easier from the machine's point of view, and also makes the human side of automation much simpler as well. In addition to being a relatively simple programming language to start with, CML automation programs can be written using a graphic interface. That means that someone with little or no programming background—such as a factory or process technician—can operate the system with no need for specialized training.

Manufacturing Facility in Space

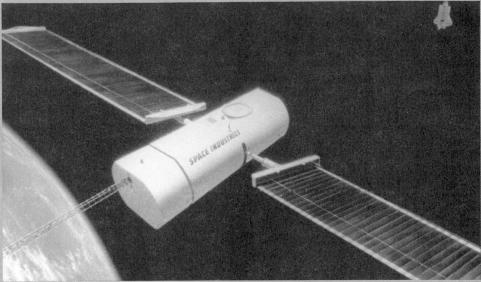

Space Industries Inc.

The first Industrial Space Facility (ISF) will be ready to launch by the end of 1990. This privately owned, human-tended, orbiting space facility will provide rental space for manufacturing materials in a microgravity environment.

The ISF, being developed by Space Industries, Inc., of Houston, and Westinghouse Electric Corporation, is expected to be used first as a materials research laboratory and power source for a docked space shuttle, which will thus be able to remain longer in orbit. But many other uses are anticipated. Business opportunities aboard the facility are expected to include:

• Purification of both pharmaceutical and biological products.
• Growth of large protein crystals to improve the quality and speed of engineering new drugs.
• Growth of large, ultrapure semiconductor crystals for high-speed computers and advanced electronic devices.
• Development of new polymers and catalysts.
• Containerless processing of improved fiber optics.
• Creation of metal alloys and other composites that cannot be produced on Earth.

The microgravity environment of the ISF will eliminate heat convection and hydrostatic pressure. It will also eliminate sedimentation and buoyancy, enabling the fusion of mixed particles or immiscible (incapable of mixing) liquids into homogeneous composites impossible to make on earth.

The ISF will not be permanently manned, but it is designed to be habitable and will provide a ''shirt-sleeve'' work environment for astronauts when docked with the National Aeronautics and Space Administration (NASA) space shuttle. The ISF is designed to work in tandem with the shuttle and will be in permanent orbit 200 miles (320 kilometers) above the Earth. NASA has already agreed to deliver two ISFs into space via the space shuttle.

As a major private-sector component of the space program, the Industrial Space Facility will provide a critical bridge between the resumption of shuttle flights and the launching of the NASA space station. The facility could also serve as a ''construction shack'' for building the station, and, once the space station is operational, provide it with a wide variety of special-purpose buildings and production facilities.

Artificial Intelligence

Perhaps the major benefit of CML is its built-in artificial-intelligence capabilities. Not only do these capabilities allow for greater versatility in programming, they also make it possible for the system to automatically modify existing programs to respond to contingency situations or to generate entirely new programs as required. That represents a terrific leap beyond conventional control systems. CML has already been successfully tested in a pilot installation in North Carolina. In that particular application, CML drives a facility that manufactures turbine blades, integrating a rotary furnace, two machine tools, two robots, an inspection system, and a host computer.

Consider the application of Cell Management Language aboard an automated space station. For the sake of illustration, we can postulate an unmanned work cell incorporating processing machinery, a controller, one or more robots, and a host computer—all essential elements, and all using different languages. Ordinarily, each of these machines would operate in total isolation from one another. But CML allows the entire system to function as an integrated whole.

For example, programmers may deliberately alter the orientation of the space station. In the process, one of the robots is jarred, and it begins to travel along the wrong path. On its own, the robot would remain oblivious to the error and would continue on as though nothing had happened. However, with CML at the helm, the system's inherent artificial-intelligence functions would recognize the error, formulate the necessary corrective maneuvers, encode them into a new program, and instruct the robot to execute.

That same adaptability would also permit easy and rapid conversion from one type of manufacturing operation to another. Rather than write individual programs for each individual subsystem, the programmer would simply compile everything in one master CML software module. The same would hold true even if new systems or equipment were added onto the original facility.

The automated tooling and systems needed to fully capitalize on future robotic opportunities in space are already available here on Earth. In one application or another, the essential technologies await only our decision to use them, either as they exist or in some appropriately modified form. This is not to say that no further challenges exist, or that the capabilities reviewed here are in any way the final word in automation technology. These systems represent only the first of many generations of robotic systems that will serve to transform the most distant possibilities of today into the practical realities of tomorrow.

A model robot for use on the space station. Robots can operate around-the-clock with no loss of efficiency.

NASA

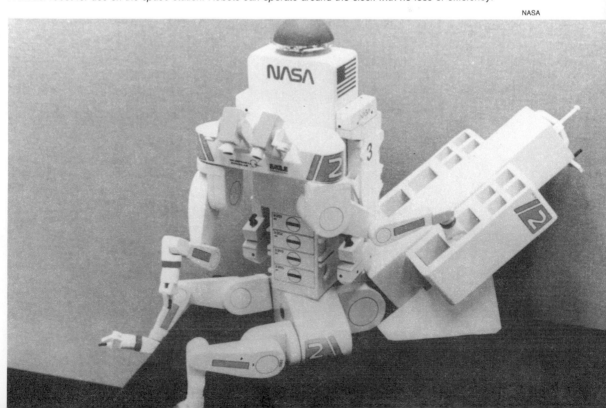

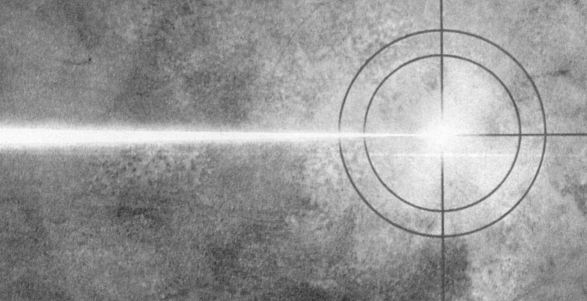

BEHAVIORAL
SCIENCES

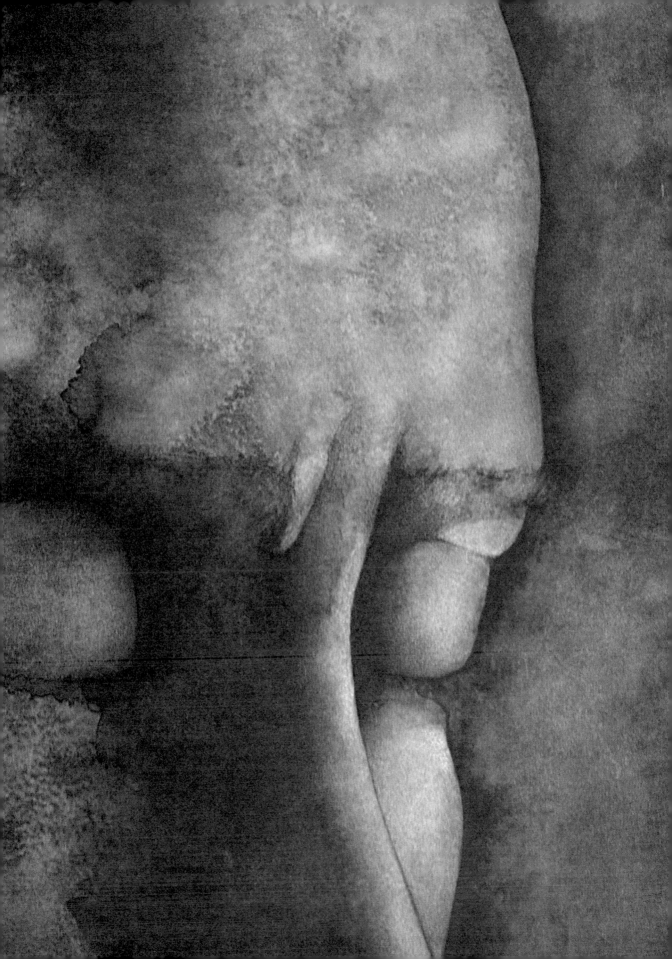

A link between heredity and manic depression has been discovered in Pennsylvania's Amish community. The traditional inbreeding among the Amish makes them particularly good subjects for genetic research.

© J.L. Atlan/SYGMA

REVIEW OF THE YEAR

BEHAVIORAL SCIENCES

In 1987 behavioral scientists discovered a genetic predisposition to manic depression, reconsidered their theories on the nature and duration of bereavement, further explored the effect of nonparental day care on children, and noted a sharp rise in IQ scores.

GENETICS OF MANIC DEPRESSION

Several studies of manic depression found genetic markers for the disorder on two different chromosomes. Specific genes that predispose a person to develop manic depression have not been identified, however.

The genetic findings support the view that manic depression, a condition marked by mood swings from deep depression to frenzied euphoria, may actually be a family of related disorders. The findings also lend credence to the idea that genetic characteristics can interact with life stresses and other psychological factors to produce serious mental disorders.

In separate studies of families in Israel and Belgium, scientists found that individuals who suffered from manic depression often had at least one of several genetic markers near one tip of the X chromosome. The markers, located with special enzymes that slice samples of genetic material at precise locations, are linked to color blindness, a chemical deficiency that causes anemia, and a process involved in blood coagulation. These traits are not necessarily accompanied by manic depression, but a specific gene predisposing its

bearers to the mental disorder may lie in the same area of the X chromosome.

The possibility that manic depression is influenced by a gene on the X chromosome has been suggested before, since more women than men are affected, and both fathers and sons seldom have the disorder. The final pair of human chromosomes (number 23) consists of two X chromosomes for females and one X and one Y chromosome for males. The Y chromosome is inherited from the father.

In another study, scientists found a genetic marker on chromosome 11 linked to manic depression among Amish families in Pennsylvania. But analysis of genetic material from families in Iceland and non-Amish families in the United States uncovered no evidence of the chromosome 11 marker in manic-depressives.

DEALING WITH DEATH

A study of people who lost a spouse or child in an automobile accident found that their emotional recovery was longer and more difficult than mental health professionals have often assumed. Four to seven years after the accident, the bereaved individuals reported marked depression and a failure to resolve their loss.

Following the traumatic loss of one's spouse or child, lasting distress is a common response to the situation, according to project director Camille B. Wortman of the University of Michigan. This undermines current theories that assume a bereaved person goes through several stages of emotional distress, such as shock, anger, and depression, followed by resolution of the loss within several years.

Wortman and her co-workers used state records to identify every motor vehicle fatality in Wayne County, Michigan, between 1976 and 1979. Surviving family members were then located. The final study included 39 bereaved spouses, who were compared with 39 nonbereaved individuals, and 41 pairs of bereaved parents, who were contrasted with 41 pairs of nonbereaved parents.

In interviews conducted in 1983, bereaved spouses reported much poorer functioning than comparison spouses in a number of areas, including depression, anxiety, social contacts, apprehension about the future, and confidence in the ability to cope with serious problems. Bereaved parents showed a similar pattern compared with nonbereaved parents, but their problems were not as pronounced as those of the bereaved spouses.

There is a chilling relevance to the study: sudden, traumatic accidents are the number one killer of people aged 44 and younger in the United States, claiming about 150,000 victims annually. Nearly one-third of these deaths stem from car crashes.

EFFECTS OF DAY CARE

Contrasting perspectives on the effects of day care for young children were offered by two new studies. One found that the quality of a day-care program is of key importance to a child's social growth, perhaps even more than family background. The other study, however, suggested that even if nonmaternal care is in the child's own home, daily separations during the first year of life can lead to a disturbed mother-infant relationship.

The first study, directed by psychologist Deborah Phillips of Yale University, looked at 166 children attending one of nine day-care centers in Bermuda. The youngsters were at least three years of age and had been in day care an average of 19 months.

In centers with higher amounts of conversation between adult care givers and children, parents and care givers alike rated the children as more sociable, intelligent, and able to concentrate on specific tasks. Day-care programs with high levels of verbal interaction among children, but not between children and care givers, scored much lower on the same ratings. Children's different family backgrounds had no effect on the results.

But a note of caution is sounded by researchers at Chicago's Michael Reese Hospital and Medical Center. They studied 110 infants of affluent parents, half of whom were cared for full-time by the mother, and half of whom had day care at home provided by someone other than the mother. Substitute care began at eight months of age or earlier.

When the infants were one year old, the investigators videotaped their behavior after several short separations from their mothers during a laboratory exercise. Infants who had early day care, particularly firstborn children, tended to ignore the mother's return, turn away from her, and refuse to communicate with her.

© Elizabeth Crews/Stock, Boston

Children in day-care centers develop better social skills when there is frequent verbal interaction with adults.

According to the researchers, this indicates that infants may perceive daily separations from the mother as rejection by her, at least during the first year of life, leading to avoidance of her during reunions.

IQ GAINS

Average scores on IQ (intelligence quotient) tests have increased dramatically over a single generation in 14 developed nations, including the United States, according to a political scientist based In New Zealand. The IQ gains range from 5 to 25 points during the period from 1952 to 1982, reported James R. Flynn.

Flynn, who collected data from intelligence-test investigators around the world, said that IQ tests appear to measure not intelligence but some type of abstract problem-solving ability that has little ultimate effect on intelligence. Otherwise, the recent leaps in IQ scores would have been accompanied by a renaissance in science, invention, and other areas of thought.

IQ scores still predict real-world achievements, such as school performance and job status, better than any other psychological measure. But Flynn contended that intelligence-test scores cannot bridge the cultural distance that separates generations in modern industrial societies, or, for that matter, Americans from Japanese or American whites from American blacks.

The single-generation IQ jump must be due to currently unknown environmental factors, said Flynn, since influences such as more education, a higher standard of living, and experience in test taking accounted for only a minimal part of the increase. A time span of 30 years is not long enough for genetic changes to boost IQ scores.

BRUCE BOWER

LEARNING TO LOVE GYM

by Emily Greenspan Kelting

School systems have inaugurated programs to instill good fitness habits at an early age. Individualized attention (above) and nonthreatening activities like hula-hooping (below) may prevent a fear of gym from taking root.

Kids love to play. By extension, gym class should be the most anticipated part of the school day—a time for high-energy activity and physical release. Yet, all too often, gym has been the class kids love to hate. It takes little prompting for many adults to recall the humiliation of being the last one picked for the team or the ignominy of doing calisthenics under the watchful eye of a drill sergeant.

For millions of American kids, the mention of gym still elicits a groan. This is particularly unfortunate in light of recent research showing that children today generally are fatter than children were two decades ago, and that their cardiovascular fitness lags behind that of active, middle-aged adults.

In separate studies in Michigan and Nebraska, 40 percent of the children in elementary school who were tested showed at least one risk factor for developing heart disease—high blood pressure, excessive levels of cholesterol in the blood, obesity, or poor cardiovascular fitness. And last year, less than 4 percent of the 18 million youngsters who took the "President's Challenge"—a test that measures endurance, flexibility, and muscle strength—scored 85 percent or above.

"The lack of youth fitness is the best-kept secret in America today," says George Allen, former coach of the Washington Redskins football team and now chairman of both the President's Council on Physical Fitness and Sports and the National Fitness Foundation, a private, nonprofit organization. "Parents think their kids are in shape because they're young, but a lot of boys and girls today can't even run a mile in 13 minutes."

Developing Good Habits

"To be in shape, kids need to work out four or five days a week, and they're not doing it. They play and they run around, which is better than nothing, but they don't get the good cardiovascular workout that they need. They ought to be developing good habits when they're young that will stay with them when they're older."

Although most educators agree that good fitness habits should be developed early, it is in America's elementary schools that the problems begin. "Most physical education programs provide only two to three hours of instruction during the week," says Dr. Ash Hayes, executive director of the President's Council. "Regular math, science, and language teachers are often drafted to run the program even though they don't understand how kids should exercise, either for fitness' sake or for developing athletic skills." California, for example, was a leader in innovative physical education programs until drastic cuts to the state's education budget resulted in the firing or reassignment of many gym teachers. Currently, less than 5 percent of California's elementary schools have physical education specialists on staff.

When playground games such as hopscotch are in the physical-education curriculum, children associate gym with fun.

Tony Tomsic/Sports Illustrated © TIME Inc.

Physical-education courses also should teach basic skills on how best to deal with sports-related injuries.

"My son Brad, who is in seventh grade, is learning a little softball, but basically it's a lot of standing around," says Ronni Cooper, a resident of Los Angeles. "The teachers are just not that interested. I'd like him to be physically fit, but when it comes down to having to choose between a phys ed teacher and a reading specialist, the P.E. teacher will come in second."

Despite recommendations by the President's Council on Physical Fitness and Sports and the American Medical Association that schoolchildren have gym classes every day, only 36 percent of children in grades 5 through 12 take daily classes. Just four states—New York, New Jersey, Illinois, and California—require that all students, from kindergarten through 12th grade, take physical education, and only Illinois requires that they take it five days a week.

A Matter of Motivation

"The story isn't so much what's happened—which is that in many homes one or both parents are in better physical shape than their kids," says Dr. Guy Reiff, professor of physical education at the University of Michigan and administrator of the President's Council School Fitness Survey since 1965. "The question is what we are doing about it. If we're going to quit raising a nation of butterballs, we've got to get kids moving. And to get them moving, they've got to be motivated."

Some 30 elementary and junior high schools in Texas, West Virginia, New Jersey, California, and New York offer a Know Your Body program in which physical education is part of a comprehensive health awareness curriculum. Developed by Dr. Ernst Wynder, president of the American Health Foundation in New York City, Know Your Body helps motivate children to do what is good for them.

"Self-esteem is based in large part on physical condition," says Dr. Wynder, "so it's crucial to give young children a thorough understanding of all the components of physical fitness." The program involves the entire school staff, and even uses school cafeterias as nutritional learning centers.

Informed Choices

"Students learn early on that the heart is a muscle that needs to be exercised, and that some foods can clog their arteries," says Carolyn McCary, a coordinator of the program in the Beverly Hills school district since 1982. "Our philosophy is that nobody takes better care of your body than you. We teach the students that by making informed choices, they will be better able to control what happens to their bodies."

First graders, for example, learn to locate their pulse, and fourth graders are taught to calculate their ideal heart rate during exercise. Students are encouraged to give blood samples every year so that their cholesterol levels can be measured, providing a clear indication that exercise and diet can make a difference in body chemistry.

"It's a fantastic program," says Isabel Bronte of Beverly Hills. "My kids are very aware of what they eat, they know exactly what chemical abuse will do to the body, and they have become exercise nuts."

While the Beverly Hills project is funded by a local family, most Know Your Body programs—as well as hundreds of other innovative approaches to physical education throughout the United States—are sponsored by private companies and foundations or by community fund-raising groups. For example, in Winchester, Virginia, a town of 21,000, some 700 members of the Judge's Athletic Association raise $25,000 annually for the physical education program at John Handley High School, which has been recognized by the President's Council as the best in Virginia. In the early 1980s the W. K. Kellogg Foundation in Michigan sponsored a three-year Feelin' Good program for 24,000 children in more than 40 elementary and junior high schools. A study of 360 of these children showed that they had significantly reduced their blood pressure and body fat and improved their exercise habits.

With a grant from General Foods, the National Fitness Foundation has created a videotape of a model physical education course to be used for teacher training. And the Campbell Soup Company has invested $4 million in Fitnessgram, a testing system that has assessed the health and fitness of some 3.5 million schoolchildren since 1983, when it was first implemented by the Institute for Aerobics Research. Students are tested for cardiovascular endurance, flexibility, and strength; they receive re-

Coed calisthenics: muscle-stretching exercises prior to athletic activity often lead to improved performance.

© Steven McCurry/Magnum

As students grow more physically fit, they show greater inclination to put strength and stamina to the test.

"We plotted certain cities around the United States on a big map in the hallway," Mr. Kiser explains. "All the kids in each class jogged together. Only laps done by everyone in the class counted. We started the program in September and finished in December. By the end, the kids had jogged 4,556 miles—to San Francisco and back."

Mr. Kiser has also started several clubs aimed at developing upper-arm strength. Children who hang from a horizontal bar or ladder for 10 seconds receive a Monkey Club card; those who hand-walk across the ladder progress to the Gorilla Club, and those who hand-walk forward and backward become members of the King Kong Club.

"I've been at Elkton 12 years," Mr. Kiser says. "When I arrived, the physical fitness scores were down at about the 20th percentile nationally. Now we rank from the 60th to 90th percentile. You've got to get kids excited before they'll go out and try harder."

A "five-minute energizer" is part of the Fitness for Youth program developed by Dr. Guy Reiff at the University of Michigan and funded by Blue Cross/Blue Shield of Michigan. Implemented in elementary schools in the Rockford and West Bloomfield school districts, the energizer consists of five minutes of vigorous aerobics performed by students twice a day right next to their desks.

"The kids realize that fitness must be pretty important if time for it is taken away from academics," says Dr. Reiff. "Both the kids and the teachers love the break. There is so much down time in the classroom anyway. This provides a psychological lift—and is often the first step in getting kids who may not be very active into motion."

At the Meany Middle School in Seattle, Washington, Ron Rall, head of the physical education department, devotes much of his free time to raising money to buy equipment for his students to use. "Kids lose interest if they are standing around waiting for their turn," says Mr. Rall. "So I make sure that every kid gets his own piece of equipment. I've bought about 160 beanbags for juggling, 36 unicycles, 150 pairs of roller skates, and enough baseball bats for an entire team.

"I also try to encourage fitness by giving extra credit for exercising at home. I give credit for everything from jogging, biking, and walking the dog to playing the piano, which builds up hand-eye coordination."

port cards (fitnessgrams) on the results of these tests, individual exercise prescriptions, and rewards (certificates, lapel pins, or patches) for improvement. According to Lee Dukes, director of the Campbell Institute for Health and Fitness, test results for students participating in Fitnessgram have improved dramatically each year.

Innovative Programs

No matter how well funded a fitness program is, its success depends on the knowledge and dedication of the teachers who run it and the willingness of the community to make physical education a priority.

With full support from his state and local school boards, James Kiser, a physical education teacher at Elkton Elementary School in Elkton, Virginia, has developed an innovative program that includes jogging and jumping rope before and after school, and a "jog across country" during daily gym classes.

A Time to Get Loose

The more varied the offerings, the greater the opportunity for kids to find a sport at which they might excel. At John Handley High School in Winchester, Virginia, juniors and seniors sign up for different gym courses every six weeks. Their choices include team sports as well as offerings like archery, badminton, bowling, handball, riflery, folk dancing, camping, and skiing.

"Gym's a time when you can let loose," says Tina Laidlaw, who graduated from John Handley last June. "I enjoyed outdoor ed the best. We spent classroom time learning the fundamentals of camping, and at the end of the six weeks, 100 of us from four classes went on a camping trip for the weekend. We went canoeing, built our own latrine, and cooked our food over the burners we had built in class. Everybody burned their eggs and toast, but it was great anyway."

Perhaps the hardest thing for physical education teachers to do is to motivate kids who have an aversion to athletics. "Gym classes are sort of a joke," says Susan Rivkin, a recent graduate of Dalton, a private school in New York City. "Last year I got out of gym for prac-

tically the whole year by managing the girls' soccer team and the boys' tennis team. All I did was make cookies for the players. I didn't get any exercise myself."

Walter Beisinger, a physical education teacher at Horace Mann, a private school in the Bronx, New York, goes out of his way to see that kids like Susan are not neglected. He starts students with a run-walk—alternately running and walking for 15 seconds, then increasing the time and distance. "Anyone, regardless of the pathetic shape he might be in, can still improve," he says. "I tell my students that they don't have to be great athletes, but they should give their bodies a little time each day.

"The importance of being fit is what I'm trying to sell them. Some kids love athletics. It's the other kids, the ones who are only interested in the theater or getting into an Ivy League college, that we really work on to get interested in sports."

Finding Time

Classroom time has always been at a premium, and demands for daily physical education classes are usually rejected on the grounds that they would take time away from academic sub-

A tug-of-war is just one activity that encourages team spirit among children regardless of athletic ability.

jects. Yet, according to Senator Richard Lugar of Indiana, a longtime advocate of youth fitness programs, "there is a strong connection between the decline in academic test scores and the sorry state of fitness and health among our young people.

"We have to indicate that physical education is one of the important studies," he continues. "Not everyone has to become a great athlete. But mental alertness and feeling good about oneself are dependent to some degree on physical activity."

A classic six-year study that ended in 1977 provides strong evidence that physical activity enhances academic performance. More than 500 students in two elementary schools—one in Trois Rivières and the other in Pont Neuf, Quebec—were assigned to an experimental program in which an hour of physical activity supervised by a gym teacher took the place of classroom time every day. During the first two years, basic motor skills were emphasized. In the following three years, the focus was on developing cardiovascular fitness and muscle strength. In the final year, the children were introduced to a variety of vigorous team sports.

At the end of six years, these students were compared to those in other classes at the two schools, who had been taught by the same classroom teachers but had participated in the standard primary school physical education program—40 minutes of physical activity a week under the supervision of a nonspecialist. The children who had taken gym classes every day showed significant gains in physical fitness and motor skills relative to those in the control group. Moreover, although the students in the control group had slightly better marks in first grade, those in the experimental program received consistently higher marks in grades two through six and also scored higher on the provincial math exam—despite the fact that they had logged fewer hours in the classroom.

Enhanced Intellectual Development

In a report on the Trois Rivières study, the Canadian Government, the Quebec provincial government, and the University of Quebec at Trois Rivières concluded that "more time can be allotted to primary school physical education without academic penalty. Although there is an ever-increasing body of knowledge to teach, this is no longer a valid argument against allocating physical education instructors sufficient time to ensure optimum physical development of the child."

The report reflects the views of many prominent educators throughout North America, including Dr. Roy Shephard, director of the School of Physical and Health Education at the University of Toronto, who served as scientific director of the Trois Rivières project. "Through its impact on psychomotor learning, physical activity enhances the total process of intellectual development," said Dr. Shephard in a presentation to the American Psychiatric Association. "Greek philosophers were correct to insist on the importance of a healthy body to a healthy mind; body and mind are closely linked at all ages, and an individual's potential can be realized only through the development of both."

With some creative planning, physical disabilities can be eliminated as a participation factor in many athletic activities.

THE HYPNOTIC TRANCE

by David Spiegel

If history has spawned skepticism of hypnosis, so, too, has the modern age of high technology. Most physicians and patients today—enamored as they are of CAT scans and computer-designed drugs, laser surgery and ultrasonic techniques—consider hypnosis as anti-quated as the pocket watch once used to elicit it. If a smoker goes to a psychotherapist and, through a brief lesson in self-hypnosis, learns to control his habit, no insurer will reimburse him the $100 treatment; but if, instead, the patient incurs thousands of dollars in surgical expenses for treatment of emphysema, his insurance company will readily pay the tab. The reason is that hypnosis is not viewed as a real procedure: it is allied in many minds with faith healing and other nonscientific approaches to disease. Thus has hypnosis been lost in the gap between holism and high technology.

Ironically, evidence is now rapidly accumulating that hypnosis is a far more powerful therapeutic tool than ever suspected. A host of scientifically rigorous studies have demonstrated its usefulness in controlling self-destructive habits, in overcoming fears, and in coping with problems ranging from physical

Austrian physician Anton Mesmer (below) believed that "animal magnetic fluid" controlled a person's health. If the fluid's flow was disrupted, the person fell ill. To cure illness, Mesmer had patients grasp iron rods projecting from a magnetized tub (left) while he made suggestive comments and gestures. Patients would then fall into convulsions, from which they emerged cured. Mesmer's disciples eventually streamlined the therapy into a procedure much like modern hypnosis.

pain to emotional loss. We have rejected hypnosis most soundly at the very time it seems most promising.

Animal Magnetism

Although trancelike states probably were induced as early as ancient Egyptian times, hypnosis was first introduced to modern Western culture by the 18th-century Austrian physician Franz Anton Mesmer. Living in an era when the prevailing scientific interests were gravitation and electromagnetism, Mesmer, like many of his colleagues, was intrigued with the notion of influence at a distance by invisible forces. He believed that the physiological equivalent of magnetism was hypnosis, which he dubbed animal magnetism, and held that disease was caused by disruption in the body's flow of "animal magnetic fluid," which could be set back in motion through the use of magnets or of his own body's magnetic fields.

One of Mesmer's methods was to have patients assemble around a magnetized tub with iron rods protruding from its sides. After taking hold of the rods and watching Mesmer make some suggestive gesture, such as passing his hands over their bodies, the ill would fall into convulsive "crises," from which they would emerge healed. Over time, Mesmer's disciples streamlined his therapy, eliminating the tub and, later, the convulsions, to arrive at a procedure much like modern hypnosis, in which the therapist intones a set of simple instructions to bring about in the willing subject a state of relaxed concentration.

Given that bloodletting was a major form of treatment in the 18th century, if hypnosis did

Top: The Bettmann Archive; above: The Granger Collection

nothing more than keep Mesmer's patients out of the hands of other physicians, they were bound to fare better than most. This made Mesmer, who developed a lucrative practice in Paris, unpopular with French physicians of the day. In 1784 his methods were investigated by a panel of experts assembled by King Louis XVI, including our own Benjamin Franklin, the renowned chemist Antoine-Laurent Lavoisier, and the notorious doctor Joseph Guillotin. The panel took a rather dim view of animal magnetism, concluding that, although cures were indeed produced, they were due to "nothing but heated imagination."

Freud's Findings

That was just the first of many flirtations with hypnosis, most followed by public rejection. Nevertheless, when Sigmund Freud began his psychological inquiries in the 1880s, he seized on hypnosis—which he studied under the great French neurologist Jean-Martin Charcot—as a powerful tool for exploring the unconscious. For more than 10 years, Freud used hypnosis regularly in therapy and remarked on its "marvelous results" in select cases. But in 1897, while a neurotic patient was under hypnosis (Freud was coaxing her to recall childhood origins of her hysteria), she suddenly leaped up and threw her arms around his neck. "The unexpected entrance of a servant," the founder of the "talking cure" recalled in his *Autobiographical Study,* "relieved us from a painful discussion."

Freud suspected immediately that the patient was responding to him as a father figure and that she might better explore her past by free-associating than through hypnosis. Thus, hypnosis was abandoned and the technique now known as psychoanalysis born. From that moment the psychoanalytic movement has been adamant in its rejection of hypnosis, despite Freud's later comment that the pure gold of psychoanalysis might in fact need to be alloyed with the baser metal of suggestion.

Hypnosis suffered yet another blow during the reign of behaviorism in the 1950s and 1960s. Taken with the scientific aura of behaviorism and its obsession with objectively measurable external actions, psychologists lost interest, ironically, in the mind. Only as it became clear that behaviorists could not deliver the bold therapeutic successes they promised did psychologists in large numbers return to the study of mental processes—particularly within the framework of cognitive psychology (an area of study, arising in the 1970s, that employs information-processing models of language, memory, and other higher mental functions). The mind once again became legitimate (indeed, recent research has uncovered direct biochemical links between mental processes and physical well-being), and there ensued a resurgence of interest in hypnosis.

French neurologist Jean-Martin Charcot used hypnosis to try to discover whether hysteria had a physiological basis.

The Granger Collection

Today two major journals are devoted to hypnosis, and scientific studies of the phenomenon appear regularly. Although there still are psychologists who doubt that hypnosis is real (social psychologists, in particular, tend to view it as nothing more than compliance in the extreme), their position is becoming increasingly untenable. A landmark study in 1969 by Thomas McGlashan and several of his colleagues at the University of Pennsylvania, for instance, found that hypnosis can provide far more pain relief than can placebos. (If hypnosis were nothing more than social compliance, patients should have obtained about the same relief from each, since in each case there existed the expectation that they would get well.) This and scores of other recent studies, taken together, lead to two indisputable conclusions: the hypnotic trance is "real"—a distinct state of consciousness, psychologically and physiologically—and it is therapeutically useful.

"Resting Alertness"

What, precisely, is a hypnotic trance? Psychologically, it has been compared to the view through a telephoto lens: one idea is brought into focus, while the field of vision is narrowed and all competing thoughts are omitted. Because the hypnotized individual focuses on only one idea, without considering its consequences or alternatives or making any stressful associations, he is extremely open to suggestion: the trance has been called a state of "resting alertness."

Physiologically, hypnosis is not so well understood. It was once thought that the electroencephalograms of people in a trance might show an unusually high number of alpha waves—periodic electrical activity in the range of 8 to 13 cycles a second—since these brain waves are associated with a mental state of relaxed attention. As it turns out, highly hypnotizable individuals—whether or not they are in a trance—generate only slightly more alpha waves than do people who are less hypnotizable. Interestingly, though, people in a trance generate less alpha activity in the right cerebral hemisphere than in the left, suggesting that the right brain is more involved in hypnosis. Studies of eye movements lead to the same conclusion. People who characteristically look to the left when asked questions favor the use of the right hemisphere, and highly hypnotizable individuals tend to look left. These findings are hardly surprising, since the right brain is more involved in intuitive and imaginative thinking than is the logical, linguistic left brain.

Perhaps the strongest evidence that the hypnotic trance is a distinct state of consciousness, physiologically as well as psychologically, comes from studies showing that subjects in a trance can induce changes in their physiological functions. Recent research at Stanford University, for instance, has demonstrated that a hypnotized subject can suppress his brain's electrical response to a visual stimulus—a response normally considered involuntary—by imagining that a cardboard box is blocking his view of the stimulus. This suppression is significantly greater in the right portion of the visual-association cortex (in the back of the brain) than in the left, suggesting that the internally generated image that dampens processing of the visual stimulus occurs primarily in the right brain. Hypnotized subjects can also raise and lower their skin temperature and control their blood flow. And hypnosis has enabled patients to eliminate warts, asthmatics to improve their bronchodilation, and hemophiliacs to control bleeding. Recent and still-controversial studies at Beth Israel Hospital in Boston even suggest that hypnosis may help individuals control their immune response.

Therapy Supplement

Hypnosis is most often valuable, however, not as a treatment but as a facilitator and intensifier of other therapies. Because the hypnotized patient is open to new ideas, the trance can be used to increase his acceptance of more conventional therapies. Hypnosis has been particularly helpful as an aid to a psychotherapeutic technique known as cognitive restructuring, which teaches patients constructive ways of thinking about, and coping with, emotional loss, physical trauma, and destructive habits. In addition, since hypnosis gives individuals "telephoto vision"—enabling them to focus on a single idea, dissociated from any unpleasant emotions—it can help patients control anxiety, phobias, and pain.

An example of the use of hypnosis in this connection is found in the case of a 30-year-old man who was referred to me after he attempted to drive his car off Route 1 near Monterey, California, into the Pacific Ocean. The patient was a veteran; while in Vietnam, he had adopted a son, whom he loved deeply. During North Vietnam's Tet Offensive in 1968, he discovered the boy's body, mutilated and dead, in a hospital.

Once relaxed through hypnosis, a pregnant woman will likely experience less labor pain and postdelivery discomfort.

Stricken with grief, he went into the jungle to kill Vietcong. Afterward he had no memory of the rampage, but returned to the United States suicidally depressed. By the time he arrived at my office, he had been in and out of psychiatric wards for more than five years.

Under hypnosis the patient recalled the events that led to his depression. I asked him to imagine a split screen, filled on one side with images of his son's death, and on the other with images of a party he **had** thrown for the boy. Over time, these symbols were simplified to a grave on one side of the screen and a cake on the other. He began, at first only in the trance state, but eventually in his everyday consciousness, to fuse the images—to connect his grief to his love for the boy. This put his loss in a new perspective and made it more bearable. Today the man is living in the community and is no longer depressed.

A similar therapeutic technique has been successful for treating rape victims. Rape is traumatic partly because the victim retains the sense of being completely vulnerable and humiliated. In therapy the hypnotized patient imagines a split screen with the rape occurring on one side and the memory of something she did to protect herself on the other. As the two images are fused, her feelings of vulnerability become more tolerable, and she can begin to accept the experience.

Breaking Bad Habits

Cognitive restructuring accompanied by hypnosis also can be used to help patients stop smoking or overeating. Most people who go to a hypnotist to break bad habits expect that they will simply be reprogrammed so that their cravings for cigarettes or midnight snacks will disappear. Such an approach harks back to the 19th-century conception of hypnosis and is still employed by some practitioners, though without much success. The problem is that it emphasizes tacit compliance and offers patients little in the way of continued reinforcement, unless they are willing to pay for repeated and often tedious visits to the therapist.

A more effective approach involves teaching patients to use their own hypnotic concentration to adopt a new point of view. It is paradoxical to tell oneself, ''Don't smoke.'' It is like saying, ''Don't think about purple elephants'': the instruction draws attention to the very activity you want to forget. In cognitive restructuring, the smoker learns to think in a new way about quitting—as an affirmative experience that protects the body rather than as an exercise in self-denial. While in a trance, he is given, and later learns to give himself, several subliminal suggestions: ''For my body, smoking is a poison.'' ''I need my body to live.'' ''To the extent that I want to live, I owe my body respect and protection.'' Hypnosis, by heightening the patient's concentration, helps fix these ideas in his mind. The therapy is self-reinforcing, for the patient feels he is doing his body a favor rather than depriving himself of pleasure. Moreover, since most people find the trance state—which they learn to induce themselves—pleasant and relaxing, it becomes a replacement for the cigarette break. Studies show that about one in four people still refrain from smoking six months after an instruction session in self-hypnosis. This is about the same success rate reported by many other smoking-cessation techniques, such as group support, among others, which often take more time and are more expensive than cognitive restructuring utilizing hypnosis.

While under hypnosis, dieters, like cigarette smokers, can learn to view abstinence not as self-deprivation but as a show of respect for the body. In addition, since the experience of being sated occurs in the brain, which processes signals from the stomach, subjects who learn under hypnosis to change their way of thinking during meals—to concentrate more intensely, for example, on their food—can often recognize satiety more easily or even produce it. In one experiment at Stanford, a hypnotized woman increased her secretion of digestive juices while eating an imaginary meal, and after 45 minutes of mouth-watering imagination, announced, ''Let's stop. I'm full.''

While hypnotized, a subject's response to touch or other stimuli is considerably reduced, and often blocked altogether.

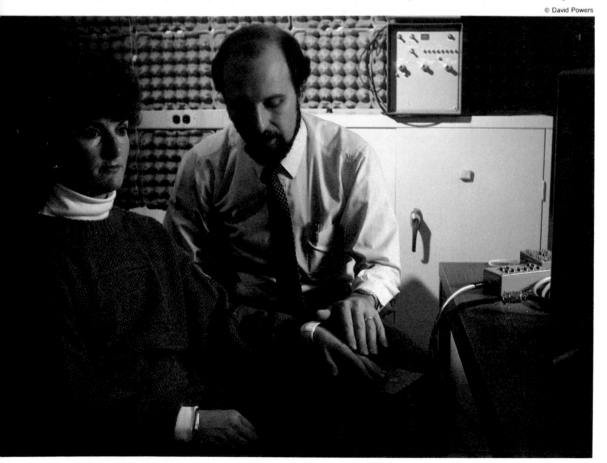

Anxiety Management

Hypnosis can also aid people in managing anxieties and phobias. Anxiety disorders are the most common psychological affliction in the United States, more prevalent even than depression. (Only alcoholism is comparable in incidence.) Since anxiety is a state both of psychological and physical distress, it makes sense that a treatment that can produce physical relaxation and mental alertness can be particularly helpful in containing it. During the hypnotic state of resting alertness, patients gain practice thinking about stressful situations without becoming anxious. They also can be taught, if they feel an anxiety attack coming on, to imagine themselves engaged in a restful activity, such as floating in a warm bath. This will interrupt the feedback cycle of psychological and somatic anxiety, a snowball effect in which the patient's initial feeling of nervousness triggers a physical response, such as nausea or dizziness, which increases the patient's feelings of distress, causing a further physical reaction, and so forth. Similarly, the patient in a trance can be fed (or better, can feed himself) suggestions that will give him a sense of control over his phobias. Airplane phobics, for instance, can be told to view the plane as an extension of their bodies rather than seeing themselves as victims trapped inside the machine. In a 1981 study at Columbia and Stanford, of 178 aerophobics offered a single training session in self-hypnosis, 52 percent were still cured or considerably improved an average of seven years after treatment.

Controlling Pain

The power of hypnosis to help people master pain is one of the technique's least controversial claims. Beginning in the 19th century, when the Scottish surgeon James Esdaile reported in his book *Mesmerism in India* that hypnosis could effect complete anesthesia in 80 percent of surgical patients—a finding later retracted under the heat of professional scorn and soon overshadowed by the discovery of ether anesthesia—repeated observations have shown that hypnosis can reduce or eliminate intense physical pain. Indeed, hypnosis has been used as general anesthesia for surgery on patients who are unable to withstand inhalation anesthesia. One such patient, during an operation to remove his diseased lung, experienced the scalpel as a pencil being drawn lightly across his chest.

Hypnotic analgesia seems to work by disciplined control of attention. Just as you may be unaware of sensations in, say, your back as you read this article, the hypnotized person can learn to put painful stimuli at the periphery of his awareness, by focusing on a competing sensation in another part of the body, by imagining that the painful area has been made numb with Novocain, or by concentrating on an imagined change of temperature in the painful region. (The effectiveness of the last of these techniques may have something to do with the fact that pain and temperature fibers run separately from all other sensory nerves in the body and spinal cord.) Pain relief can persist indefinitely after the patient emerges from the trance. Thus, hypnosis even can be useful in controlling chronic pain—the pain of cancer, say, or arthritis—freeing the patient from long-term use of narcotic analgesics, with their disabling side effects, including addiction. Children are especially good candidates for this form of pain relief, since they tend to be highly hypnotizable. In 1982 Stanford psychologists Josephine Hilgard and Samuel LeBaron found that leukemic children who underwent bone marrow aspirations were able, with hypnosis, to reduce pain by 30 percent during the procedure.

Patient-controlled Therapy

All these uses of hypnosis, from relieving pain to softening trauma, have one feature in common: they aim to enhance the individual's control over his behavior or emotions—over anxiety attacks, eating binges, episodes of hysteria, or bouts of suffering. Ironically, many patients and physicians still associate hypnosis with a loss of control, leading them to reject the trance as something magical—and pseudoscientific. Through much of its history, hypnosis did enable therapists to impose their suggestions on an entirely passive subject (the very word, *hypnos,* is Greek for *sleep*); today, however, we know that the therapy is most productive when subjects take an active role—learning to induce their own trances and to mobilize their own inner resources toward a therapeutic goal. In an age when increasingly aggressive, high-technology medical interventions have triggered a renewed interest in patient-controlled therapy—when the growing use of drugs for psychiatric therapy, for instance, has been met by a Food and Drug Administration (FDA) recommendation that mild hypertension be treated when possible by relaxation training, not medication—perhaps the time is finally ripe for hypnosis to take hold of the public's imagination.

© Punch/Rothco

"And now for the news. Those who are squeamish about news may wish to switch off at this point."

MIXED MESSAGES
FROM THE MEDIA
by Cathy Perlmutter

Policeman caught selling cocaine! Drug use among police officers rising! Fire burning in a warehouse! Suicide in a subway station! Child falls from 17th-story window and lives! Corruption in City Hall! Beirut death toll rises! London's worst fire since 1982! Two airliners nearly collide over the Atlantic!

Weather. Sports. Finally, the good news: This year marks the 40th anniversary of the bikini bathing suit!

And that's the way it was, according to a recent 10:00 P.M. local television news program. O.K., this particular program was aired in New York City, a market renowned for its lurid appetite. But almost anywhere in the coun-

try, if you open the newspaper, or especially if you switch on the TV or radio news, the lineup isn't likely to be much more encouraging. Inexorable as the tides, the media send out waves of this every day.

How do you react to the daily tidings of tragedy? The bad news can present psychological dilemmas. Psychologists say that people's reactions are as diverse as their personalities. Some people may be haunted for days by major catastrophes—like the space shuttle *Challenger* accident—or "minor" ones, like the murder of a distant stranger. On the other hand, there are the people who let it all roll right off them.

Is there a healthy way to respond to the bad

news? Have you ever wondered if it's possible to be a well-informed citizen without having ice water running through your veins, or alternatively, being afraid to leave the house? And is the problem with the world, the news media, or with ourselves?

These are some of the questions we asked journalists, psychologists, and media critics. There was plenty of disagreement about the answers. But all agree that through deeper understanding of the news media—and of our own reactions—we can find a better way to deal with the news and the bad news.

What's News?

"People everywhere confuse what they read in newspapers with news," essayist A. J. Leibling once wrote. He was, of course, referring to the vast difference between everything that happens on the planet, and the particular events that editors select for use in newspapers, magazines, or broadcasts.

In choosing from billions of possibilities, there's no doubt that the media tend to go for the jugular. Why is bad news considered more newsworthy than good? "News is something that deviates from the norm, and that's very often unpleasant," says television news consultant Jim Thistle, associate professor and acting director of the Boston University School of Journalism.

The importance of exposing people to the worst was proved in recent years by the war in Vietnam, Thistle argues. "The horror of Vietnam was plunked into people's living rooms, and people said, 'We shouldn't be in this war.' Television is credited with turning people around on Vietnam."

Of course, much of the bad news that the media choose to emphasize—the "Dog Bites Baby" stories—doesn't even approach the significance of Vietnam. Competition for readers or audience means media choose to "titillate instead of illuminate" with trivial but gripping footage or headlines of warehouse fires and freak accidents.

Of course, the news media aren't entirely to blame. Psychologists point out that the media wouldn't dish it out—the endless replays of Christa McAuliffe's parents' reaction to the *Challenger* explosion, for example—if the public didn't want to consume. "I think there's a certain attraction to being emotionally aroused by the news," says psychologist Tom Cottle, Ph.D., popular cohost of a morning television talk show in New England. "I wish I could get a nickel for everybody renting a horror movie tonight. We love to be frightened."

The result of the public's taste for thrills, and the media's race for ratings, is summed up in a particularly cynical newsroom adage: "If it bleeds, it leads." Paradoxically, the bad news that fascinates many people may also undermine some people's psychological well-being. Sonya Friedman, Ph.D., psychologist, radio host, and author of numerous best-sellers, including *Smart Cookies Don't Crumble* and *A Hero Is More Than a Sandwich,* says she witnessed plenty of news-induced depression among single women last year, in the wake of a media brouhaha over a study contending that women over 30 have little chance of getting married.

"One of the leading factors in the deterioration of mental health is the feeling of a lack of control," says Dr. Friedman. "That's why cataclysmic events, like earthquakes, or AIDS, or some study telling women that looking for a man is a dead end, have such a big impact. We feel totally undermined."

The feeling of lack of control develops not only because the items that the media report are so terrible, but because they are presented in a fragmented way, says Neil Postman, Ph.D., professor of media ecology at New York University, and author of *Amusing Ourselves to Death: Public Discourse in the Age of Show Business* (Viking, 1985).

Television news is particularly bad in this regard, he contends. "The problem with TV news is that the language that usually accompanies the pictures is minimal, and it does not lin-

ENGLEMAN

"You watched the late news again, didn't you?"

ger long enough to provide context. It seems to be a mélange of isolated, meaningless events.

"I think the most pleasing part of the news of the day is the weather, because at least if the man says, 'There's a snowstorm brewing in Texas, it's moving east, and will reach Boston on Thursday,' you have a sense of continuity. It gives you a feeling, not of potency, but of understanding the forces of nature."

But most of the bad news is explained so badly, says Dr. Postman, that "I think the overall psychological effect is to increase the sense of impotence; that in the end there's nothing we can do except go back to the kitchen and get another piece of apple pie."

The Eye of the Beholder

Then there's a slightly different school of thought that contends that the fault, dear public, is not so much in the media, but in ourselves.

"Basically, the news media does a pretty good job. It's people's irrational and crazy ideas and perceptions that tend to create misery," says Barry Lubetkin, Ph.D., clinical psychologist and director of the Institute for Behavior Therapy in New York City, the nation's largest private behavior-therapy clinic.

"I find from my practice that people's response to bad news, and news in general, is very highly correlated with the way they handle life issues," says Dr. Lubetkin.

He cites some of the unhealthy responses of his clients to bad news:
• *Personalizing*. "Whatever the bad news is, they hook it up to themselves rather than recog-

nizing it as a random coincidental event that has nothing to do with them. It confirms the pessimistic, depressed outlook that they have anyway."
• *Phobias*. "Sometimes you will see fear of crowds, fear of subways, fear of dark places develop." Dr. Lubetkin notes that after the *Challenger* explosion, a number of phobics seemed to get worse, particularly airplane phobics. They thought, 'If with all that scientific expertise, the *Challenger* blew up, how can I trust an airplane that gets much less scrutiny?' "
• *Numbness*. "Then there's the group that numbs out," says Dr. Lubetkin. "They hear bad news, or read it, but they put on blinders and earplugs and remain indifferent."
• *The Wild Response*. "There's another group that somehow uses bad news to justify carrying on their lives in a wild way. They say, 'What the hell, the world's going to pot anyway, let me just enjoy myself and act without conscience.' "
• *Charmed*. "Some people welcome the randomness of violence—not that they look forward to it, but they tend to believe they lead a charmed life. The randomness of bad news allows them to continue with the illusion that nothing can touch them, that they'll always be in the right place at the right time."

What's a better response? "Probably the most adaptive way is what I call reasonable vigilance," says Dr. Lubetkin. "That means these people think, 'The world is unpredictable, the world is basically unfair, it metes out bad and good luck independently of what I hope, pray, dream, or desire. I have to accept this as a basic reality of life. I will be reasonably vigilant, I won't pick up strangers hitchhiking, but I accept a certain amount of risk, which is part of being a human being.' "

For patients who do have inappropriate news-related phobias or anxieties, Dr. Lubetkin recommends a technique called relabeling. "Relabeling is challenging irrational beliefs," he explains. Patients who were nervous about flying in the wake of the *Challenger* tragedy, for example, were helped by focusing on all the planes that take off and land successfully each day.

Good News Is No News?

Isn't it simpler just to turn it off? Joyce Anisman-Saltman, a Connecticut psychotherapist and sometime comedienne who teaches executives and clients all over the country how to put more laughter in their lives, wholeheartedly endorses this approach. "Every time I'd read the newspaper, I'd go, 'Tsk, tsk,' 'Oh my God,' 'Honey, did you see that?', 'Isn't this terrible!' "

So she went cold turkey—she simply no longer reads news stories or watches television news. As evidence that this technique works, Saltman points out that vacationers usually don't read the newspapers. "When we're trying to recharge ourselves, we instinctively stop reading the newspaper to feel better.

"I accept that one of my shortcomings is that I'm not a well-informed person. I'm good at other things," she adds.

There are two problems with the cold-turkey solution. First is our responsibility as citizens of a democracy to stay informed. And second is, as Dr. Lubetkin puts it, "You can't turn it off forever."

Fortunately, there are plenty of other things you can do to deal with the news in a better way.

A Selective Approach

The first step is to be a choosy news consumer and recognize that all news sources are not alike. Television is more explicit than newspapers and tends to aim for the emotions rather than the mind.

If you do watch television news, you may want to opt for the 6:00 P.M. version rather than the later shows. News consultant Jim Thistle points out that news directors are looking for a fresh lead on the later show, and are more likely to opt for a dramatic-but-not-very-important crime or fire. The morning news tends to be the most "user-friendly," Thistle adds.

Most experts say that, in general, newspapers are a better choice than television or radio, because they have space for more explaining. Some newspapers are more responsible than others, though. And selective reading of your favorite newspaper may also be necessary. As one eminent journalist put it, "A headline is not an act of journalism, it is an act of marketing." If the headline reads, "Ax Murderer Strikes Again"—and you know it will upset you—you don't have to "buy" the story by reading it.

Psychologists emphasize that there are many ways to consciously adopt a healthier attitude to the bad news. "Take whatever you read and diminish your reaction by one-half," explains Dr. Friedman. "Then ask yourself whether you have any control over the situation, whether you can make a difference. If the answer is 'no,' you must recognize that that is one part of civilization you are not a factor or participant in, and which will roll along without your involvement.

"But if there is any way your involvement—a vote, a letter, a donation—can make a change for the better, you owe it to your mental health to do that, to take control," adds Dr. Friedman.

"Remember now—four parts violence to one part sex."

© Cole/Rothco

BORN TO BE SHY?

by Jules Asher

We've all met shy toddlers—the ones who cling to their parents and only reluctantly venture into an unfamiliar room. Faced with strangers, they first freeze, falling silent and staring at them. They seem visibly tense until they've had a chance to size up the new scene. Parents of such children are likely to say they've always been on the timid side. "It's just his way," one might say.

Despite parents' observations, psychologists have tended to resist the notion that such traits are inborn, concentrating instead on the importance of early experience in the development of character. Today, however, evidence from several lines of research indicates that at least some behavioral traits, such as extreme shyness, are enduring aspects of personality that are grounded in inborn ways of responding physiologically to the environment. In short, they're part of some people's basic temperament.

Harvard University psychologist Jerome Kagan has found this in his long-term studies of human infant development, and psychologist Stephen Suomi of the National Institutes of Health (NIH) has seen the same thing in his developmental studies of monkeys. Both Kagan's "extremely inhibited" kids and Suomi's "uptight" monkeys often behave in similar ways when faced with novel situations, and they have similar physiological reactions as well.

An Enduring Trait

Kagan, in his classic developmental studies with psychologist Howard Moss and colleagues almost a quarter-century ago, found that for traits such as dependence, aggression, dominance, and competitiveness, individual children did not remain consistent from age 2 or 3 to age 20. But they were unchanged over the years in one trait—which he then called "passivity" and now calls "behavioral inhibition." In an unfamiliar situation, the children might be cautious; around strangers, they might be shy.

The "inhibited" kids, as adults, had unusually stable and high heart rates in response to mild mental stress. At the time, Kagan recalls, this was an intriguing physiological finding, but hardly one he saw as a clue to an underlying biological vulnerability. Steeped as he and his colleagues were in the prevailing behaviorism of the day, they assumed they had simply detected "an acquired fearfulness shaped by parents."

But when he and other researchers began finding apparently genetic differences in temperament from infancy between Chinese-American and Caucasian children in the mid-1970s, Kagan started to look for the biological underpinnings of the enduring trait they had come upon. He decided to compare very inhibited and very uninhibited children—the 10 percent at either end of the spectrum—rather than average children, since "Otherwise, the biology is just giving a little push, and you lose it all."

Long-Term Study

In 1979 Kagan and psychologists J. Steven Reznick and Nancy Snidman started to follow the development of extremely inhibited and uninhibited children (using two groups, starting at 21 months of age in one group and 31 months in

the other). In this study, they tracked the children's heart rates and other physiological measures as well as observing their behavior in novel situations.

The children have now been studied through their sixth year, and though the very shy children no longer behave exactly as they did when they were 2, they still show the pattern of very inhibited behavior combined with high physiological responsiveness to mild stress.

These children, in addition to their continuing timidity, show a pattern of excessive physiological responses to mildly stressful situations that would be unlikely to faze their more easygoing peers. Their unusually intense physical responses to mental stress—which include more dilated pupils and faster and more stable heartbeats—indicate that their sympathetic nervous system is revved up. Higher salivary cortisol levels and indicators of norepinephrine activity round out the picture of an overactive "stress circuit" under mildly stressful conditions. (see the box, "A Tour of the Stress Circuit," on page 63). These temperamental characteristics are so stable that Kagan, looking at the early indicators of behavioral inhibition at 21 months of age, can predict how children will score on several measures of stress reactivity at 5½ years old.

Kagan believes that very shy children tend to become "uncertain" when placed in an unfamiliar situation—a predisposition that may be related to their easily aroused stress circuit. Inhibited toddlers typically cling to their mothers and are very slow to venture into a strange playroom. "These children case the environment very vigilantly," notes Kagan, adding that they also tend to suffer from "stage fright"; very uninhibited children typically speak within the first minute in the lab, but very inhibited children will wait as long as 20 minutes before making a comment. Often conspicuously tense in posture and voice, the very shy children also perform worse than other children on visual matching tasks, leaning either toward impulsivity—and wrong answers—or too much reflection and late answers.

Judging by mothers' reports, Kagan says that the very timid children were, as a group, more colicky, constipated, and irritated as infants than were other children. Many have allergies that have continued into middle childhood, while the uninhibited children in Kagan's study are virtually allergy-free. Since one effect of the stress hormone cortisol is to suppress the immune system, he wouldn't be surprised to find a connection between high reactivity to stress and susceptibility to certain physical illnesses.

Primate Correlations

While Kagan was conducting his early studies of child development in the 1950s and 1960s, psychologist Harry Harlow at the University of Wisconsin, Madison, was doing his own classical research on infant monkeys' reactions to separation from their mothers. Harlow showed that while some baby monkeys became depressed, others emerged relatively unscathed. In the 1960s and 1970s, Suomi, working with Harlow, zeroed in on the depression-prone monkeys—the ones he would later identify as "uptight"—and found that they had behavioral and physiological characteristics closely resembling those of Kagan's timid children.

During the first month of life, the uptight monkeys responded to the stress of a strange situation by being slow to explore. They also lagged slightly behind in motor-reflex development and had poor muscle tone. During infancy, under the stress of brief separations, they became less playful and showed the sharp rises in blood cortisol and the unusually high and stable heart rate seen in Kagan's shy toddlers. They also showed many signs of anxious behavior, such as clasping and grimacing, and had other physiological signs of stress.

Suomi has found that uptight monkeys, like Kagan's shy children, do not often outgrow their abnormal physiological response to stress. Those who, when 22 days old, had elevated cortisol levels in response to mild stress responded to such stress at 1½ years old with the highest heart rates and cortisol levels found among their age group. When these monkeys were later separated from their peers for periods of a week, they continued to show signs of anxious behavior and to have abnormal physiological responses. Once they were reunited, however, everything again appeared to be normal.

As late as adolescence—4 to 5 years old in monkeys—those who were uptight at birth continued to react abnormally to stress, but at this stage they tended to become hyperactive. As adults, they regressed in the face of stress, showing the depressed behavior seen in infancy.

A Genetic Predisposition?

The extreme timidity of Suomi's simians and of Kagan's kids seems to have a genetic foundation, the researchers agree. Since most of the monkeys in Harlow's original colony were reared together in nurseries and peer groups, "parenting" clearly was not influencing their individual ways of reacting to stress. Further evidence that uptightness is probably an inherited trait has been accumulating for years in Suomi's breeding colony, the descendants of Harlow's monkeys, in which about one in four monkeys is born uptight. For example, Suomi found that siblings and half-siblings (rhesus monkeys are rarely monogamous) are more likely to react similarly to stress than are unrelated monkeys.

Evidence that humans may have a special biological predisposition for extreme shyness is derived from the studies performed by behavioral geneticists Robert Plomin of Pennsylvania State University and David Rowe of the University of Oklahoma, who found that identical twin pairs are particularly prone to react alike to strangers.

What does this predisposition mean for the babies who inherit such a legacy? Are they destined to be fearful children, hyperactive teenagers, depressed adults? The answer, so far, seems to be "not necessarily." Suomi's current work suggests that, under the right circumstances, being born uptight need not be a social handicap.

While clearly not a perfect model of human behavior, rhesus monkeys share enough brain systems and patterns of social behavior with humans to make for some compelling comparisons. And because monkeys develop faster than people do (by the time Kagan's youngsters have reached second grade, Suomi's monkeys have already reached reproductive maturity), four monkey generations can be compressed into the same time frame as one human generation, offering a long-range view of how heredity and environment interplay.

Because the monkeys in Suomi's colony have been carefully studied over many generations, he knows their pedigrees, their childhood experiences, their adult behavior, and their individual characteristics. For example, he has found that monkey mothers, like humans, have varied styles of child rearing; some are quite nurturing and protect their offspring from stress, while others reject, even punish, their children. Such rearing styles are pretty well fixed after one baby has been raised. In addition, the mother's own temperament—whether she herself is emotionally uptight—affects the manner in which she raises her babies.

Photos: Courtesy Stephen J. Suomi/National Institute of Child Health and Human Development

Shyness may result from a combination of genetic and environmental factors. A monkey born and raised by an emotionally uptight mother almost invariably turns out timid. But when the young monkey is placed with a relaxed, nurturing foster mother, it clings to her only briefly (right) before becoming outgoing and adventurous (below).

Psychologist Jerome Kagan (left) of Harvard University watches as a timid child quickly adjusts to a strange playroom when his mother is present. But the same child may take up to 20 minutes before venturing to speak (below) when only strangers are in the room.

A Tour of the Stress Circuit

When uptight monkeys and shy toddlers are stressed, they have similar abnormal physiological reactions. Most of these responses are also seen in adults with clinical anxiety and depression, although shy children do not necessarily grow up to have these disorders.

The reactions center on a biological pathway known as the "HPA axis" or "stress circuit," the feedback loop connecting the hypothalamus with the pituitary and adrenal glands. A stressful situation triggers a cascade of chemical events.

When emotional centers in the brain are activated, chemical messengers such as serotonin and norepinephrine are sent to the hypothalamus, signaling it to secrete corticotropin-releasing hormone. This causes the pituitary gland, just beneath the brain, to release adrenocorticotropin hormone (ACTH) into the bloodstream. ACTH, in turn, stimulates the adrenal glands atop the kidneys to spill the hormone cortisol into the blood. Cortisol triggers a state of heightened bodily arousal to cope with the challenging situation. This state is reflected in a number of measurable changes, including increased heart rate, blood pressure, muscle tone, and pupil dilation.

Patients in the throes of serious depression typically show numerous signs of overactivity or poor regulation of this stress circuit. (Some clinicians theorize that early deprivation and stressful events may make a genetically overactive stress circuit even more active.)

The physiological similarities between uptight monkeys and depressed people have led Suomi to look at how antidepressant drugs affect uptight infant monkeys. Suomi has found that the drug imipramine, used to treat depression and panic attacks in humans, has virtually the same therapeutic effects in anxious monkeys. Such infants, treated with the medication and then separated from their peers, play and explore more than their untreated uptight peers. Separating monkeys, Suomi says, seems to elevate norepinephrine activity in the brain, and imipramine lowers it.

"We're finding that drugs will have different effects depending upon the conditions under which they're taken," Suomi explains. For example, imipramine affects uptight monkeys' stress circuits more powerfully when they are stressed than when they are not, apparently because the animals metabolize the drug faster under stress.

Suomi says that such studies can reveal how environmental events affect both physiological processes and the actions of drugs themselves. However, he emphasizes, they do not suggest that very shy youngsters should be given medications.

"The jury is still out on the effectiveness of pills—for monkeys or for humans," he says, "but we know that sensitive, nurturant parenting can help."

The Role of Learning

Although the monkeys' genetic heritage seems to play a considerable role in making them uptight or not, learning may also influence how they develop. For example, independent of her genetic contribution to her infant's behavior, an uptight mother might pass on her own emotional tendencies to her offspring simply by providing a model of overreactive behavior or through her particular caretaking style.

To test the relative influences of genetic endowment, caretaker style, and caretaker temperament on infant behavior, Suomi is using the monkey equivalent of foster parenting. He is breeding uptight and calm monkeys, then separating them at birth from their biological mothers and placing them with substitute mothers chosen for various combinations of rearing styles and temperaments. Thus, for example, a naturally uptight baby might end up raised by a nurturing but uptight mother, or by one who is relaxed but punitive.

In one such study, infants—half of them uptight, the other half calm—were assigned to foster mothers within a week of their birth. Each caretaker-infant pair lived together except for a

Triumphing over Timidity

Shyness is a widespread condition. Studies by psychologist Philip Zimbardo and colleagues at Stanford University have revealed that 80 percent of Americans say they were shy at some time in their life, and 40 percent say they're still shy.

According to psychologist Jonathan Cheek of Wellesley College, about half of the latter group seem to be the temperamentally inhibited types studied by psychologist Jerome Kagan of Harvard University, and the other half became shy in early adolescence. The temperamentally shy, even those who don't show their problem behaviorally, usually continue to have excessive physiological arousal under mild stress. Both types can be helped to overcome their problem, particularly through relaxation techniques, but Cheek says the temperamentally shy have a tougher, longer road.

Shyness is not necessarily a barrier to success. While some shy people choose to work in low-level, virtually invisible jobs, others may become famous in their fields. According to Kagan, both poet T. S. Eliot and Austrian writer Franz Kafka were shy from a very early age.

Some shy people even become performers. Zimbardo counts among the "shy extroverts" such celebrities as Johnny Carson, Carol Burnett, Barbara Walters, and Michael Jackson. Clearly, some shy people, even those that apparently have the genetic dice loaded against them, can come up winners.

Barbara Walters

Carol Burnett

Johnny Carson

Michael Jackson

20-minute separation once a week during the first month. While the infants were on their home turf with their foster mothers, the mothers' caretaking style was the dominant influence on their behavior. Regardless of their inherited temperament, infants with punitive mothers behaved more anxiously than those with nurturing mothers.

But when the infants were tested during the mildly stressful separation periods, neither the mother's rearing style nor her temperament influenced the infant's behavior; only inherited temperament predicted how the monkey would react to stress. Uptight infants, even with easygoing, nurturing mothers, showed the abnormal stress-reactivity pattern.

After six months the baby monkeys were separated from their foster mothers for four-day periods, relieved by three-day reunions in the cage. Under these quite stressful conditions, heredity again asserted itself: during separations, uptight youngsters became noticeably disturbed and passive, and their cortisol levels shot up higher than those of their easygoing peers. By the third or fourth separation, the temperamentally uptight mothers also showed signs of anxiety.

At 9 months the infants were separated from their caretakers and placed in peer groups, where they are still being studied. While characteristically slow to adjust to these new circumstances, the uptight monkeys are for the most part thriving, according to Suomi. In fact, a few lucky enough to be raised by nurturing mothers are now the dominant monkeys in their groups—a sure sign of simian social success. But, not surprisingly, the one unfortunate monkey who was triply handicapped—born uptight and raised by a foster mother who was both uptight and punitive—is struggling at the bottom of his peer group's dominance hierarchy.

Overcoming Timidity

How did the naturally timid monkeys overcome their handicaps and rise to the top of the social ladder? In a sense, they cultivated the right connections. The uptight babies who eventually became dominant did so after Suomi introduced older females into the group to act as "foster grandparents." (Such older monkeys are usually available in natural groups.) Having learned to appreciate good caretaking from their nurturing mothers, the uptight monkeys apparently were more motivated than others to seek out similar relationships with the older females. In

the rhesus matriarchy, such relationships translate into power, and the lucky ones got it.

Suomi is guardedly optimistic that, at least for monkeys, nurturing parents can indeed make up for an inherited vulnerability. But what does this mean for the 10 to 15 percent of human babies who Kagan estimates are born with the potential to become very shy? Can they avoid it? Can their parents help them?

Kagan says there's nothing deterministic about the biological vulnerability of very shy children. "Nature gives the infant just a very small temperamental bias," he emphasizes. "The proper environmental context can change it profoundly. It takes more than simply a biological vulnerability to produce an inhibited child. You need a stressor plus vulnerability."

"Most parents are fatalistic," says Kagan, "and if you let a child remain fearful for a very long time, then it may become hard to change." However, there's evidence from his study that even though very timid toddlers tend to stay shy, such children can improve with help from their parents. Kagan found that 40 percent of the originally inhibited children—mostly boys—became much less inhibited by 5½ years, while fewer than 10 percent became more timid.

Based on interviews with the parents, Kagan believes that they helped their children overcome shyness by bringing other children into the home and by encouraging the child to cope with stressful situations. He cites as an example two boys in his study who were very inhibited at 21 months and showed all the characteristic physiological signs. "At 5½, they were uninhibited, and their heart rates had changed. There is plenty of malleability in the system. But these children happened to be born to very sensitive, educated parents who decided to change the kids."

He advises parents of very shy children to recognize their problem early, protect them from as much stress as possible, and help them learn coping skills. "Parents need to push their children—gently and not too much—into doing the things they fear," Kagan says.

The work of Kagan and Suomi, whose separate research programs have been closely coordinated since 1981, has helped to clarify the delicate interplay and influence of both heredity and environment on behavior and development. In the case of inborn shyness, biology clearly sets the stage, but learning helps to write the script. Many scenarios are possible, including some with reasonably happy endings.

BIOLOGY

Without authorization, Gary Strobel of Montana State University inoculated 14 elm trees with a gene-altered microbe that may provide resistance to Dutch elm disease. In the uproar that followed disclosure of the unsanctioned tests, Dr. Strobel himself cut down the trees.

REVIEW
OF THE
YEAR

BIOLOGY

As research moves from the laboratory to the outdoors, genetics, environmental studies, and agriculture grow closer together. And as studies in those areas advance, the basic backbone of biology—observations of life—continues to teach scientists more about how the world works.

EVOLUTION

Two fossils, one living and one extinct, are altering scientists' understanding of evolution.

The living fossil, the coelacanth, is a large fish, until 50 years ago known only from its fossilized remains. But in 1938 an African fisherman netted a living coelacanth. This year, West German scientists observed the strange eight-finned fish in its native habitat, several hundred feet underwater.

For reasons yet to be explained, the fish occasionally adopts a headstand position, and sometimes swims backward or belly-up. The coelacanth was observed moving its fins in synchrony, much like a walking animal. Such a method of locomotion suggests that the fish may not only be a living fossil, but also a missing link between fish and animals.

A long-extinct creature, the crablike trilobite, reignited the debate over the pacing of evolution. In the past decade or so, the concept of punctuated equilibrium—evolution as a process that progresses in infrequent but dramatic jumps—has taken precedence over Darwin's concept of a slow, gradual process.

An analysis of Peter Sheldon of Trinity College in Dublin of 15,000 trilobites found in Wales indicates that the organisms changed gradually over time. Studies with other species support punctuated equilibrium, and proponents of that theory are sticking to their guns. Sheldon's work ensures that the debate over abrupt versus gradual change will continue to remain a hot topic in biology.

Whatever the pacing of evolution, the process seems to have passed bees by, at least in regard to an 80-million-year-old bee embedded in resin. The bee, discovered in the collection of the American Museum of Natural History, is nearly twice as old as the previous record holder, a 45-million-year-old sample. The similarity between the ancient bee and the modern variety suggests that bees have not felt the evolutionary push to change that many other species have.

ANIMALS AND PLANTS

A British study of red deer shows that the sound of the male's mating call is enough to affect the fertility of red-deer females, causing them to ovulate. To show that sound can induce the hormonal prelude to ovulations, Karen McComb of Cambridge University played audiotapes through loudspeakers in the red deer's compound. While bird songs can induce ovulation, this is the first time sound has been seen to influence reproduction patterns in mammals.

In the world of flowers, German researchers induced petunias to bear red flowers where pale pink was expected. The feat was accomplished by implanting petunia cells with a corn gene that produces a protein capable of making a red pigment.

Just as bees dance on their return to the hive to tell others where nectar-bearing flowers are, ospreys also communicate news of their catch. Scientists found that not only do other ospreys in the colony pick up hunting clues by observing what others bring back and from what direction they come, but successful hunters also call and dance on their return to alert others.

A semipalmated sandpiper set an avian record by flying 2,800 miles (4,500 kilometers) in four days from Massachusetts to northern South America. The shorebird made its historic flight in 1985, and researchers verified it in 1987. Its feat was discovered when it was killed by a hunter who mailed the bird's band back to the U.S.

The World Wildlife Fund declared a "panda

emergency" in March 1987 to draw attention to a new census showing a reduction in the number of pandas. The foundation blames habitat destruction and accidental ensnarement for a 200-panda drop in the past decade, leaving only 700 in the wild.

On the other hand, sea lampreys made an unwelcome comeback in the Great Lakes. Years ago the lampreys, which attach themselves to other fish and feed on their vital fluids, invaded the Great Lakes via a canal around Niagara Falls. They killed much of the salmon and trout before scientists found a chemical that killed lamprey larvae. But the larvae have become less sensitive, and now the lamprey has returned with a vengeance.

GENETICS AND THE ENVIRONMENT

In June, Gary Strobel of Montana State University injected 14 American elm trees with genetically engineered bacteria. He hoped to enable the trees to resist Dutch elm disease, a fungal infection that came to the U.S. 50 years ago and has decimated the population of American elm trees. But Strobel never saw the fruits of his labor. Because he had not received permission from the Environmental Protection Agency (EPA) to release a laboratory-created organism, a furor erupted and he destroyed the trees himself, three months after he had begun the experiment. Strobel later admitted that in an unrelated 1984 experiment, he had introduced altered bacteria into the soil of four states, also without permission.

While genetically engineered vaccines have been used before, 1987 saw the first authorized release of genetically altered bacteria into the environment. After four years of attempts, University of California at Berkeley scientists secured permission to test a bacterium designed to make plants frost-resistant.

The bacterium was created by snipping a

Biologists see the long-extinct crablike trilobites as evidence that evolution is a slow, gradual process.

gene from a common bacterium. With the gene intact, the bacterium acts as a seed for ice formation; without it, ice doesn't form as readily. Researchers hope the engineered bacterium will crowd out the natural variety when it is released in crop fields.

Hot weather and vandals damaged plants treated in the first release in April, necessitating a second planting. The scientists say the bacteria do not appear to have spread outside the treated fields.

The Patent Office announced a plan to begin issuing patents on genetically engineered organisms more complicated than bacteria (which it has already patented). But the attempt was stymied when Congress put the plans on hold.

PRODUCING PLANTS AND DRUGS

A Davis, California, company, Plant Genetics Inc., has developed artificial seeds from which it hopes to develop disease-resistant plants. Lettuce cells were grown in tissue culture and exposed to disease-causing chemicals. The surviving cells were converted into embryos, and coated with a degradable chemical.

The same basic concept of growing plant cells in culture is being used to develop better tomatoes and butter-flavored popcorn. Cells from corn and tomato plants are grown in culture, induced to differentiate, and their progeny surveyed for the desired characteristics.

The interaction between the lowly dung beetle and an antibiotic widely used in cattle has caused some concern among scientists. Antibiotic in the cattle's feces make the dung less attractive to the beetles, which play an important role in breaking down the dung. Scientists fear that lower numbers of beetles will leave more dung in the field, with detrimental effects on grasslands.

Two successful experiments reported in 1987 suggest that animals may someday become pharmaceutical factories. Scottish researchers hooked a sheep gene to a genetic "switch" turned on during milk production, and injected it into mouse embryos. As hoped, the adult mice produced the protein in their milk. The scientists then put similarly modified genes from two human proteins, one used in treating hemophilia and the other for a genetic form of emphysema, into sheep.

A Massachusetts company, Integrated Genetics, Inc., induced mice to produce TPA, an enzyme used in the treatment of heart attacks. The gene that produces TPA was hooked to a portion of a gene normally turned on when the mice lactate; the hybrid gene, inserted into the mice as embryos, caused them to produce TPA in their breast milk. The eventual goal: to get the gene into cows, where the collection and purification will be much easier.

JOANNE SILBERNER

© Susanna Pashko/Envision

Dogs use their keen sense of smell to detect the pheromones—chemical messages—deposited by their fellow canines.

A Sense of SCENTS

by Katherine Ambrus

Humans communicate with words that we can speak, read, or write. But how do animals communicate? Dogs growl and cats hiss when they feel threatened, but what do they do when they are interested in a cooperative relationship? Many animals—from bears to dogs to insects—can send messages with a language of chemicals. These chemicals, called pheromones, are different for each species. Various chemical combinations can relay different messages: to attract a mate, to find food, or to warn others against predators. Scientists have recently been able to isolate and even make pheromones in laboratories, so they can now study their effects on animals in controlled experiments.

Animals broadcast pheromones by releasing the chemicals into the environment. Some animals release pheromones through specialized glands. Rabbits have glands under their chins, ants have them on their legs, minnows have them on their skin, and monkeys have them on their hind ends. Other animals, such as rhinos, dogs, and bears, deposit a peculiar odor in their urine or feces. The odor then disperses through the air or water for other animals to receive. Bees and butterflies flap their wings in order to help transfer their pheromones.

Animals can detect each other's pheromones with a keen sense of smell. Some animals use olfactory cells in their noses, but insects use their antennae. Most people can distinguish more than 4,000 odors. German shepherd dogs, however, have about 44 times the number of olfactory cells humans have, and can thus distinguish many more scents. Bloodhounds, foxhounds, and retrievers are especially good at following a trail of odors. But ants, bees, and snakes are just as good. An animal is able to follow a scent because it can continuously sense when it is losing the trail. Thus, dogs are often seen sniffing back and forth in a zigzag motion.

Scientists have discovered that olfactory cells are directly connected to a part of the brain called the limbic system. It regulates motor activities, and sex, hunger, and thirst drives. It is thought that a pheromone directly stimulates a particular response in an animal. A male moth that detects a female moth's sex pheromone may not have a choice but to fly toward her.

Who Are You?

One way insects and animals can recognize each other is by means of pheromones. Each member of a family, group, or species has a unique set of chemical odors with which other members can identify and respond. Each species may have identical mixtures of chemicals, but the proportions of each chemical may vary from one individual to the next. Dogs, for example, often sniff the area where urine or feces have been deposited. With just one sniff they can tell if the depositor was another dog, if it was a male or female dog, and if the female dog is sexually active. Wolves can tell if the depositor was a dominant or submissive male. A dominant wolf has larger pheromone-releasing glands and urinates more often and in greater quantites than a submissive wolf. Scientists have further demonstrated this recognition through odor in laboratory animals. A male mouse was allowed to choose between a chamber with a male mouse of a different species, a chamber with another male of the same species, a chamber with a female of another species, and a chamber with a female of the same species. The male mouse preferred the chamber with the female of the same species. The experiment was then repeated with the female of the same species removed. The male mouse still preferred the same chamber because of the residual odor. Scientists claim that only the female of the same species can attract the male mouse, and that very specific chemicals stimulate his recognition behavior.

Other species can differentiate only between a familiar scent and a nonfamiliar scent. The blind goby fish, for example, lives in burrows in pairs. The male recognizes the female by means of a pheromone. Fish other than his mate that enter the burrow do not have the appropriate pheromone and will be attacked. A desert wood louse defends its burrow in a similar manner.

A common pheromone is often distributed between a mating pair, a family, or a group of animals. Rats, for example, crawl under and walk over each other and deposit drops of urine on each other. Rabbits also deposit scents upon each other. Social insects spread a common odor throughout a hive or nest to identify members of the colony. In honeybees, particular chemicals may be released from food waste or nest materials and will be absorbed onto bees'

Highly territorial animals such as wolves stake out their turf by means of pheromones. The timber wolf at right can tell whether the scent on the tree is from a dominant or submissive wolf. The gray wolf below rolls in urine-marked snow to pick up the scent.

© Bucky Reeves/Photo Researchers

The blind goby fish recognizes his mate by her pheromones, and he will attack any other fish that enters his burrow.

bodies. Any bee without the same odor will be attacked. However, if a foreign bee is placed in the hive and protected in a cage, it will soon absorb the odor of the colony and be accepted.

An important aspect of recognition is between the mother and her offspring. Sheep, goats, and black-tailed deer recognize their young by sniffing them at the rear area where pheromones are released. A mother ewe will not acknowledge her own lambs if plastic pants are placed over their hindquarters, covering the pheromone glands. Both rats and rabbits also use pheromones to identify their offspring; if they cannot smell the proper chemicals, they will attack, and may even kill, their own young. Unless a mother can recognize young animals as her own, she will reject them.

No Trespassing

An important message that animals need to communicate is who lives where. Many animals mark their living, feeding, and breeding areas in order to inform others. By depositing a scent around one's territory, an animal can also recognize its own home range. Wolves and dogs urinate on trees and logs. Often common points are used for marking, and one individual can tell by the strength of the odor if many others are in the area. Sometimes several wolves of a pack will even wait in line to urinate at the same place. Brown bears and bison urinate on the ground, roll in the urine, and then rub their

scents onto trees. Rabbits mark their territory by rubbing a pheromone from their chin glands onto shrubs and logs. Black rhinos spread their feces around by kicking at piles of dung with their hind legs. Honeybees and wasps deposit specific chemicals from their feet as they walk near or through the entrance to their hives. These pheromones let other animals know that the territory is already occupied. They also help to prevent overcrowding and competition for resources.

This Way

Some animals mark a trail with pheromones for themselves and others to follow. Ants, for example, deposit pheromones from glands on their legs as they march. These chemical signals can lead other ants to a food source. As more ants march on the trail, more chemicals are deposited. The ants can then follow the same trail home. Termites deposit trail pheromones from their abdomens. A bark beetle will send out chemical messages to other bark beetles when it has found an old or sick tree in which to burrow. This one beetle may stick to the tree's resin, but it can still release a pheromone in its feces. This pheromone, called an aggregation pheromone, attracts thousands of other beetles to come and colonize the tree. Under mass attack, the tree is left defenseless.

Rattlesnakes release a chemical in their venom. At first they only strike their prey and then wait for the venom to act before they begin to feed. Although the victim may be able to get a good distance before the venom enters its bloodstream, the rattlesnake can follow its trail because of the pheromone. This way the rattlesnake avoids injuries by its victim's teeth or claws. Since only the rattlesnake is sensitive to its own pheromone, the chemical trail does not invite others to the meal.

Watch Out

Other pheromones relay warning signals. An injured minnow, for example, releases a pheromone from its skin glands. The chemical tells other minnows of the possible danger and to flee the area, a so-called fright-reaction. Schooling fish often contain alarm pheromones that protect the entire school rather than each individual. Tadpoles develop glands with alarm substances as soon as they are able to swim. Water snails receive chemical signals when one gets crushed, and respond by burrowing into the bottom sediment. Earthworms, beetles, and ants also release alarm pheromones when one of their number is injured. This chemical warning system allows at least some members of a given species to escape from an attack.

Sex Pheromones

The first pheromones discovered in the late 1950s were sex pheromones in female moths. These pheromones were isolated from abdominal glands and were noted to attract male moths of the same species. Sex pheromones are released by one sex at specific stages of life, at

© Pat & Tom Leeson/Photo Researchers

A Rocky Mountain bighorn sheep finds its way to a potential mate by sniffing out airborne pheromones.

specific times of the year, and under specific conditions. Changes in weather, light intensity, nutritional levels, and population density bring about the release of sex pheromones. Only under optimal conditions will an individual be able to successfully mate; these chemicals may actually regulate the reproductive rates of many animals. They may be released by either males or females. One pheromone may only attract a

Chemical communication. Deer recognize family members and maintain proximity to one another through pheromones.

© Leonard Lee Rue III/Animals Animals

mate, while others are needed to stimulate the mating process. And yet another pheromone may be needed to stimulate the secretion of reproductive hormones; the presence of the male odor sparks the release of the female sex hormones in mice, cats, pigs, and sheep. Mating, it seems, is not a random, but a controlled process.

Scientists have considered the possibility of using sex-attractants to control insects and pest populations. It seems simple: attract one sex of a gypsy moth, cabbage looper, cottonpest, or the pink bollworm, and then trap it with a sticky resin. The practice, however, is difficult because sex pheromones require such specific conditions. For example, the way the chemical is released may reduce its attractiveness. If it is released too fast in too large quantities, the pheromone may no longer be attractive. The biggest problem so far has been keeping the chemical as pure as it is when released under natural conditions. In order to develop this potential, biological, chemical, and technical methods need to be researched. Intervening in nature's communication system requires perfection. Nevertheless, the prospect of reducing crop losses by using pheromones deserves attention.

Human Pheromones

Scientists are not certain if actual human pheromones exist. Many people may give off an odor when they sweat, but the effect on other people varies. Women, on the other hand, can recognize the smell of musk, an odor used in some perfumes, much more easily than men. They are also more sensitive to musk during their menstrual cycles. Many fragrances are commercially produced to give a sense of "freshness" to greeting cards, fabric softeners, and dishwashing liquids. Robert Henkm, a biologist at Georgetown University, is studying the possibility of odors reducing stress and anxiety in factory workers and violent behavior in prisons. If they do exist, however, human pheromones do not necessarily cause dramatic behavior changes. The biggest difference between human and animal communications is that people have the free will and consciousness to ignore a signal, whether it is a chemical signal or another type.

A Different Kind of Language

Scientists are just beginning to uncode the chemical language of pheromones. The variety of pheromones is possible because of the incredible number of different chemical combinations. A single ant gland, for example, may contain more than 40 different chemicals. Dog urine contains several hundred.

The ability to communicate with animals in their chemical language has both advantages and disadvantages. Reducing insect and rodent populations may promote healthy trees, fruits, and vegetables. However, altering critical messages about mating times, mother-offspring identification, and food sources could reduce the potential for a species to survive. An understanding of pheromones is more than an opportunity to interfere with natural processes. It is a calling for a deeper appreciation for nature's complexity.

© Franz J. Camenzind

A coyote establishes its ownership of an old moose carcass by urinating on it. Less aggressive animals who feed on the moose will do so at their own risk.

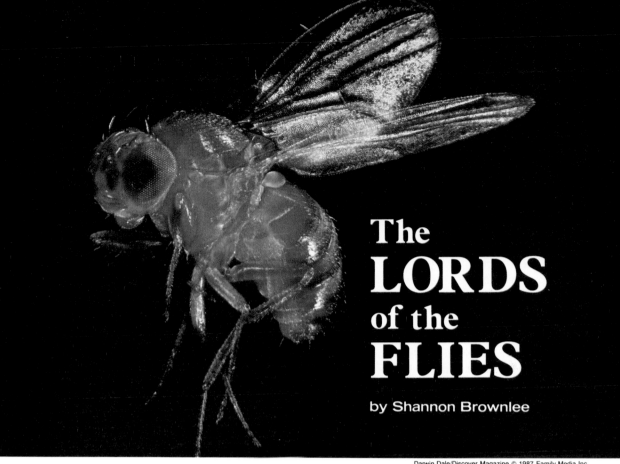

Fruit flies of genus Drosophila *have the simple chromosomes and short reproductive cycles ideal for genetic testing.*

The LORDS of the FLIES

by Shannon Brownlee

Each of the hundreds of flat-bottomed test tubes lining the shelves of the biology lab holds about a dozen fruit flies incessantly crawling over one another, their wings shimmering like miniature oil slicks. If these flies had imaginations, the lab would give rise to Frankensteinian dreams. To the naked eye, they resemble the fruit flies one might see hovering over ripe bananas on a summer's day. But look at one through a microscope. It leaps into focus, its body enormous, glossy; its head, thorax, abdomen, and legs covered with short black bristles. There are even a few on its wings. All perfectly normal. Not the eyes. They're sepia, a dull variation on the red eyes of normal flies. One of its genes for eye color has been mutated. Here's a fly with one good eye and a shrunken lump where its second should be. Here's one with four wings instead of the usual two. And here's another with an extra pair of perfectly formed legs—attached to its forehead where its antennae should be.

Bizarre deformities aren't remarkable in fruit-fly labs. They're the stock-in-trade of molecular biologists, whose attention these days is focused on a newly discovered piece of DNA (deoxyribonucleic acid). Deep within the insect, inside the nucleus of each cell on chromosome number 3, are several copies of a fragment of DNA called the homeo box, which may one day provide the answers to some of biology's most perplexing questions.

What is the Homeo Box?

The homeo box is a short stretch of genetic material embedded within a gene. It's composed of a specific sequence of 180 molecules, called base pairs, the molecules that make up the rungs of the double helix. Virtually identical versions of it have been found in at least 20 fruit fly genes. The homeo box's promise stems from the fact that most of the versions discovered are in developmental genes, the ones involved in the process of constructing a fly.

More significant, says Allen Laughon, a molecular biologist at the University of Colorado, is that "we're going to know how complex organisms evolved from simple ones." Homeo boxes have also been plucked from the DNA of a number of vertebrates—including humans—and their presence in such diverse animals has begun to shed light on a question that's as difficult to answer as it is profound: What are the threads binding evolution and development in all creatures? Of all the genes in the body, those controlling development seem the likeliest to have played a significant role in the appearance of new species.

Embryology of a Fruit Fly

During embryogenesis (formation of the embryo), a fruit fly—or any other animal—undergoes an astonishing transformation, a process by which a single cell—the fertilized egg—blossoms into the millions of specialized cells of the adult. Three hours after fertilization, when the insect-to-be is little more than a hollow, football-shaped blob, its 6,000 cells have already been assigned their destinies. They know which way is up and which down in the embryo, as well as which end is the front and which the back. The cells at the front will develop into a head; those in the middle will become two wings, six legs, and the thorax; those at the back will form the 10 segments of the abdomen.

Only a few of the genes involved in this process have been known for more than a decade, and those few were discovered only after nearly a century of analyzing fruit-fly genes. Modern genetics began in earnest around 1908—long after Mendel bred his peas—when *Drosophila melanogaster*, the common fruit fly, was taken into a lab at Columbia University by Thomas Hunt Morgan. In Morgan's lab, and later in others, flies were systematically mutated with radiation or chemicals, and bred and cross-bred to produce thousands of strains, each with its characteristic genetically controlled deformity—the indirect evidence of mutated genes.

Since Morgan's time, more than 1,000 genes in the fruit fly's small genome of 5,000 to 10,000 have been identified. Several hundred of those are for "housekeeping"—they code for proteins that the fly's cells need every day. Another hundred or so are less prosaic. They do things like give color to the fly's eyes and allot the right number of bristles to each leg. The remaining genes are the most interesting: they control the organization of the embryo.

Several—but not all—of these developmental genes have a seemingly capricious property. Mutations in them cause parts of a fly to grow in the wrong places. For example, a mutation in the gene Antennapedia makes legs sprout where antennae should be. A mutation in Ultrabithorax gives a fly four wings by turning the third segment of the thorax into a copy of the second, the segment that carries the wings.

Homeotic Genes

Such genes, which hold a particular fascination for geneticists, are called homeotic. By 1980 it was known that a number of the fruit fly's homeotic genes were situated in two clusters, called complexes, on the right arm of the third chromosome. Between them the complexes direct the formation of much of the fly's anatomy.

The discovery of these clusters gave rise to two provocative theories about homeotic genes.

William McGinnis, a Yale University molecular biologist, poses with a swarm of fruit flies. McGinnis found that homeo boxes—a DNA fragment found in certain fruit-fly chromosomes involved in the organism's development—also occur in beetles, mice, and even humans.

George Lange/Discover Magazine © 1987 Family Media Inc.

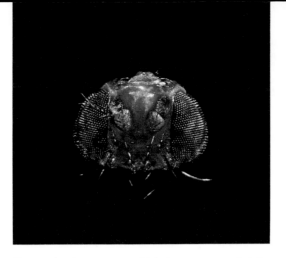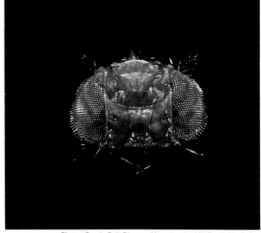

By mutating just one gene, biologists can create fruit flies with "sepia" eyes (left) rather than normal red ones.

The first was a wildly speculative notion proposed by Antonio García-Bellido of the Centro de Biología Molécular in Madrid, who portrayed homeotics as master-switch genes, each controlling a suite of other genes, flicking them on and off at just the right moment during embryogenesis. The fate of all fly cells, he suggested, might be controlled by just a few genes.

Edward Lewis, Caltech's grand old man of *Drosophila* genetics, propounded the other theory. Lewis had worked for more than 30 years on genes located in what turned out to be one of the homeotic complexes—work, according to Matthew Scott of the University of Colorado, "that's the real foundation of everything the rest of us do." Lewis postulated that the fly's homeotic genes had evolved from a single gene in a much simpler, millipede-like ancestor. The original homeotic gene, he said, took care of pattern formation, i.e., the arrangement of body parts, in the fly's ancestor. Duplicates of this gene, spliced in near the original, mutated and added layers of complexity to the evolving fly's form.

Lewis's theory had great appeal. For one thing, it explained how very different body forms could have come from minor genetic changes over millions of years. Developmental genes direct a creature's formation; changes in them cause changes in body form; and natural selection decides which ones are kept.

Building Intricate Patterns

According to Lewis's theory, changes in genes governing development pave the way for new species to become more complex. You start with one gene that does one job, like making legs. Copy it, and the duplicate will control something else—like inhibiting legs from appearing on certain body segments. This way you can build more intricate patterns. The fact that a mutation in Antennapedia causes antennae to be replaced with legs, for example, suggests that the gene or genes controlling antennae somehow default to those controlling legs.

The theory also struck an aesthetic chord. "If you look at invertebrates," says Laughon, "there are many different body plans, and they're certainly diverse. But there are some underlying themes in the way development occurs." Lewis's theory addressed the existence of rules and patterns, as yet undefined, that transcend the marvelous welter of biological life. Biologists seek these rules, trusting nature to disclose them. "The ultimate goal is understanding the common features, or perhaps the common constraints, on the evolution of all those body plans," says Laughon.

"Lewis's idea was beautiful," says William McGinnis, a molecular biologist at Yale. "Some of it may eventually turn out to be wrong, but it was so beautiful it just had to be tested."

A Single Ancestral Gene?

That's what McGinnis set out to do in the spring of 1983, while he was a postdoctoral fellow in the laboratory of geneticist Walter Gehring at the University of Basel. McGinnis persuaded Michael Levine, also a postdoc, and graduate student Ernst Hafen to join him in searching for evidence that homeotic genes all arose from a single ancestral gene.

Earlier that year, another of Gehring's postdocs, Richard Garber, had cloned a short piece of fly DNA, which turned out to contain

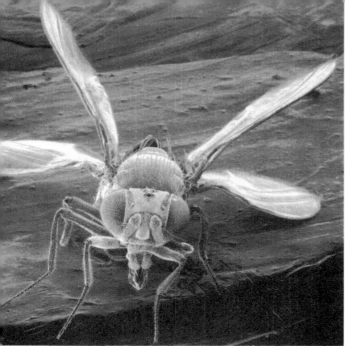

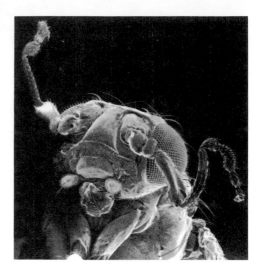

Most homeo boxes discovered so far are involved in the process of "constructing" the fly. Manipulation of such developmental genes has yielded a fruit fly with extra wings (left) and a bizarre mutant with legs where its antennae should be (above).

Photos: David Scharf/Discover Magazine © 1987 Family Media Inc.

the homeo box, though nobody knew it at the time. Garber did know that the clone was special: it came from a piece of Antennapedia, and it was homologous to a fragment of DNA from another fruit-fly gene. That is, the two gene segments had a similar genetic code, which is unusual. (Biologists can tell when two pieces of DNA are similar because both will stick to a third, complementary piece of DNA.)

Within three months, McGinnis and his team had evidence that five of the homeotic genes had strikingly similar sections. "The homologous regions didn't just dribble off at the ends," McGinnis says. They matched from the first base pair to the last. "They had very sharply defined limits, like the walls of a box," he says. They called it a homeo box—a box within the homeotic genes.

Simultaneous Discovery

Meanwhile, Scott also had stumbled upon the homeo box in the spring of 1983, while doing a postdoc in Thomas Kaufman's lab, where the complex named for the gene Antennapedia was first recognized. He was mapping mutations in a number of the complex's genes, including Antennapedia and a gene called fushi tarazu, which means "insufficient segments" in Japanese. (Called ftz—pronounced *futz*—for short, this gene isn't homeotic, because it doesn't put body parts in the wrong place when mutated; it produces flies with half the usual number of body segments, a defect that kills the embryo

before it can mature.) Scott was running fragments of the neighboring ends of Antennapedia and ftz out on a gel, a substance that separates DNA fragments according to size. When he added a clone of a fragment of Antennapedia, he was amazed to see it clinging where it had no business doing so—to a piece from ftz. "I thought it was a mistake at first," he says. He repeated his experiment. Same result.

Upon finding the homology between Antennapedia and ftz, Scott chose a very different tack from that taken by the McGinnis team: he decided to track down the sequences of the base pairs from his two regions. "I had to get the sequences," he says. "The homology could have been anything," including "nonsense" DNA, stretches of base pairs that litter genomes but apparently don't code for anything.

After a few weeks, Scott had his DNA sequence. He wrote out the letters corresponding to the base pairs from the homologous regions of the two genes. He then had to decipher what protein each region would code for. (Genes can be thought of as recipes for proteins, which are made of amino acids. Every protein has a different mix of these ingredients. A particular protein's sequence of amino acids corresponds to the sequence of the base pairs that code for it.)

Once he had transplanted the base pairs into amino acids, Scott compared the string of acids coded for by the Antennapedia homeo box with that from ftz, underlining on a piece of paper in blue pencil those that matched up. When he finished, his paper was covered with blue marks. Out of 60 amino acids, 51 were identical in both sequences—a remarkable degree of similarity for proteins coded for by such different genes.

McGinnis heard of Scott's discovery through the grapevine. Scott learned of McGinnis's work from Welcome Bender, a biochemist at Harvard who was providing DNA clones to both labs. Both were surprised to hear that somebody else had his homology. McGinnis, Levine, and Hafen hustled off a paper to *Nature* describing the existence of the homeo box in five different locations within the homeotic complexes, and it was published in March 1984.

Providential Yeast Research

Scott's paper was delayed by his move to Colorado. "I was all messed up, trying to begin my faculty job, writing grants, and setting up my lab," he says. Allen Laughon, one of the lab's first postdocs, who had been working with yeast as a graduate student at the University of Utah, soon arrived, and Scott gave him the task of analyzing the workings of the homeo box. He was the man for the job. "I knew from the first inklings, the first glimmerings of the homeotic

genes, that I wanted to come work with flies," he explains.

His yeast research turned out to be providential. Laughon had studied an unusual protein, of a type until then identified only in yeast and bacteria, that had the capability to attach itself to DNA, generally near the starting point of a gene. There was clear evidence from bacteria that by latching onto DNA in this way, these proteins could somehow turn genes on or off.

As Laughon examined the homeo box's protein, it began to look familiar. The homeo box codes not for an entire protein but for a little piece of it, called the homeo domain. To Laughon's practiced eye, part of the amino-acid sequence of the homeo domain looked remarkably like some of the amino-acid sequences of yeast and bacteria DNA-binding proteins. The agreement between the sequences in certain key places was so strong, in fact, that Scott and Laughon suspected that the homeo domain itself might be able to bind to DNA.

It was an extraordinary concept, because this meant that if the homeo domain was also like the yeast and bacterial proteins in the way it acted, a gene containing a homeo box might regulate other genes, as García-Bellido had postulated. The homeo domain could provide the

George Lange/Discover Magazine © 1987 Family Media Inc.

Blender biology: Michael Levine of Columbia University whips up an earthworm "broth" from which he extracts DNA. The earthworm's homeo box can then be isolated by a technique called a Southern blot.

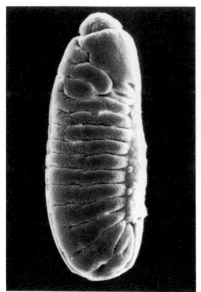
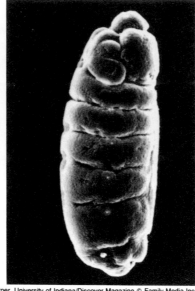

Geneticists have discovered the gene that maintains the correct number of body segments (far left) in a fruit fly embryo. By mutating the gene, an embryo is produced with half as many segments as normal (near left). Such mutants die before maturing.

Photos: F.R. Turner, University of Indiana/Discover Magazine © Family Media Inc.

biochemical means for this by serving as a sort of Velcro patch for taking hold of the DNA of other genes.

Blender Biology

In the meantime, McGinnis was pursuing further proof for Lewis's theory. He was convinced that the homeo box existed not only in other homeotic genes in the fruit fly, but also in those of other invertebrates. He went to a bait shop to buy some experimental subjects, then back to the lab to do a little blender biology. He put a few earthworms into the machine, pushed the button, strained the resulting "broth," and performed some biochemistry to get DNA. He spread the DNA out on a gel in what is known as a Southern blot, and the clone of the homeo box stuck. No sooner had he found the homeo box in earthworms than he did blender biology on beetles and *Drosophila virilis,* another fruit fly. In both cases the homeo box was there.

With the success of the barnyard blots, as he called the experiments, McGinnis began looking for the homeo box in animals higher up the evolutionary ladder. "We had a bunch of *Xenopus* [a South African toad] and calf DNA lying around the lab," he says, so he tested those and found the homeo box. He sought it in chickens, mice, and humans. And found it— five to 10 copies in the DNA of each of the species he tested, including humans.

The implications of this were stunning and twofold. First, it meant that Lewis was probably correct. The homeotic genes in *Drosophila* probably did arise in a more primitive invertebrate, only to be copied a number of times in the fruit fly. Second, the presence of the homeo box in invertebrates strongly suggested that there were genes regulating development doing very similar things in diverse species—and that a common set of rules might apply to the embryos of flies, chickens, and people.

Homeo-mania

Homeo-madness set in. Molecular biologists working in fields ranging from yeast to oncogenes gossiped about the latest word on the homeo box. Labs that had been sifting through other developmental genes in fruit flies quickly shifted their focus to homeotic genes. The journals were swamped with homeo-box papers. For the next six months, there was hardly an issue of *Cell* that didn't carry at least one paper on the subject, and for a brief time the homeo box even made the popular press.

The homeo box's mass appeal could be traced to its presence in mammals: the public may not give a hoot about worms and flies, but it does care about mice and people. Even scientists were startled by the similarity between vertebrate homeo boxes and those in the fruit fly. One homeo domain from *Xenopus* has the same amino-acid sequence as that from Antennapedia at all positions save one. Two homeo domains in human DNA are 90 percent similar to three in fruit flies.

The conservation of the homeo box through such a variety of species is remarkable, given that nature is so haphazard—especially since the common ancestor of insects and vertebrates lived in the Precambrian, more than 600 million years ago. The conclusion was inescapable: the homeo box serves a similar function during development in many species.

Segmentation Speculation

Some scientists speculated that the homeo box had to do with segmentation. After all, it's found mostly in the homeotic genes, which control the pattern of segments in *Drosophila*. Vertebrates are segmented, too. During its early stages, a chick, or frog, or human embryo looks a bit like a worm. Running up its back is a double row of pillowy mounds of cells, called somites (from the Greek *sōma*, for body), which give rise to musculature and skeleton. Many embryologists think of somites as imperfect and temporary segments.

Homeo fans began suggesting that in invertebrates the box might be contained in unknown genes controlling segmentation in the early embryo. Since no one knew (or knows) much about the genes controlling human development, the segmentation theory was difficult to dispute. Beyond that, at the time, nobody had yet been able to pull a homeo box out of the DNA of an unsegmented creature, like a bacterium or a nematode (roundworm).

If the genes (and their constituent homeo boxes) that regulate the arrangement of body parts were to be found in all animals, wrote British embryologist Jonathan Slack in 1984, "we really can anticipate that the problem of pattern formation, one of the deepest mysteries in biology, is on the point of final solution." Small wonder that *Nature* called the homeo box the biological equivalent of the Rosetta stone.

As often happens, the euphoria dissipated. The mysteries of pattern formation haven't been easily unraveled, and critics of homeo-madness have emerged. Among their main targets are molecular biologists who were ensnared in the syllogism that the homeo box governs segmentation in all species. Just because it's found in genes regulating segmentation in *Drosophila* doesn't mean that it's necessarily located in segmentation genes in other organisms, which may not even have such genes. "I never believed this," says Scott. "The homology between insect DNA and human suggested to me that the homeo box wasn't related specifically to segmentation—but that maybe it was related to more fundamental aspects of pattern formation during development." And, in fact, the homeo box has recently been pulled from the DNA of sea urchins and yeast, two unsegmented creatures. So much for the segmentation theory.

The Homeo-Box Hook

Before the homeo box came along, most biologists figured that understanding the genetics of development in vertebrates, especially humans, would be impossible for many years to come. They talked about having hit the wall. This wasn't surprising. Says Scott: "We haven't got 75 years of genetic analysis of mutants in humans as we have for the fruit fly." Or, as another molecular biologist puts it, "You can't very well go around asking weird-looking people to breed with each other." Until the discovery of the homeo box, the genes that choreograph the dance of cells in the embryo seemed unreachable, hidden within the immortal coil's embrace.

But now scientists are fishing for developmental genes in invertebrates, using clones of the homeo box as a hook; any vertebrate DNA sequence homologous to the homeo box is almost certainly contained in an important gene. At least six homeo boxes have already been found in human DNA, and 12 in that of mice. Half of those 12 are clustered on two chromosomes, just as they're clustered in the homeotic complexes on *Drosophila*'s chromosome 3.

In April 1986, a paper appeared with unambiguous evidence that a gene containing the homeo box is active before a human embryo is 10 weeks old. With a technique involving radioactive probes, biologists in Europe and the U.S. have watched "homeogenes" turn on in mouse embryos only eight days after conception.

A Look Ahead

Laughon and Scott's suggestion that the homeo domain can cling to DNA has been borne out experimentally. Not only that, but the homeo domain binds to specific sequences of base pairs. The next step is finding the locations of those sequences. Are they at the beginning of other developmental genes? And if so, are those genes regulated via homeo domains? With each new experiment, the homeo box opens a door on what Scott calls huge vistas. Scientists may say they're seeking facts, even the truth, but for many of them, real excitement lies not in the answers, but in finding new questions.

DRUGS from the SEA

by Eleanor Smith

People in every culture have looked to nature's chemistry to relieve them of pain and disease. Chinese and Native Americans relied on herbal remedies and stimulants for thousands of years, grinding the roots and fruits of medicinal plants to cure their ills and enhance spiritual experiences. And since the late 1800s, when Western scientists isolated morphine from the sap of the opium poppy, thousands of potent drugs from natural sources have become part of the armament of modern pharmacologists.

Medicine's weapons today include digitalis, from the flowering foxglove, for heart disease; a wealth of antibiotics, many derived from fungi, to treat infections; and aspirin, from the bark of a willow tree, for pain and fever. In fact, nearly one-half of all drugs currently in use have their origins in nature, primarily in land-based plants.

Turning Seaward

By the middle of this century, terrestrial species were yielding few new chemicals. So scientists, eager to explore an untapped realm, turned to the sea.

Early efforts to find active substances in ocean dwellers have yielded drugs with antiviral activity, which were designed from unusual segments of DNA first found in a sponge in 1951. Despite this early encouragement, technical obstacles had dampened optimism among researchers until recently, according to marine

chemist William Fenical. He explains that "most of those early discoveries did not lead to new drugs." But with advances in methods to detect and separate complex chemicals, Fenical says, the past few years have brought "sophistication of the science, as well as solid evidence that there will indeed be marine pharmaceuticals."

Today dozens of scientists around the world, particularly in the U.S., Japan, and Australia, are scouring the seas for marine organisms with novel chemistry. Many of the experts met to discuss their work during a May 1987 symposium on "Biomedical Importance of Marine Organisms" at the California Academy of Sciences.

In addition to possibly unraveling some of nature's ecological mysteries, scientists agree, chemicals found in sea species offer hope of finding new ways to treat cancer, heart disease, acquired immune deficiency syndrome (AIDS), and other scourges of society. Just last year the National Cancer Institute (NCI) launched an

Specimens of exotic plants and animals collected from the ocean floor may yield entirely new classes of medicines for treating disease.

ambitious program to collect and screen compounds from marine organisms that might show selective activity against certain types of human tumors.

Two paths of technological development have converged to allow this new search for active undersea substances. With improvements in scuba gear and submersible research vessels, it is safer than ever to spend time underwater exploring for and collecting specimens. And sophisticated instruments now enable chemists to separate natural substances efficiently, accurately, and with a high degree of purity.

Moreover, discoveries of powerful new types of chemicals in marine organisms have spurred greater cooperation not only among different scientific disciplines, but also between academic researchers and the pharmaceutical industry.

Ecological Considerations

In order to determine which of the myriad marine species should be collected and tested for unusual, potentially useful compounds, natural-products scientists need to rely on a knowledge of ecology. They observe interaction among different species, the habitats they are adapted to, and the defense mechanisms they employ. "If an organism is poorly defended physically, it stands a higher chance of being defended chemically," says John Faulkner, marine chemist at the Scripps Institution of Oceanography in San Diego.

For example, the soft-bodied sea hare (genus *Aplysia*) possesses a powerful means of fending off predatory fish and lobsters. *Aplysia* can not only safely eat certain red algae, which contain a set of toxins, but it turns the algae's defense to its own advantage. The sea hare concentrates within its digestive gland the poison it ingests, then transports some of the compounds to its skin, secreting a bitter-tasting mucus that in turn discourages its own enemies.

Nudibranchs, gaily colored sea slugs, were able to give up their shells during evolution because they carry out a similar strategy. They dine on certain toxin-containing sponges and, like their relative *Aplysia*, concentrate the noxious chemicals in their digestive glands. The chemicals are later exuded in an unappetizing skin mucus. Some nudibranchs feed on others of their kind, Faulkner points out, so that chemicals can "pass up the food chain to the predatory nudibranchs."

"The shell-less mollusks do a lot of the chemist's job for us," Faulkner adds. Instead of searching through sponge or algal tissues for the first clues to a potential drug, he and his colleagues collect sea hares and nudibranchs. Then, with sensitive detection methods such as high-pressure liquid chromatography and mass spectroscopy, the scientists identify the concentrated chemical contents of the creatures' digestive glands and mucus.

Fish Assays

In the laboratory meanwhile, marine-products researchers can check to see if specimens they have collected might contain substances that deter native predators from feeding. In experiments a fish's preferred food is coated with a sponge extract, for example, and offered to fish kept in an aquarium. If hungry fish refuse to eat, the researchers know the sponge extract contains a feeding deterrent.

Many bioassays in the lab have employed goldfish, which Faulkner describes as "ecologically irrelevant" subjects for tests of extracts from marine species. One of his own assays uses spotted kelp fish, which are fed adulterated shrimp from a pipette—a laboratory dispenser similar to a large eyedropper. In Faulkner's "barfing fish assay," the kelp fish's face will turn bright red, "like a person eating hot curry," as it spits out any distasteful morsel. A kelp fish's violent reaction offers strong evidence that an adulterant contains a natural feeding deterrent. Then, Faulkner says, "by following up feeding inhibitors in marine organisms, you can sometimes find pharmacologically active chemicals."

Chemicals isolated from extracts of sea dwellers are tested further, in simple assays that judge their ability to kill bacteria, viruses, or tumor cells cultured in the lab. Once a newly identified compound shows activity in such assays, however, it is still a long and complicated way from becoming a useful drug. Possible toxic effects on animals and people must be weighed against therapeutic promise. Often, a set of look-alike compounds must be synthesized to determine whether small chemical modifications might reduce toxicity without robbing the potential drug of its action against infection or cancer. This approach provided medicine with the antiviral drugs Ara-A and acyclovir, both of which are modified versions of unusual DNA building blocks isolated from a sponge in the early 1950s.

Years of Study

The time from discovery of a promising marine-derived pharmaceutical to the end of clinical trials averages 10 to 14 years. As with any new drug, the costs are enormous, ranging from $30 million to $60 million. Neither universities nor government agencies can afford to take a drug all the way from discovery to synthesis, and from clinical trials to market, according to Robert Jacobs, a pharmacologist at the University of California, Santa Barbara. "By and large, the pharmaceutical companies are the ones equipped to conduct clinical trials," he says.

To share the cost and labor, cooperative arrangements between academic scientists and industrial laboratories have been formed to study natural products from the sea. "Collaborative efforts between university research groups and pharmaceutical companies offer the best hope for developing marine pharmaceuti-

Above: © Al Grotell; below: © Dr. Deborah M. Roll

Scientists have concentrated on substances produced by sea organisms for self-defense. Chemicals manufactured by the purple sea squirt (above) to help it maintain living space on the ocean floor also may prove effective against cancer cells. Nudibranches (right and bottom right) and sea hares (bottom left) feed on poisonous algae and sponges. The toxins are concentrated in their digestive glands and secreted as a bitter-tasting mucus that deters predators. The chemical contents of their digestive glands and mucus are now being evaluated for possible medical applications.

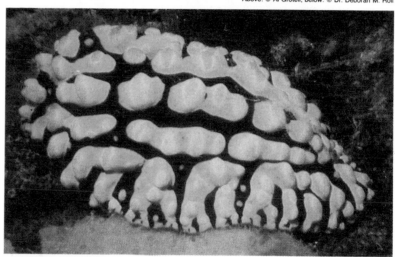

Harbor Branch Oceanographic Institution, Inc.

© Al Grotell

cals," Faulkner says. He and his colleagues work with scientists at a number of pharmaceutical firms.

The $28 billion-a-year pharmaceutical industry guarantees return on its investment either by patenting new compounds as they are discovered, or by purchasing the option to produce a new compound from the university that discovered and patented it. A patent or option gives the company exclusive rights to manufacture and market a drug. Pharmaceutical companies stand to make huge profits from a unique, bioactive compound. Fenical estimates that a new, improved arthritis drug would reap a billion dollars a year for the company that develops it.

Environmental Impact

To conduct chemical and pharmacological tests, scientists must have adequate supplies of the active compounds. So far, the principal source of new materials is organisms collected in the wild. What effects does "harvesting" of sponges, algae, and other marine organisms have on their native habitats?

Scientists who take specimens for research insist that collection, particularly in shallow water by scuba divers, has negligible ecological impact. Marine chemist Phillip Crews of the University of California, Santa Cruz, says he and his divers cull only abundant species. He compares this type of collecting to "going into a redwood forest with an ax—you just can't destroy a reef."

Faulkner even points to complications that arise because his group is so restrained in their collection methods: "We have trouble finding where we did collecting before. It's all regrown. We take no more than one in 10 specimens in any location, and we have a policy of staying away from tourist areas."

Yet some researchers admit that while shallow-water culling by divers has no lasting environmental effects, collection to supply industry may not be so benign. Clearly, other methods for acquiring sufficient quantities of marine compounds must be found. Alternatives include chemical synthesis, a painstaking and expensive way to re-create the molecular structure of a compound already identified as interesting. Modified molecules, or analogues, may indeed be found to work as well as or better than the original, and they may be easier and less expensive to synthesize.

High-Tech Alternatives

Other alternatives to collection include aquaculture. A Caribbean species of *Trididemnum,* which produces didemnin B, an antitumor

A Harbor Branch Foundation chemist uses liquid chromatography to separate and purify chemicals from sea organisms.

Harbor Branch Oceanographic Institution Inc.

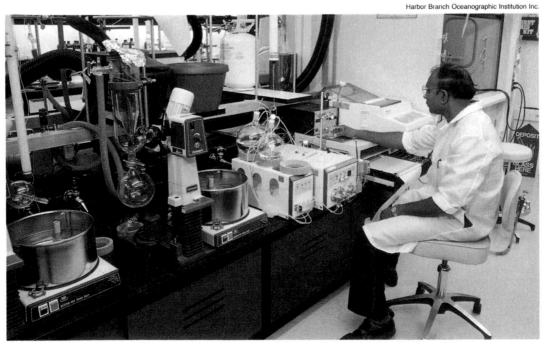

Submersibles allow divers to scour the deep ocean floor for undiscovered sources of therapeutic drugs.

agent, is now being cultured at the University of Hawaii. In some instances, cultivation of microbial symbionts—microorganisms that live in the host organism—reveals that the symbiont actually possesses the biologically active chemistry attributed to the host.

Production of an active compound or a close molecular relative can also be achieved through genetic engineering. The gene for the compound of interest is identified and isolated from the natural host, and is then introduced into the genetic material of more easily grown organisms such as *E. coli* or yeast cells. Cultured on an industrial scale, the new microbial hosts with the spliced-in gene will produce the compound, which usually can be purified with relative ease.

While research continues on the best means to produce adequate quantities of compounds from the sea without harming habitats, scientists around the country are making progress on a number of new pharmaceutical leads. SeaPharm of Princeton, New Jersey, the nation's first pharmaceutical company devoted solely to development of marine-derived drugs, is optimistic about two of their compounds. "We're aiming to have clinical trials as soon as possible on both," says SeaPharm president

Juan Carlos Torres. "One is an antitumor agent, and the other is an antiviral compound."

In 1983 SeaPharm joined forces with the Harbor Branch Foundation, a nonprofit research institute in Fort Pierce, Florida, to collect and screen marine compounds for activity against tumors, fungi, and viruses, or for effects on immunity. Scientists aboard Harbor Branch research vessels can conduct preliminary assays at anchor by the site where samples were found. Should a specimen yield an extract that gives encouraging preliminary results, SeaPharm divers quickly can collect more.

Under a $3.5 million contract with the NCI, SeaPharm scientists are now searching shallow waters in the Indo-Pacific region, and deep waters in the Caribbean and the Atlantic Ocean, for potential new drugs. NCI began an ambitious program in the fall of 1986 to collect and screen compounds from marine organisms for selective activity against slow-growing, solid human tumors, such as lung, colon, and breast cancers, according to Matthew Suffness, director of the NCI's Natural Products Branch. Chemotherapy with existing drugs already helps against fast-growing tumors such as leukemias, Suffness notes, but few agents are available to kill the slower-growing ones. NCI's program will also look for compounds to selectively attack the AIDS virus, a high priority for new drug development.

New Drugs in the Works

Meanwhile, scientists in California are working on a variety of marine-derived chemicals with exciting properties. In 1979 Faulkner of the Scripps Institution collected a sponge, *Luffariella variabilis,* in the tropical waters off Palau. He and U.C. Santa Barbara's Jacobs subsequently discovered that the sponge contained a powerful new anti-inflammatory and analgesic agent, manoalide, which had already been named by Paul Scheuer, a chemist at the University of Hawaii who collected and isolated the same compound at about the same time. Manoalide's development has been taken up by Allergan, Inc., a subsidiary of SmithKline Beckman based in Irvine, California. Allergan is currently conducting toxicity tests in animals, in preparation for clinical trials in humans.

One of the drug's apparent advantages, Jacobs explains, is that "manoalide works very early in the pain and inflammation process. Unlike any existing drugs, it blocks the release of the initiating enzyme and thus prevents pain and inflammation from occurring."

Inflammation results from a complex interplay among the chemical messengers that the body's cells use to communicate with each other and coordinate action. When a skin cell encounters an irritant, for example, an enzyme in its cell membrane called phospholipase A2 begins a biochemical cascade. Mediators in the cascade mobilize white cells from the immune system, and stimulate surrounding skin cells to divide, in an attempt at repair. In some skin disorders such as psoriasis, the messages are inappropriate, and skin cells mistakenly proliferate.

Manoalide blocks the action of phospholipase, and may prevent the "second messenger"—which is calcium—from spreading the word that tells tissues to swell, according to biochemist Larry Wheeler, head of the group at Allergan that is investigating the new agent.

"We think it can be used in conditions such as arthritis, muscular dystrophy, and some progressive skin diseases," says Jacobs. "But because we're dealing with a substance that inactivates an enzyme never before inactivated, it's going to be awhile before we know if manoalide will ever be a useful drug."

At Scripps, Fenical and his marine chemist colleagues have isolated another intriguing anal-gesic and anti-inflammatory compound from a Caribbean soft coral, or sea whip, *Pseudopterogorgia elisabethae*. Like manoalide, pseudopterosin represents a novel class of chemicals. It, too, acts early in inhibiting the production of pain and inflammation, though at a different step than manoalide. In experiments with mice, pseudopterosin was more potent than indomethacin, a standard, aspirin-like drug for arthritis and other inflammatory conditions. It also seems relatively free of toxicity, according to Fenical. If further research and development is successful, pseudopterosin could eventually be used to treat psoriasis or arthritis.

U.C. Santa Cruz chemist Crews is hopeful about three compounds he has isolated from the *Jaspis* group of sponges, natives of the South Pacific. One compound, jasplakinolide, looked like it would be useful against *Candida* fungus, a common cause of vaginitis in women, and of a mouth infection called thrush in people whose immunity is weakened, such as transplant recipients or AIDS patients. But studies found jasplakinolide to be too toxic. Crews says less toxic analogues of the original molecule are being tested by his industrial partner, Syntex Corporation of Palo Alto, California. The other two compounds derived from other *Jaspis* species have meanwhile displayed antibiotic and antiparasitic activity in early tests.

Most encouraging is progress with didemnin B, a potent antitumor agent first discovered in 1976 in an extract of a Caribbean tunicate, a bloblike creature also known as a sea squirt. Led by Dr. Kenneth Rinehart, scientists from the University of Illinois isolated a class of chemicals they called didemnins, after the tunicate genus *Trididemnum*. Didemnin B was found to be the most effective in reducing the size of tumors in animals.

The compound has been synthesized by chemists, and is the first marine compound ever to enter clinical testing in humans as a natural product from the sea. It is currently being tested for safety and efficacy in patients with a variety of cancers, under NCI's auspices. If all goes smoothly, didemnin B or one of its chemical relatives will become an important new cancer-fighting agent.

Speaking at the academy symposium, Fenical displayed optimism that has been lacking for many years in those who have been panning the ocean for new therapeutic products. "We're confident now that we're on the right track, that we will accomplish what we set out to do."

The DEADLY GAME of STEROIDS

by Roger W. Miller

Athlete Information Bureau

Canadian weightlifter Terry Hadlow and countless other athletes have taken steroids illegally to build muscle bulk and to reduce recovery time between workouts. What improvement from steroid abuse occurs, however, is more than offset by adverse side effects.

Politics and sports usually don't mix too much, but the legacy of just such a mixture some 30 years ago has left modern America with another serious drug problem—abuse of anabolic steroids.

The Soviets provided the politics in the 1950s when they gave their athletes—both men and women—a male hormone called testosterone that apparently helped the competitors build muscle. As a result, they dominated many international sports events at the time.

An American doctor, who was later to regret his action, sought to even the score in those coldest of the Cold War days by developing for our athletes a variation of a drug that was related to testosterone. The doctor came up with a form of anabolic steroid for use by weight lifters that was supposed to build muscle while minimizing masculinizing side effects. The weight lifters who found that the prescribed 5-milligram (mg) pills helped build muscle assumed immediately that 10 mg, or two pills, would add even more muscle, 15 mg more yet, and so forth. The race was on.

Widely Used and Abused

Today anabolic steroids are widely abused by young athletes in search of bigger muscles. This drug abuse involves boys not yet in their teens; high school, college, and professional athletes; and bodybuilders of both sexes.

A more recent problem, according to experts on the subject, is the use of anabolic steroids by law enforcement officers who are lifting weights and using steroids to make themselves more imposing to criminals. The *Miami Herald,* in a May 19, 1987, article, quoted a Florida police chief as saying more police officials should be aware of the problem, adding: "There's a great potential for an officer abusing steroids to physically mistreat people." In fact, possibly the first misuse, or, as the medical people say, the first "nonclinical application," of anabolic steroids was by the Nazis in World War II, who gave them to their troops to make them more aggressive.

Steroids were first developed in the 1930s to build body tissue and prevent the breakdown of tissue that occurs in some diseases. But a Food and Drug Administration (FDA) review of these drugs years later failed to find evidence that they were effective for those purposes.

Anabolic steroids can produce a host of side effects and adverse reactions. They include liver cancer, cardiovascular problems, sterility, testicular atrophy, jaundice, and masculinization of female fetuses in pregnant women taking steroids, among others. What's more, steroids don't mix with some other drugs, a fact that can add to the list of unwanted consequences. Actually, the total side-effect picture is unknown, for it remains to be seen what complications will develop for today's iron pumpers who take steroids in large quantities and for extremely long periods of time. It is known that some Communist athletes in the 1950s were given so much testosterone that many of the men developed large prostates and had to be catheterized (have a tube inserted in the penis) in order to urinate. And some women athletes had to submit to chromosome tests to prove that they were really women because of the extensive masculinizing effects of the drugs.

Muscle-Gain Controversy

Although the numerous side effects of steroids are unquestioned, the drugs' ability to increase muscle mass has not been fully verified. The current *AMA Drug Evaluations,* published by the American Medical Association, says the evidence on the muscle-building ability of steroids is "equivocal." Writing in the September 1987 issue of *Clinical Pharmacology,* researchers Michael W. Kibble and Mary B. Ross concluded that steroids increase muscle mass and strength "only in persons who are already weight-trained and who continue intensive training while maintaining high-protein, high-calorie diets."

What muscle gain there is may be offset by injuries associated with use of the drugs. That possibility was noted in a *Journal of the American Medical Association* article (January 20/27, 1987): "It seems likely that their use may expose athletes to the risk of injury to ligaments and tendons and that these injuries may take longer to heal."

Weight lifting has gained enormously in popularity in recent years. Not all that long ago, musclemen were looked on as freaks of sorts. Even as recently as 1973, *The Wall Street Journal* ran a front-page feature story on the U.S. heavyweight lifting champion under the headline: "Weight-Lifting Champ Frets as U.S. Yawns Over His Achievement." The champ was quoted in the story as saying, "Do you think I like having people make fun of me?"

But that was four years before the Arnold Schwarzenegger movie *Pumping Iron* transformed barbells and big biceps into status symbols. The movie sent young men thronging to health clubs and gymnasiums. There they found out about steroids.

Knowledge of the value of weight lifting gradually spread, as athletes in other sports, particularly football and track, but also some baseball players, put on muscle to play their games better. It was only a matter of time before pumping iron—and using steroids—got into high schools and even junior high schools.

Women have also taken to pumping iron and using steroids, as have young men who are not even interested in athletics. In using steroids to build muscle, women athletes run a particular risk, as some of the side effects, including male pattern baldness and a deepened voice, are irreversible.

Some young men are interested in taking steroids because they believe a more muscular physique will make them look more appealing to young women. Or they don't want to look like "wimps," which seems to be the word of choice these days for degrading a young man's masculinity.

The popularity of anabolic steroids is attested to by the growth of a large black market and the development of quack steroid products. Conservative estimates put the black-market gross at $100 million a year. A lot of the black-market products come from underground labs and foreign countries and are of questionable quality and purity.

Some doctors have readily written prescriptions for athletes. Robert Voy, M.D., chief medical officer for the U.S. Olympic Committee, tells of a small study that he did indicating that 30 percent to 40 percent of the steroids used by bodybuilders came from physicians. However, he believes those figures are dropping as doctors become more aware of the drugs' dangerous side effects. Malpractice suits are further cutting into the mindless prescribing of these drugs.

Many athletes claim they take steroids to help mend their bodies after injuries. But the *AMA Drug Evaluations* calls this a "medically trivial indication." The only uses FDA allows on anabolic-steroid labels are for treating certain types of anemia; certain kinds of breast cancer in women; and hereditary angioedema, a type of allergic reaction to some insect bites, foods, viruses, and so forth.

Some athletes claim that steroids quicken recovery from sports injuries, despite medical evidence to the contrary.

Testing for Steroids

Despite such limitations, use of anabolic steroids by football players has become notorious. In a celebrated case late in 1986, a University of Oklahoma All-American was barred from a bowl game because he tested positive for steroids. In 1987 the National Football League (NFL) checked for steroids for the first time in training camps and set standards for steroid levels. A player who tests positive is sidelined for 30 days; two additional positive readings of equal or higher levels result in being barred from the league. The NFL has also started an education effort that includes a videotape on the dangers of steroid use.

Testing to detect steroids has been used for a number of years in major track-and-field and weight-lifting events. These days some athletes look for ways to cheat the test, as evidenced in a recent bodybuilding magazine in which a British lifter bragged of using water-based steroids because, he said, they couldn't be detected after a day or two. Dr. Voy, the U.S. Olympic medical director, scoffs at that idea. "Let them think that's true," he remarks.

Testing is becoming more sophisticated all the time. The magazine *Muscle & Fitness* notes in its August 1987 issue that: "Steroid detection today exists in the nanogram range, or one *billionth* of a gram." (Italics original.) In some cases, the magazine adds, detection can be made of one-quarter part per billion.

While testing may be better, it apparently has not stopped the growth of the drugs' popularity. Experts such as Dr. Voy; Bob Goldman, D.O., author of *Death in the Locker Room;* and FDA's Don Leggett, who handles enforcement efforts against illegal steroid sales, agree that the problem has become more widespread, involving younger children and more groups.

Enforcement Efforts

FDA, the U.S. Justice Department, and the Customs Service are cracking down on the steroid black market. In May 1987, their efforts resulted in a 100-count indictment against 34 people, including a former British Olympic medalist. The indictment charged that counterfeit steroids were manufactured and smuggled from a pharmaceutical lab in Tijuana, Mexico. The individuals had a potential of doing $70 million worth of steroid business a year.

But enforcement efforts aren't going to do it alone, especially with some coaches pushing steroid use on young athletes. "Our children have got to know what steroids really are," says FDA Commissioner Frank E. Young, M.D., Ph.D. "These things aren't a simple shortcut to building muscle. They're complex chemicals that the body doesn't handle easily, particularly in the amounts being taken by many weight lifters and athletes. Anabolic steroids can be dangerous—deadly dangerous." FDA, the Department of Education, and the Drug Enforcement

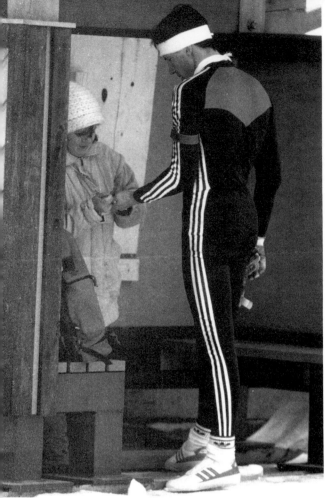

© Sportschrome

Widespread steroid abuse has led to testing of both amateur and professional athletes. The biathlon champion above submits to the blood test required of all winners at the World Cup games. Computerized results (below) register steroid levels as low as one-billionth of a gram.

Focus on Sports

Administration (DEA) have joined together in sponsoring a public education program on steroids, aimed mainly at youngsters.

One problem with trying to educate youth is that young people tend to believe they're immortal. Death, they think, is for old people. Another difficulty is that many of the bad effects of steroids might not show up for a decade or two after the user begins taking the drugs. Cardiovascular problems and liver tumors 10 years down the road aren't going to get much consideration from a high school senior trying to make first-string linebacker. Young athletes should know that there are dozens of other steroid reactions, and that some, such as acne and uncontrollable 'roid rages (aggressive and combative behavior), might cause immediate difficulties. Our sports-loving society probably also needs to reexamine the fanaticism embedded in the philosophy that "winning isn't everything—it's the only thing."

There's little doubt that steroids can affect human behavior. And withdrawal from steroids can bring on problems that may make an abuser want to go back on the drugs, or take other drugs. Steroids may be considered an ongoing physical necessity for an athlete or bodybuilder when he or she finds, upon withdrawal, that some weight and muscle mass are quickly lost. (There is evidence to indicate that the weight loss is really just water, as steroids cause water retention in the body.) Also, depression can result from withdrawal, prompting some former abusers to turn to amphetamines for a lift.

Steroid Metabolism

A look at how the body uses testosterone, which anabolic steroids mimic, gives an idea of why steroids are so dangerous. Testosterone is secreted by the testes in mature men in quantities of 2.5 mg to 10 mg daily. (Those who use steroids to build muscle often "stack" them—i.e., take a combination of brands in quantities of 100 mg or more daily.) Testosterone stimulates and maintains many of the sex organs, including the penis, prostate gland, and the semen sacs. The hormone also, as explained in *Remington's Pharmaceutical Sciences,* "stimulates the development of bone, muscle, skin, and hair growth and emotional responses to produce the characteristic adult masculine traits."

Women produce little testosterone: thus, their use of steroids leads to the development of masculine characteristics such as balding, facial hair, enlarged clitoris, and deepened voice.

THE BAD NEWS ABOUT STEROIDS

Established side effects and adverse reactions from anabolic steroids

Acne	Hirsutism (hairiness in women—irreversible)	Peliosis hepatitis (a liver disease)
Cancer		
Cholesterol increase	Increased frequency of erections (boys)	Penis enlargement (young boys)
Clitoris enlargement		
Death	Increased risk of coronary artery disease (heart attack, stroke)	Priapism (painful, prolonged erections)
Edema (water retention in tissue)		Prostate enlargement
	Jaundice	Sterility (reversible)
Fetal damage	Liver disease	Stunted growth
Frequent or continuing erections (mature males)	Liver tumors	Swelling of feet or lower legs
	Male pattern baldness (in women—irreversible)	
HDL (which helps reduce cholesterol) decrease		Testicular atrophy
	Oily skin (females only)	Yellowing of the eyes or skin
Heart disease		

But if testosterone is basically a sex hormone, how can too much of it in the body stunt growth, or result in female breasts for males, or cause cardiovascular problems such as heart disease or stroke? The answer requires an appreciation of the human body. When testosterone levels get too high, the hypothalamus within the brain takes note. It acts to shut down processes in the body involving testosterone. In an adolescent, bone growth stops.

The feminization of male breasts is another example of action by the hypothalamus. With excessive testosterone in the blood, that brain unit sends a signal to the pituitary gland to stop producing the hormone gonadotropin, which in turn stops the testicles from producing more testosterone. The process may remain shut down when steroids are discontinued, leading to an imbalance of male and female hormones within the body—and the development of unsightly, enlarged breasts that even can produce milk.

Cardiovascular problems can come about as follows: steroids cause fluid retention, which in turn can lead to high blood pressure. Steroids also lower high-density lipoproteins (HDLs) in the blood. HDLs help rid the body of cholesterol. Too much cholesterol in the body leads to the formation of plaque on the walls of arteries. Eventually the arteries get clogged, possibly causing stroke or heart attack.

Legitimate Steroid Use

A few anabolic-steroid compounds are available by prescription. They come in tablet or injectable form. The listing of these drugs in the *Physicians' Desk Reference* runs less than 10.

However, the August 1987 issue of *Muscle & Fitness* magazine listed 22 steroids that are "commonly tested" for. Dr. Voy, in a 1986 speech to the American Pharmaceutical Association, said there are about 80 testosterone derivatives available, including the veterinarian supply.

Records of U.S. sales of anabolic steroids are incomplete. However, such sales are recorded in Norway, where a 42 percent increase was noted in one nine-year period.

The recommended dosages for steroids used for legitimate purposes may range from 1 mg a day to as much as 400 mg intramuscularly (by injection into a muscle) every three to six weeks. These amounts are a far cry from those being "stacked" by some bodybuilders.

There seem to be some indications, in reading the muscle magazines, that the popularity of steroids is waning among bodybuilders. Writing in *Musclemag,* columnist Garry Bartlett said: "Drugs will only ruin your chances of developing a championship physique. My advice to you is to avoid steroids like the plague."

And in *Muscle & Fitness,* Lee (Mr. Olympia) Haney says: "You will ultimately make your best bodybuilding gains if you avoid steroid usage and just concentrate on hard training and good nutrition. But many young and impressionable body builders get on drugs within a couple of weeks or months of starting to pump iron. . . . The gains they make are lost very quickly—within a few weeks—once they get off the juice. You're much better off—both in terms of health and ultimate bodybuilding gains—if you train naturally."

Physiology or Medicine

by Elaine Pascoe

The 1987 Nobel Prize in Physiology or Medicine was awarded to Dr. Susumu Tonegawa, a Japanese scientist working in the United States, for solving a mystery that had long puzzled medical researchers: how the human body can produce antibodies custom-tailored to act against the millions of different disease agents capable of attacking it.

In a series of experiments that the Nobel committee termed "convincing and elegant," Tonegawa showed that the genes that code for antibody production are shuffled randomly on their chromosomes, yielding a nearly endless potential for variation. By increasing understanding of the mechanisms of the immune response, his work was expected to lead to improvements in the effectiveness of vaccines and to advances in efforts to fight immune disorders such as Acquired Immune Deficiency Syndrome (AIDS) and the autoimmune diseases, disorders in which the immune system attacks the body's own tissues.

Other researchers had reached conclusions similar to Tonegawa's. But the Nobel committee noted that after the publication of his experiments, which were conducted at the Basel Institute for Immunology in Switzerland during the 1970s, he dominated the field. Tonegawa thus became the first Japanese to win the Nobel Prize in Medicine, and only the second person since 1961 who did not have to share the honor. (The other was Dr. Barbara McClintock, who won in 1983 for research into genetics.) The cash award for 1987 came to $340,000.

The Antibody Paradox

Antibodies are proteins produced by certain white blood cells, the B lymphocytes, in response to antigens—viruses, bacteria, toxins, and the like—that enter the body. They are frontline troops in the body's war against such invaders, acting to neutralize the antigens in any of several ways: by dissolving them; and by coating them so that they become ineffective; by changing their surface structures so that they clump together and are easily found and ingested by other white blood cells, called phagocytes. (Antibody production is only one part of the immune response, a complex and still incompletely understood series of reactions that include the actions of still other white blood cells, called T lymphocytes, and various blood proteins.)

As a rule, antibodies are specific, capable of recognizing and neutralizing only one type of invader. Each antibody is a Y-shaped protein molecule, formed of long and short chains of amino acids that appear in a set order. Among antibodies of the same class, the base of the Y is constant. (Scientists have identified five types of human antibodies based on the makeup of this constant portion.) But at the tips of the

Dr. Susumu Tonegawa (left), recipient of the 1987 Nobel Prize for physiology or medicine, shakes hands with fellow M.I.T. professor Robert Solow, the 1987 Nobel laureate in economics.

AP/Wide World

arms, the sequence of amino acids varies, and it is this variation that targets the antibody to a specific antigen and enables it to latch onto the surface of that antigen. A common analogy compares the mechanism to a lock and key: the base of the Y is the key handle, and the branches are the end notched to fit a specific lock.

Thus, to protect the body, the B lymphocytes must be capable of producing different antibodies against millions of possible antigens. The puzzle that stumped researchers until the 1970s was that, despite the variety of antibodies the B cells produce, these cells contain only a limited number of genes to code for antibody production. Put another way, each B cell can produce only one type of antibody, yet the number of potential antibodies far exceeds the number of B cells.

Genetic Change

Working with B cells from mice and using advanced techniques of molecular biology, Tonegawa was able to explain the apparent paradox. He compared genes that code for antibodies in embryonic mouse cells with those in adult cells and found that as the cell matures, bits and pieces of the genes are shuffled and recombined in random patterns. Rather than inheriting a set genetic code, each cell in effect begins with a group of genetic components, which it assembles into antibody genes. The fact that billions of different combinations are possible, Tonegawa concluded, allows the body to mount a specific antibody response against each antigen.

The theory that genetic change accounts for antibody variation was first put forth in the 1960s by two scientists at the California Institute of Technology (Caltech), William Dreyer and Claude Bennett; what was missing was an explanation of the mechanism involved. Tonegawa was tenacious in completing the series of crucial experiments that revealed it. In September 1987, he shared the $15,000 Albert Lasker Medical Research Award with two other scientists who were working on the problem—Dr. Leroy Hood, chairman of the Division of Biology at CIT, and Dr. Philip Leder, chairman of the Department of Human Genetics at Harvard.

Dr. Susumu Tonegawa was 48 when he received the Nobel award, and had lived and worked away from his native Japan for 22 years. He was born in Nagoya, and earned a bachelor's degree in chemistry from prestigious Kyoto University in 1963. Shortly after joining the staff of the university's virus-research labora-

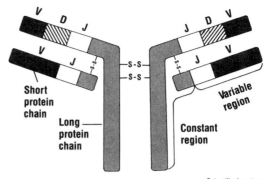

Scientific American

Human antibodies are made of four protein chains, two short and two long, bound together by sulfur (S) bonds. The arrangement of the V, D, and J genes determines the individual characteristics of the antibody.

tory, he went at the urging of his director to the United States for postgraduate work at the University of California at San Diego.

After receiving a doctorate in biology in 1969, he did further postgraduate work at U.C. San Diego and at the Salk Institute, and in 1971 he joined the staff of the Basel Institute for Immunology in Switzerland. It was there that he carried out the series of experiments that won him the Nobel Prize—and, along the way, earned him a reputation as a brilliant problem solver and an independent, hardworking, and somewhat aggressive researcher.

In 1981 Tonegawa returned to the United States as a full professor in biology at the Massachusetts Institute of Technology (MIT), where he has continued to focus on research into immunology. According to co-workers, he often arrives at his lab after noon and works straight through until 3:00 A.M. or later. He is married to Mayumi Yoshinari, a former Japanese television reporter who enrolled as a graduate student in brain and cognitive science at MIT; they have one son, Hidde, who was nine months old when the Nobel award was announced in October 1987.

As the first Japanese to win the Nobel Prize in Medicine, Tonegawa received wide praise in his native country. However, some observers in Japan and abroad found an ironic twist in the award: Tonegawa has been openly critical of what he sees as a lack of opportunity for creative research in Japan, where he says consensus is favored over individuality, and young scientists rarely find funding or encouragement for their projects. He has said that he has no plans to return to Japan.

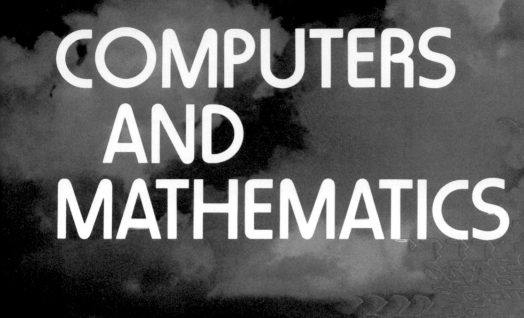

COMPUTERS
AND
MATHEMATICS

Computer-generated chaos? Programs developed to monitor stock prices and sell accordingly bear partial blame for the dramatic stock market plunge of October 19, 1987. When prices began to fall, computers started to sell at a rapid enough pace to cause the stocks to fall even further. This drop precipitated still further selling. By the end of the day, stock averages had fallen 508 points. Since then, markets and brokerages have imposed limits on computer trading.

REVIEW
OF THE
YEAR

COMPUTERS AND MATHEMATICS

Manufacturers continued to refine both computer software and hardware in 1987, introducing systems that are faster, easier to operate, and with a greater range of capabilities. Using supercomputers, mathematicians were able to recalculate some of the great constants of science. Computers also earned a degree of notoriety in 1987, as analysts heaped blame for the October stock market crash on the practice of computerized trading.

COMPUTERS AND THE PLUNGE

Computerized trading on Wall Street gained strong popularity in 1987. But when the stock market plunged in October, computers became one of the villains. Computers programmed to track stock prices second-by-second automatically entered buy or sell orders when certain conditions existed. But since the programs lacked the factor of human judgment, they contributed to the chaos when a flood of sell orders hit the stock exchanges on the morning of October 19.

In comparing the falling stock prices with their own buy-sell instructions, programs suddenly kicked in and began to add to the crisis by automatically selling off even more stock. By the end of the day, more than 600 million shares of

stock had been sold, and the Dow Jones Industrial Average had fallen 508 points.

In a typical program, the computer compares the price of stock index futures contracts—a form of trading that involves contracts to buy or sell a group of stocks at some future date—with the current price of the stocks themselves. Because the contracts and the actual stocks trade on different exchanges, their prices sometimes let traders make a quick profit by buying one and selling the other simultaneously. But it takes the high speed of a computer to spot those moments and act on them.

When actual stock prices fell rapidly on October 19, the programs went to work. But by selling stock too fast, the decline accelerated, the price gaps were exaggerated, and even more automatic selling followed. Only when the plunge continued to accelerate did the computer trading decline. By then a full-scale panic was under way.

Despite its problems, computer trading will continue in some form. But after the Crash of '87, the markets temporarily placed limits on the practice, and some brokerages announced their own embargoes until new programs—with more built-in safety factors and perhaps an added dose of human judgment—could be written.

NEW DESKTOP MACHINES

The battle of the giants of personal computing raged anew in 1987 as Apple introduced the Macintosh II, a high-performance machine aimed at the business market, while IBM responded with its new P/S 2 family of personal computers. The introductions brought the competing computers closer together in appearance, performance, and operation.

Apple's Macintosh II looks much like its IBM competitor. Its large, low-slung cabinet contains most of its electronics and disk drives, a separate video monitor, and a keyboard. In exchange for its increased size, users get a faster 32-bit central processor, an expandable memory, monochrome or color output, and seven expansion slots for adding electronic circuit cards that give the machine an even wider range of capabilities.

Apple preserved the Macintosh's extensive graphics capability and the hand-held mouse (which simplifies the computer's use by controlling most of its operations), but doubled its operating speed by using Motorola's 68020 microprocessor.

Late in the year, Apple released a new operating system that allows all Macs with 1 megabyte or more of memory to run multiple programs simultaneously in separate windows on the screen.

IBM's new P/S 2 computers range from low-end machines compatible with the company's existing PC line to future desktop computers similar to the Macintosh II. The desktop computers will use a new operating system, O/S 2, being developed by the Microsoft Corporation.

The new system, graphics-based, uses a mouse to pull down menus on a screen and to select actions for the computer. It also resembles the Macintosh in allowing users to open multiple windows on the screen, each containing different information. Microsoft released the first version of O/S 2 in 1987, with enhanced versions expected in 1988.

THE "STACKWARE" PHENOMENON

HyperCard is a breakthrough in how personal computers manage, display, and retrieve information. By year's end, hundreds of applications using HyperCard had been introduced. Industry experts even forecast HyperCard to be the largest area of software sales in 1988 and 1989.

In HyperCard, all the information on the Macintosh screen is treated both as a single file card and as part of an unlimited database. The information—text, graphics, and sound—plays back through the computer's speaker. Groups of cards are called "stacks" or "stackware."

A typical stack might be an address book. Each card contains the standard name/address/phone number information. But it could also have a photograph of the person, a brief recording of his or her voice, and up to 32,000 characters of information. The cards also are interactive. Ask for "Smith," and HyperCard finds all the Smiths. Use the mouse to click on Joe Smith's phone number, and it is dialed automatically for you.

Such capabilities are possible because the program allows users to create on-screen "buttons" that are programmed to perform specific actions. The programming links cards, or stacks, together so that all the Smiths—or all the

refrences to, for example, "yellow canary"—can be found quickly.

Stackware on the market or being developed in 1987 included a reference guide for world travelers and encyclopedia-like collections of information on a wide variety of subjects, including a human anatomy guide for medical students, a compilation of ancient Greek literature (complete with maps), and training guides to using other computer programs, among many others.

CHIP MAKERS IMPROVE CIRCUITS

The chips that form the heart of all modern electronics, providing memory, computing power, switching, and a host of other functions, are shrinking in size while growing in capability. At Case Western Reserve University in Cleveland, Ohio, scientists displayed chips coated with a carbon-metallic film only one molecule thick. By lowering electrical resistance, the film, according to Dr. Scott E. Rickert, has the potential for allowing chips to operate thousands of times faster than they do at present. Research continues to make the film-coating process commercially feasible.

Another process, replacing the standard silicon in a chip with gallium arsenide, expanded as companies gradually solved the problems of using the more brittle substance. The effort is noteworthy because gallium arsenide transmits electricity much faster than silicon and generates less heat. One computer company, Cray Inc., said that its Cray-3 supercomputer, due out about 1990, would use gallium arsenide chips and be capable of performing 10 billion calculations per second.

Pi IS FOREVER

The value of pi (3.1416 . . .) to more than 134 million decimal places seems to have little value. But Japanese researcher Yasumasa Kanada of the University of Tokyo did it anyway, using a day of time on an NEC SX-2 supercomputer and printing out the results. The exercise does, in fact, have some value, showing how fast new supercomputers actually are, and helping to validate sophisticated mathematical formulas.

If pi is constant, some constants are not, or at least they can be changed. In 1987 scientists agreed to change several long-accepted scientific constants. The gravitational constant went down. So did Planck's constant used in quantum mechanics. But Avogadro's number, used in chemistry, went up. The mass constant of both electrons and protons went down.

All the changes were slight, occurring in the fourth or higher decimal place. The changes occurred because new instruments and new techniques allow more precise measurements.

JIM SCHEFTER

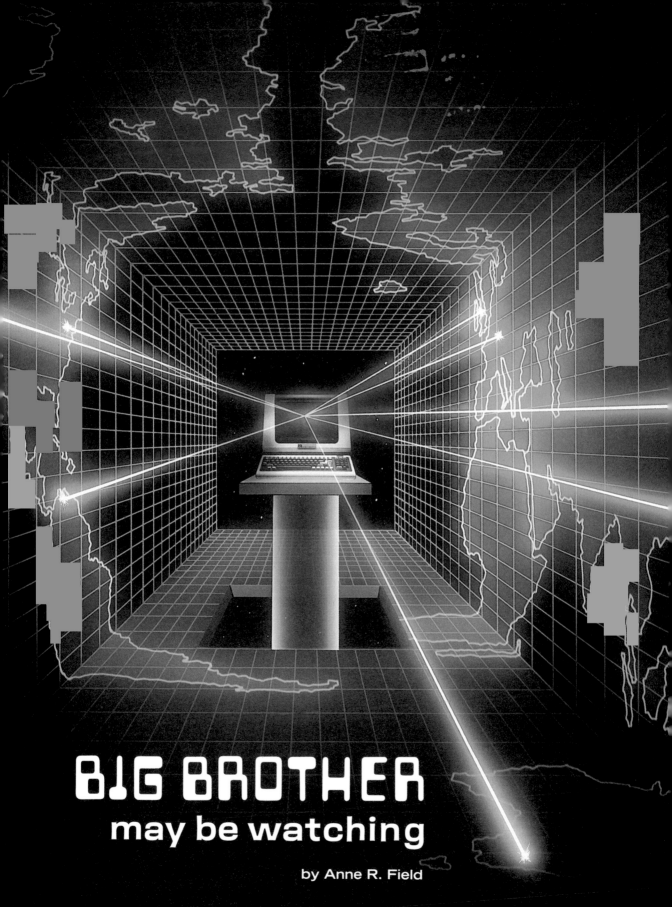

BIG BROTHER
may be watching

by Anne R. Field

All Rudine Pettus wanted was a place to live. But as the clerk-typist applied for apartment after apartment in the spring of 1981, no one in the Los Angeles area had room. Not until she was well into her search did one rental agent explain why: a dispute with a previous landlord had gotten Pettus on a computerized list of potentially undesirable tenants sold by a company called UD Registry Inc. A California law requires that people be informed if they're on such a list. But Pettus says she "had no idea such a thing existed."

Pettus is a casualty of the information age, and she's not alone. Computerized databases are proliferating fast. The top five credit-rating companies have records on more than 150 million individuals. About 85 federal databases contain some 288 million records on 114 million people. And it's not just the volume of information that's frightening. Advances in computer technology are making it easy to do what was impossible not long ago: cross-match information almost at the touch of a button to create portraits of individuals—and even to try to predict their behavior.

"People are leaving an electronic trail of transactions with various institutions—educational, financial, governmental, professional, criminal justice," says Clement Bezold, co-author of a recent study on the subject commissioned by the Information Industry Association, a trade group. The result could be an invasion of privacy unparalleled in any modern democratic society.

Boon or Bane?

No clear legal definition of privacy exists, but experts agree on a few basics: it means the right to keep personal affairs to yourself and to know how information about you is being used. The issue has big implications for information companies. "I think the industry feels that [individuals must sacrifice] a certain amount of privacy in the information age," says Peter A. Marx, an attorney specializing in computer law. The public disagrees. A 1984 Harris Poll found 75 percent of respondents "very" or "somewhat concerned" about threats to privacy. Says Bezold: "We have to make sure the information revolution is a boon, not a bane."

It's been a boon to Harvey A. Saltz, the president of UD Registry. Every day he sends a squad of employees to dozens of southern California courts to gather information involving bankruptcies, evictions, property damage, and other landlord-tenant disputes. The workers type information from current cases into portable personal computers, then enter it into Saltz's main computer via phone lines. Saltz combines this information with credit reports he buys from companies such as TRW Inc. The $9 fee that UD Registry charges for the data doesn't include any advice on how to use it. But landlords get the idea.

Pretending that she was from out of state, Pettus says she eventually lined up an apartment from a landlord who didn't check UD's list. But then she got into a dispute at the new place over leaks—and refused to pay rent until they were fixed. After the landlord tried to evict her, they settled out of court with the understanding that the incident would be kept off the list, says her attorney. But because UD Registry includes landlord-tenant cases regardless of their outcome, the dispute was listed anyway. It took Pettus months to find a new home—where she has lived now for more than three years.

Government databases form the most cohesive web of information on individuals: some 15 agencies mix and match data. Ostensibly, they are restrained by the Privacy Act of 1974, which requires the consent of individuals before an agency collects and uses information on them for a purpose different than was originally intended. But there's a big loophole: if the agency wants the data for "routine use," little notice is necessary. Privacy experts say that the few perfunctory checks that are made take a backseat to efficiency.

Computer matching started in the late 1970s as part of an effort to reduce welfare fraud, and the Reagan administration has expanded its use. The Veterans Administration (VA) uses it to keep federal employees from receiving excess benefits. The U.S. Education Department looks for federal employees who are delinquent on student loans. Although exact figures are hard to come by, the number of matches tripled from 1980 to 1984, with more than 2 billion separate records being exchanged during that period, according to the Office of Technology Assessment (OTA). Now a special presidential committee is looking into how to expand computer matching.

Spending Habits

The 1984 Deficit Reduction Act already has gone a step further. It requires that states set up verification systems to head off cheaters. These computer systems will use Social Security num-

© Roger Ressmeyer

Using vast computer banks, the IRS exchanges data with state and local tax offices to verify accuracy of tax returns.

bers as the key for linking dozens of government databases.

The most aggressive agency may be the Internal Revenue Service (IRS). Its debtor master file, created in 1986, is used to withhold tax refunds owed to borrowers who default on federal loans. So far it lists about 750,000 people who owe money to the Education Department, the Housing and Urban Development Department (HUD), the VA, and the Small Business Administration (SBA), according to the OTA. The IRS even experimented briefly with buying lists from direct-mail companies—to find out if the spending habits of targeted individuals jibed with their reported income.

That test was dropped. But the upshot of such federal and state projects, says Priscilla M. Regan, an analyst with the OTA, is that the U.S. "is starting to move toward a national database." A damning report, released last summer by the office, said: "The opportunities for inappropriate, unauthorized, or illegal access to and use of personal information have been expanded."

This leads to big problems. As anyone who has run afoul of a computer knows, incorrect information is hard to fix. Raulinea Howard learned the hard way. In 1982 a Massachusetts computer match uncovered $11,000 in a bank account that she supposedly hadn't reported to welfare officials. Howard insisted that the account wasn't hers, but the department threatened to cut off her aid anyway. Eventually, she traced the account to a woman with a similar Social Security number. Howard was one of many cases inaccurately uncovered by a state program to match welfare lists with state bank records. "The process had glitches," concedes Joseph V. Gallant, associate director of the state's Public Welfare Department. "But we've ironed them out."

Whether computer matching is worth the trouble is hard to tell. Joseph R. Wright, Jr., deputy director of the Office of Management and Budget (OMB), says it has saved money, although he doesn't have figures. And the IRS says that in 1985 it recovered $2.5 billion in taxes that would have gone uncollected. But the OTA study and another by the General Accounting Office (GAO) argue that few agencies have adequately calculated the cost-effectiveness of computer matching.

Not Just Government

Of course, government databases are only half the story: lots of private companies sell information about individuals. For example, Chicago-based Docket-Search Network Inc. sells a service called Physician's Alert. It consists of information on patients who have filed civil suits; its clients tend to be doctors in high-risk specialties, such as obstetrics and orthopedics, among others. Like most suppliers of data, president Michael G. Eckstein claims that his product does nothing to threaten individual privacy per se. ''We are in the information business,'' he says. ''We do not instruct our clients on how to use the data.''

Probably the most ubiquitous sellers of private information are credit-reporting companies. Unlike most database suppliers, these companies, which gather a wide range of information from department stores, banks, and finance companies, are regulated under the Fair Credit Reporting Act of 1970. The act says that all negative records have to be purged from credit reports after seven years. But companies don't have to let people know when they've been added to a databank or whether they're being investigated.

That's noteworthy because credit bureaus are expanding their businesses. The federal government uses them to verify applications for loans. And some credit companies sell data for checking out the backgrounds of potential employees. TRW says that while it doesn't do this, it is feeling market pressure to start. With no laws governing the use of this information, job applicants are at the mercy of prospective em-

© George Dritsas/Light Images

Automation aftereffect? Government investigators can access computerized records of an individual's finances.

Via computer, the FBI provides state and local police with more than 300,000 items of criminal data each year.

Courtesy FBI

How Computers Are Helping to Invade Your Privacy

The increased use of computers in recent years has resulted in massive amounts of information on individuals that can be collected, cross-matched, and manipulated to generate much more detailed profiles of U.S. citizens than ever before—sometimes in a matter of seconds. This information can affect everything from credit ratings to welfare eligibility to your chances of renting an apartment or landing a job. Here's who may have a lot of information on you:

• *Internal Revenue Service*. Increasingly, the IRS is exchanging data with state and local tax authorities to check the accuracy of tax returns.

• *Social Security Administration*. Your Social Security number, which third parties need to tap into computerized information on you, is available to at least 125 government and private agencies.

• *Motor Vehicle Departments*. About 40 states will sell direct-mail firms the information you provide when registering a vehicle or applying for a license. This reveals your age, sex, Social Security number—even, through deduction, your income range.

• *Federal Bureau of Investigation*. The FBI's National Crime Information Center has more than 10 million centrally stored records of criminal histories—all available to state and local authorities.

• *Courts*. Some states are computerizing their court documents—making it easier to monitor everything from eviction to criminal proceedings.

• *Credit Bureaus*. The five largest credit-reporting companies control records on more than 150 million individuals.

• *Banks*. Most banks are allowed by law to give out information on customers' accounts and credit histories to state government investigators.

• *Life Insurance Companies*. By tapping a central database run by a company called the Medical Information Bureau, they can find out details about your medical history from claims information provided by insurers.

• *Direct-Mail Companies*. By combing through some of the above records and various other information, they churn out lists of specific individuals whom salespeople or political campaigns may want to contact.

ployers who don't bother to take more than a thumbs-up-or-down reading. "Some customers are very harsh," says one credit bureau executive. "But it's their money. They can do what they want."

Taste Test

Few people know this as well as Joseph Miller. In the spring of 1985, Miller, now 26, quit his job at a large retail store in New York to look for a better position. He remained unemployed for

An automobile accident report soon finds its way into databases at motor-vehicle departments and insurance companies.

© Michael Grecco/Stock, Boston

months as several potential jobs fell through. Then, in September, he received a notice of his dishonorable discharge from the Army—an odd occurrence, since he'd never been in the service. The truth was out: a former college roommate was using his name. "I realized that my Social Security number was stored in I don't know how many databases across the country," recalls Miller. "He had jail records, bad credit—all under my name." Unable to persuade credit agencies to change his records, he has applied for a new Social Security number and driver's license.

Most people will never face such problems, of course, but they may be affected in subtler ways—by experts who use databases as marketing tools. Dataman Information Services in Atlanta, for example, provides basic data. It compiles real estate and mortgage information from courthouse records in 48 states and sells it to companies as diverse as Citicorp and Neiman-Marcus. It also compiles phone numbers of homeowners for telemarketers. A subsidiary of Metromail Corp., a big direct-mail company, it has access to Metromail data as well. Says William Flaherty, Dataman's chief executive officer: "If you gave me your name and address, I could match that name with Metromail's files and probably tell you how old you are, how many children you have, and how old your house is."

Other market researchers are more sophisticated. They buy census data, which divide the country into 250,000 neighborhoods of about 250 households. Using these figures as a foundation, the marketing companies break the country into 40 or so socioeconomic groups. Combining this with up to 100 other databases, they guess at an individual's tastes. For example, National Decision Systems in Encinitas, California, has determined that an individual who falls into a category dubbed "high-tech frontier" will be five times as likely to buy a Japanese car as one not in the group.

Watchdogs

For now, few laws govern the use of databases. An effort to enact a medical records privacy act, similar to the Fair Credit Reporting Act, failed several years ago. And few states regulate the quality and accuracy of databases. One bill, recently reintroduced in the Senate by Senator William S. Cohen (R-Me.), would set up official boards to oversee computer matching of federal databases.

© Halstead/Gamma Liaison

The Secret Service consults computer data to help protect President Reagan and visiting foreign dignitaries.

Cohen's approach is modeled after those used by countries such as Sweden, West Germany, and France. Most European countries have some form of legislation regulating the use of government databases—and sometimes private ones. In France, for example, a watchdog commission created in 1979 oversees government, private, and university use of electronic information. It regularly steps in when it thinks cross-matching is getting out of hand. The commission has even required that mail-order companies inform consumers when their names are transferred from one computerized list to another.

Without regulation in the U.S., say proponents of the Cohen bill, privacy may become more threatened as technology advances. A new technique called computer profiling is a case in point. It combines sophisticated software with databases to create profiles of people who are likely to exhibit certain characteristics. The Secret Service, for one, is reported by privacy analysts to be developing a system to help identify people with the tendencies of assassins. Says one privacy observer: "If [these databases] are ever all connected, it will be Big Brother Inc."

Fighter pilots soon will rely on an array of software systems to combat everything from bad weather to armed threats.

SOFTWARE CATCHES
THE TEAM SPIRIT

by Louis S. Richman

From the fertile, science fiction–soaked imaginations of computer software engineers is springing a dazzling new vision of a futuristic office environment where the 21st-century TV cartoon character George Jetson might feel at home. Software that will enable people to collaborate across barriers of space and time is one of today's hottest frontiers of computer research. Like an electronic sinew that binds teams together, the new ''groupware'' aims to place the computer squarely in the middle of communications among managers, technicians, and anyone else who interacts in groups, revolutionizing the way they work.

Groupware boosters make breathtaking, if extravagant-sounding, claims for what this new technology will do. Linked desktop terminals running the new software will coordinate schedules and route messages. Novel products will emerge as networks of computer workstations guide teams of workers through large shared databases; a pharmaceutical company, for example, might search a database of organic chemicals for possible new drugs. Managers will confer with colleagues, suppliers, and customers via wall-size video screens as cameras connected to computers record and store their conversations. And—hold onto your space helmets—even meetings will become more effective as today's low-tech conference rooms turn into multimedia "war rooms" controlled by software that helps keep everything on course.

The Group Approach

Software that supports group work may not be as far-out as it sounds. Advanced prototypes are already in use at a handful of research labs around the country; the first commercial products are beginning to reach the market. Says Jerry Wagner, a professor of management information systems at the University of Texas Business School in Austin: "This technology could be one of the most important contributions to management effectiveness in business history."

In the new effort to develop software that helps teams of people work smarter, necessity is running in tandem with opportunity. Software engineers need better ways to manage teams of programmers writing vastly more complicated computer codes; as programs grow more intricate, the risk increases that the work of engineers collaborating on one of dozens of subsystems will distort the work of other teams. At the same time, companies are looking for opportunities to transform their huge investment in office automation equipment into tools that actually, finally, pay off in productivity gains.

Engineers at the Microelectronics & Computer Technology Corp. (MCC) research consortium in Austin, Xerox's Palo Alto (Calif.) Research Center (PARC), and Tektronix Laboratories in Beaverton, Oregon, have made groupware a priority for their research. "We've reached the limits of what individuals can do," says Laszlo Belady, director of MCC's software research program. "The biggest problem we face isn't so much a technical problem as a human coordination problem." Belady is quick to add that solving the problem casts software designers in a new role: "As hard scientists, we've found it uncomfortable dealing with the messy, ambiguous relationships that exist among people in groups."

Says Benn Konsynski, a professor of management information systems at Harvard Business School: "Coordinating people is the business problem managers want to solve." Thomas Malone, who teaches the same subject at MIT's Sloan School, thinks companies will benefit most from software that helps quicken their "information metabolism," the speed with which they digest and respond to information. A team Malone heads has been working for over two years on a program called Information Lens, with funding from GM, Wang, and Xerox.

User-Friendly Servants

Information Lens blends into the office like a supercompetent servant with a team of scattered masters. It draws on an artificial-intelligence programming tool that allows each user to tailor the system to his personal needs. The computer

Electronic scratchpad? Broderbund's For Comment software would have allowed Abraham Lincoln and 14 collaborators (left) to compose, revise, and comment on the Gettysburg Address—and comment on the comments (right).

can be instructed to discriminate among electronic messages—recognizing the difference, say, between a routine announcement of a new pencil-procurement policy and an urgent reminder that your boss wants your group's report before the end of the day. And from other computers' databases, it can cull information that relates to the projects a group is working on, routing the information speedily to each group member's terminal and automatically updating his files. Malone thinks commercial versions of the system designed to work on personal computers could be ready in two to three years.

Transforming groupware from an engineers' plaything into user-friendly programs for business poses formidable problems. "The pace of acceptance of these new tools will be determined by the abilities of the most technophobic member of a work group to use it," says George P. Huber, a professor at the University of Texas Business School. Commercial software developers, having perfected word processing and financial spreadsheet programs to a market-saturating fare-thee-well, have a powerful incentive to try to solve the problem. Among the biggest new markets for business applications software are the roughly 280,000 networks that companies have bought to link their computers together, but so far have discovered few ways to use. Microsoft and Lotus Development are making software that supports group work a major focus of their research, but both estimate that they are about three years away from launching products.

Pride of place for bringing the first easy-to-use programs to market belongs to two California companies, Action Technologies and Broderbund. At its start-up in January 1985, Action Technologies introduced a product called the Coordinator that is based on a stunningly simple theory of human communication. It is the brainchild of a cerebral Chilean émigré named Fernando Flores, who served as finance minister in the government of Salvador Allende.

Action-oriented Conversations

Business, according to Flores, is essentially the completion of a set of action-oriented conversations such as requests, offers, counteroffers, and promises. The trick to effective team coordination, he says, is having work groups label their conversations accordingly. The Coordinator lets a user compose a message on a personal computer, assign it one of Flores's conversation categories, and transmit it via standard telephone lines to other users. The system tracks each user's conversations, reminds him of his pending commitments, and keeps a record of the status of a group project.

Gtel, a California-based seller of telephone equipment, uses the Coordinator to track inventory at its 20 retail outlets and four warehouses, assemble daily store-management reports, and communicate between headquarters and the field. Denise Schubert, Gtel's personal-computer manager, estimates that the new system yields better data and costs $4,500 a month less than the electronic-mail system it replaced. But Schubert is most impressed with the fact that Gtel's store clerks, most of them aged 17 to 24, were able to start using the system after just

Electronic brainstorming in the corporate meeting room: video teleconferences combined with group software can integrate meetings with the work individuals perform independently.

© Robert Holmgren

Xerox's Media Spaces program allows engineers to confer by video, swap data, and store a record of their meetings.

a day's training. The Coordinator is winning converts among managers at General Motors' EDS subsidiary, whose account managers are using the system at GM offices in Dayton. It is also being tested at Aetna Life, where Bonnie Johnson, a corporate technical planning manager, says, "This is the first effective group communications tool I've seen."

Broderbund introduced a program called For Comment last November. It enables a team of up to 16 members to collaborate on writing, reviewing, and editing documents that can contain up to 236 single-spaced pages. Users relay a common document they are working on—a business plan, for example—through their network of personal computers, suggesting revisions and adding up to five levels of comments, and comments on comments.

The software tracks and saves each draft revision as well as all the commentators' contributions, creating a record of the ideas that influenced the group-decision process. To prepare a finished document, the author simply moves suggested changes from the comment block into the main text almost as easily as an intent teenager in a video-game arcade zaps an onscreen space invader. "Our background developing computer games gives us a big advantage in understanding how to make software easy to use," says Joanne Bealy, For Comment's product manager.

Hypertext

In the research labs, software engineers are taking two approaches to create programs that will transform networks of computers into more advanced collaboration tools. The first, called hypertext, allows groups working in the same building or at a distance to use their linked computer screens as a shared work space. The second, using electronic meeting rooms, harnesses the computer to increase the amount of information that can be brought to bear in face-to-face meetings. The computer is at the heart of both approaches, capturing the communication among team members, tracking and updating the information exchanged, and rendering it back precisely to all of its users.

The term "hypertext" was coined in the 1960s by Ted Nelson, an exuberant Stanford University computer scientist who had the extraordinary idea of creating a computer-linked global information source he called Xanadu, after the mythic palace in Coleridge's "Kubla Khan." Today researchers at Xerox PARC, MCC, and Tektronix are plucking hypertext from the realm of fantasy and trying to shape it into a focused research tool. Working with networks of powerful Xerox and Sun workstations equipped with large display screens that can be divided into windows, hypertext programmers segment data into interconnected, idea-size chunks called nodes.

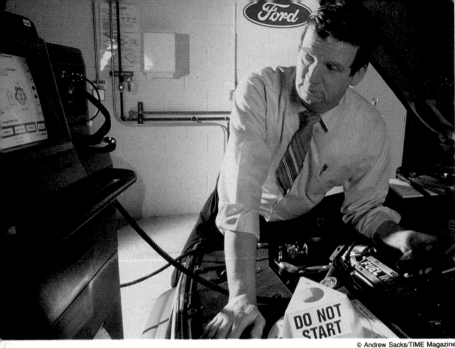

Automated repair manual: Ford mechanics soon will be able to identify hard-to-diagnose engine problems by simply accessing a nationwide computer system from touchscreens in the workbay.

© Andrew Sacks/TIME Magazine

Hypertext pulls together data from disparate sources and prompts the user to check information that may bear on what he's doing. In a simple commercial application, a toy company's market researcher checking a node called "Frisbee sales" might confirm that adolescent males are the toy's biggest buyers. Searching another node called "population trends—Minneapolis," he might discover that the city's male population aged 12 to 18 is decreasing far faster than the national average. By linking the two nodes, the researcher could conclude that his company should reduce its Frisbee distribution to the Twin Cities.

Individual hypertext users can navigate freely among nodes, following established links. As they roam, they can add new nodes and link them to the existing network, enriching the foundation of associated ideas and creating a sort of nonlinear electronic encyclopedia. More-limited systems that allow users to browse through data without adding new information or creating new links are beginning to find commercial applications. This summer, Ford plans to automate its repair manuals, using a browsing system called Guide to help mechanics service its 1988 models. Sold by Owl International, a year-old company based in Bellevue, Washington, the software will run on Hewlett-Packard computers connected to touchscreens at mechanics' workstations. Instead of having to leave the repair bay to leaf through volumes of grease-stained manuals, a mechanic using Guide will simply touch symbols on the com-

puter screen to search through servicing instructions stored on compact disks in the computer's memory.

Into the Conference Rooms

Software developers are also aiming to crack business's last computer-free inner sanctum, the conference room. For all the time managers spend in meetings, the process remains more a tribal rite than a structured, scientific process. After much talking and little listening, decisions too soon forgotten emerge by a process that no participant can describe. Armed with powerful workstations, researchers are mounting an assault on the meeting room and trying to integrate meetings with the work that individuals do independently. "We use computers in every other aspect of our work," says Mark Stefik, who designed an electronic meeting room called Colab at Xerox PARC. "Yet each time we came to meetings, we had to leave them behind in our offices and resort to flip charts."

The Colab room in Palo Alto accommodates eight participants seated around a U-shaped table at computers linked by cables. Facing the table at the front of the room stands a glowing 4- by 8-foot (1.3- by 2.6-meter) projection screen that serves as an electronic chalkboard. Unconventional as the room looks, what goes on inside it is positively bizarre. A meeting moves through three stages, beginning with "idea generation," proceeding to "idea structuring," and ending with evaluation. In the generation stage, participants hammer away at keyboards, creating a frenzied staccato as they simultaneously enter their thoughts into computer memory. As new ideas are entered, they pop up automatically on other participants' screens and on the electronic chalkboard.

Moving to the structuring stage, participants abandon their keyboards and shift ideas into related groups by using a mouse to shove a block of text across the screen and click it into place. Once the ideas are grouped to everyone's satisfaction and the clicking subsides, the group settles down to evaluate its work, supplementing the sorted thoughts with additional information drawn from members' personal databases. Colab's developers think all this chatterless clatter brings far greater cohesiveness to meetings. The computer records each participant's comments and displays them for all to see as the meeting progresses, a process Stefik describes as "what-you-see-is-what-I-see," or WYSIWIS (pronounced "whizzy-whiz"). The problems are equally obvious. Speed, unshakable concentration, and acute manual dexterity help a lot in getting one's point across.

Creative Chitchat

Like latter-day Dr. Jekylls, the researchers at Xerox PARC and MCC, which is building its own electronic meeting room, are studying computer-coordinated meetings by experimenting on themselves. At the University of Arizona's College of Business and Public Administration, researchers headed by Jay Nunamaker are investigating how ordinary executives adjust to this new idea. Arizona built a Decision and Planning Laboratory in 1985, and tested it on over 200 planning executives from such organizations as IBM and the U.S. Army. The lab lets users enter their comments anonymously. Managers like the candor the process allows, and the test groups have been uniformly enthusiastic.

The work groupers' ultimate strategy is to marry the computer's memory with video and audio equipment. A small team of researchers headed by Robert Stults is exploring that far-out edge of technology at Xerox PARC in an experiment called Media Spaces. In May 1987, Stults and his team equipped a half dozen offices at Xerox's Palo Alto labs and four Xerox offices in Portland, Oregon, with video cameras, monitors, microphones, and speakers, and wired them together with recording gear—all controlled by computers. They even wired the coffee lounges to capture all the creative chitchat that goes on during what employees used to think of as breaks.

Media Spaces allows group members using these multimedia offices to see each other as they confer; the camera projects each user's image on television monitors in his colleagues' offices. Tapping into the computer's database, Media Spaces conferees can swap text and graphic data back and forth and exhibit them in windows on each other's screens.

In time a new participant in the system will be able to command his computer to search a vast library of meetings recorded on video disks, zero in on a specific conversation, and play it back to reconstruct the rationale for a decision that the group made before he joined it. Stults thinks advanced versions of Media Spaces may emerge by the end of the century. "Right now we may look like just a bunch of overage kids playing at a funny farm in Palo Alto," says Stults. "But when this technology is ready, it could take off fast."

Computer workstations equipped with display screens that can be divided into windows allow data to be segmented into related idea-size blocks called nodes.

Xerox

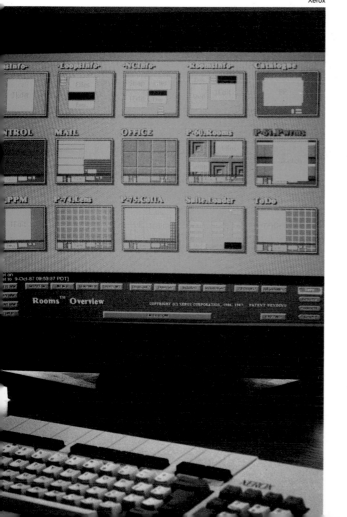

© Barry Hetherington

COMPUTERS IN THE CLASSROOM

by Alison B. Bass

The rusting carcasses of two stripped cars border the street in front of the Hennigan Elementary School in the Roxbury section of Boston, Massachusetts. The building's drab beige walls are pockmarked with graffiti, and the grass is long and unkempt. All the doors fronting the street are locked, and the only open entrance is hidden around the side.

Inside, the environment is cheerier.

Splotches of crayoned paper conceal the concrete walls, and a dark hallway opens up into large, open rooms filled with noise, light, and children. The children are seated around three circular banks of computers, staring at the green CRT screens and chattering with one another. One little boy's screen shows a square inside a square, and the squares are different colors. The boy is proud of his accomplishment and eager to explain how he did it. But two desks down sits an even smaller child whose screen is blank. Her hands are silent, her eyes are on her lap.

Both students are part of "Project Headlight," a pilot program designed to incorporate computers into the regular curriculum at Hennigan School. Initiated in 1985 by Seymour Papert, professor of mathematics and education at Massachusetts Institute of Technology (MIT), Project Headlight is an ambitious attempt to improve the educational climate in one public school.

"We chose Hennigan because it is central to the problem of education in the United

States,'' says Papert, a mathematician, computer scientist, and self-styled anthropologist. ''It's an inner-city school with a range of problems: single parents who are just trying to survive, not much education at home. It is a culture on the margin of literate society.''

Educational Software

Into this milieu, Papert has introduced 252 personal computers donated by IBM, and a programming language known as LOGO. Originally designed by Papert in the 1960s, LOGO has since spawned hundreds of other educational software programs and is close to becoming a cult. Every year a week-long LOGO conference is held at MIT—an event that one bemused observer calls ''a chapel to LOGO.'' Two of LOGO's more promising spin-offs are included in the Hennigan experiment: LOGOwriter, a package that combines programming with word processing; and LEGO/LOGO, software that allows children to use the computer to manipulate toys built with parts from LEGO building sets.

Students at Boston's Hennigan School (facing page) participate in Project Headlight, a program that incorporates computers into the regular curriculum. The program's founder, mathematician Seymour Papert (below), finds that computers help children visualize and grasp mathematical concepts in a manner not possible with books.

Based on plain English, LOGO allows children to draw all kinds of geometric shapes, symbols, and complex pictures with the computer. Their ''pencil'' is the Turtle, a fuzzy gray apparition that can be directed to move in any direction on the screen. The Turtle allows children to visualize and grasp mathematical concepts in a way that they can't with textbook problems.

When drawing a circle (or rather, a polygon that approximates a circle), for instance, children can command the Turtle to go forward (FD) 2 (a Turtle step is roughly the size of one pixel, or dot on the screen), turn right (RT) 12 degrees, and then repeat that sequence 30 times. In creating that simple shape, children pick up some interesting facts. They learn that whenever a Turtle is turned around a total of 360 degrees (12×30), it will be facing the same direction as when it started. They learn that 180 degrees is half a circle, or half of 360 degrees. And as they move on to other shapes, they learn that no matter what shape the Turtle draws, it must turn a total of 360 degrees if it creates a closed curve. According to Papert, these are powerful geometric concepts not always obvious to young children. With the Turtle, they can see these concepts, make them happen, in front of their eyes.

''In directing the Turtle, children also have to make judgments about the size of numbers as well as spatial judgments,'' Papert says. ''For instance, I've seen many small kids who don't know the difference between 10 and 10,000. But they pick up that difference very quickly with the Turtle; if they command it to go 10,000 steps, the computer will say, 'I don't like 10,000 as input.' ''

Mastering Concepts

Most important, Papert says, LOGO allows children to draw from their own experience in mastering a concept. He revealed that secret one day to a diminutive nine-year-old at Hennigan with braids almost as long as her pinafore. The girl, along with the rest of her fourth-grade class, had been assigned to draw a map of the solar system. But new to Hennigan and to LOGO, she was having difficulty designing a simple sun.

Papert, who had been watching the class work, gently drew the child to her feet. Holding her hand and talking quietly, he took a few steps forward and then turned to the right. He repeated that sequence with her until they had turned together in a complete circle. Intimidated at first by the big, gray-haired stranger, the little girl blushed fiercely through the first go-around. She stopped blushing when she understood.

"The reason why children don't learn math is not because it's hard, but because it's not related to their experience. They can't do anything with it that seems worth doing, and so it feels deadly to them," Papert explains later in the "Turtlecove," a small room at Hennigan allotted to the MIT group. As usual, he is dressed casually in a white-ribbed turtleneck sweater and black wool pants. His eyes are large and luminous behind thick glasses, and his gray-pepper beard swallows up the lines on his face.

"In the real world, people always learn by experience," Papert says. "A lot of theorists and thinkers about education agree it would be a powerful way to learn in the classroom. But up till now, nobody knew how to provide experiences that embody the kind of math knowledge that we think children need to have. So mathematics is taught mainly by rote, and many children are turned off.

"Now we have a technology that children can use to make something they're interested in—whether it's pretty shapes with LOGO or cars with LEGO. The computer provides children with a way of appropriating mathematical knowledge—and using it in a very personal way."

Conquering Math Anxiety

In the 1950s, primitive computers were on the scene, and the early pioneers of artificial intelligence were grappling with many issues. While still based in Geneva, Papert began commuting to London to work with one of the most powerful computers then in existence. Built by the mathematician Alan Turing, the computer had a memory of about 2K—one-thirtieth the memory of a simple Apple IIc. Yet it filled a room as big as a barn. There Papert met John McCarthy and Marvin Minsky, now widely considered to be the founders of artificial intelligence (AI).

Minsky eventually persuaded Papert to come back with him to MIT, where they jointly ran the AI Lab through the late 1960s. But Papert was still working with child psychologist Jean Piaget when he conceived the idea of the computer as an element of cultural and educational change.

"On the one hand, Piaget is telling us that children are wonderful learners, that they redis-cover this vast amount of knowledge as they grow," Papert explains. "But on the other hand, as I began to see in the schools, children, far from being wonderful learners, seem to be incapable of learning even the simplest things. How does one explain this paradox?"

He came to the conclusion that children learn best when they have materials from their own culture with which to build. For instance, even children who drop out of school can readily count change or read comic books. But when knowledge is not well represented in the culture and, in fact, is feared by that culture—as is math and, to a certain extent, grammar children falter. Computers, Papert theorized, could be the solution—if and when they became small and affordable enough to be used in the classroom.

By the 1980s, computers had indeed become manageable enough for the classroom, and the push to bring them into the schools began. IBM and Apple personal computers, often donated or discounted, found their way into elementary and secondary schools as well as universities. In the public schools, however, they were used mainly for drill and practice in the basic skills—something that could often be done just as effectively with paper and pencil. As one educational expert charged, computers were being cast in the same sad mold of rote teaching that has characterized much of U.S. public education.

"Historically, American public schools have embodied the idea of education as a passive experience for students," wrote Marc Tucker, executive director of the Carnegie Forum on Education and the Economy, in a 1985 national report on computers in education. "So it was natural that school personnel would view the machine as just one more device to deliver instruction, like a sort of automated drill sergeant delivering commands."

A year later, in a speech to a National Governors' Association task force, Tucker was a bit more optimistic. He reported that computers were being used in more "creative" ways in a few isolated places around the country. One of those places was the Hennigan School. Tucker had visited Project Headlight in its first year of operation, and observed a group of nine-year-olds playing with LEGO/LOGO.

"But this was no ordinary LEGO set," Tucker told the governors. In addition to the building-block modules, gears, shafts, and wheels found in most LEGO sets, this set also

© David M. Doody/Tom Stack & Associates

Mastering computers is relatively simple when it includes an element of fun. The two students above, receiving instructions via headphones, practice basic math skills on a computer that produces farm animals and other visual rewards on the screen for each correct answer. The girls at right learn some of the finer points of computer operation by working their way through a maze. A fourth grader (below) programmed the computer to draw a map of the planets revolving around the Sun.

Above: © Don & Pat Valenti/Tom Stack & Associates; below: © Barry Hetherington

COMPUTERS AND MATHEMATICS   **115**

contained electric motors that could be mounted onto the cars and other toys the children made. Also available were touch and light sensors that they could add to their creations. The sensors and motors could be connected to the computer, which, in turn, made it possible for the children to use data coming from the sensors to control the motion of the things they built.

Learning Engineering

One little boy, for instance, had built a car that was supposed to follow a track made by laying a piece of adhesive tape on the floor. The car stayed on the track with the aid of a light sensor placed under its "hood." When the car wandered from the adhesive tape, the sensor showed that the floor was dark, and the computer program the boy had written directed the wheels to turn until the sensor showed that the floor was light.

"In this workshop, boys and girls learned more math and science and technology at the fourth-grade level than I had ever thought possible," Tucker reported. "Consider the car that followed the adhesive tape. The instruction to the computer was in the form of: if the value returned by the sensor is equal to or less than x, then turn b degrees to the right. If, having maintained this direction for a specified interval, the value returned by the sensor does not increase above a specified value, turn so many degrees to the left, and so on. . . .

"Bear in mind that what is being given in this lab is a class in engineering, a first exposure to the pleasures of equipment design, in which the participants are exposed to the use of mathematics and science in a way that is clearly enthralling."

No Sweating the Mistakes

Kyle is a handsome nine-year-old from Roxbury who has trouble reading and writing. He has disrupted class so many times that he has been banished to a special-needs workshop. There he has been given the opportunity to play with LEGO/LOGO. Last week he built a tractor and kept running it back and forth on the floor, making delighted vroom noises as the wheels spun along. This week he is learning how to direct the computer to run his tractor for him. He likes the idea of being able to add a sensor that will keep his tractor from bumping into walls.

Jack Gray, a Harvard student who is working with Papert's group, tells Kyle he will help him write the tractor program. But Kyle will have to take notes so he doesn't forget how to do it. One of the teacher aides who has been sitting nearby interrupts: "I don't know if he can take notes." Gray looks momentarily discouraged. Then he says, "O.K., Kyle, I'll take the notes; you type them in."

Kyle types in TO and then turns to Gray and asks him, "How do you spell tractor?" "I don't know," Gray replies. "What do you think?" Kyle struggles for a few minutes with the TR sound. But after a few hints from Gray and a few more false starts, he finally spells it out loud and types it onto the screen: TO TRACTOR. Gray begins running through the instructions step-by-step: TALK TO "C" (C is the power outlet where the motor is plugged into the computer) ON FOR "40" (go forward for 4 seconds) LISTEN TO "6" (the sensor is plugged into button number 6 on the computer interface) WAIT UNTIL. . . .

But Kyle has lost interest. He is no longer looking at the screen, and is busy screwing and unscrewing the tiny wires that connect the tractor with its computer interface. A few minutes later, he throws a glance at me taking notes and asks suspiciously, "Is she a computer lady?" Gray replies, "Yeah, I think she is." But Kyle continues to squat moodily on his heels, his fingers busily working tiny strands of wire.

Later, Steve Ocko, a filmmaker who helped develop LEGO/LOGO and has been working with the teachers at Hennigan, explains: "Kyle loves playing with LEGO. In class he has a very short attention span, but we have to pull him off the LEGO toys. Kyle is also on the verge of getting thrown out of public school and put in a special school. He knows this is his last chance. He probably thinks you are here to test him, and that scares him."

In reality, no efforts are being made to test the Hennigan students on what they learn from LEGO/LOGO. The MIT researchers say that it is extremely difficult to measure in any systematic way what concepts the children are picking up. They view Project Headlight as an experiment to study how children learn with computers, not as a benchmark test from which to develop standards. As a result, they have little hard data to show experts in education and computer science.

"Tests tell how well kids learn by rote, which is why so much of their education consists of abstract facts and rules," says Mitch Resnick, an MIT graduate student in computer science who worked with Ocko in designing

Elementary engineering. Fifth graders at the Hennigan School constructed vehicles from LEGO building blocks (above). They then connected their creations to the computer, which the students programmed to make the vehicles move (right).

LEGO/LOGO. "But what's really important for kids to learn, the actual process of learning—that's a hard thing to test. And how do you test whether you've gotten kids excited and curious about learning?"

As Resnick is fond of saying, play is not a four-letter word at Project Headlight. The children are encouraged to learn by exploration, by discovery, and by making mistakes. And when they do, they are asked to figure out what went wrong, correct it, and move on. "The children learn they don't have to sweat the mistakes," Ocko says.

The same goes for the teachers. Papert is encouraging the Headlight teachers to experiment and to integrate the computer into their own curriculum—whether math, science, social studies, or English—and then study the results. He sees his role in all of this as adviser, not the all-knowing headmaster.

Open Classroom?

"The strategy is not to tell the teachers what to teach. There's already too much of that. . . ." Papert pauses and, in a characteristic gesture, drops the thought and starts afresh. "Yesterday, somebody from the U.S. Department of Education came to MIT to talk to us about computers in education. He wanted to know how we can use computers to bypass the teachers. He had this idea: let's get the best teachers in the world and then embody in the computer their ways of

teaching. Well, we're doing the opposite at Hennigan."

Papert freely acknowledges that Project Headlight is an attempt to bring back the open classroom of the 1960s. Only this time, he says, teachers have a more powerful and seductive medium to work with and a specific approach. "The free-school movement of the 1960s collapsed partly because it was tied to a political movement of the time, and partly because there were some subject matters that nobody knew how to teach in a noncoercive way. With the computer, we're in a much better position to have a second shot at free schools."

Some observers are not so sure. Joseph Weizenbaum, professor of computer science at MIT, says that a more open, less rigid approach to education is a fine idea. "Seymour may, in fact, have found a better form of teaching. But what does that have to do with computers?" he asks. If anything, he says, an overemphasis on computers obscures the real issue, which is the need to fundamentally restructure the educational system and deal with the social problems that hinder children's natural urge to learn.

"Children may not be motivated in school because they're hungry or they've been abused at home or for any number of reasons," Weizenbaum says. "Simply introducing computers avoids the question of why children may not be motivated in school. It converts a social problem into a technological problem and then tries to solve it by technical means. In that sense, the computer serves to inhibit the asking of important questions about the way our society raises and teaches its young.''

Will Children Think Like Computers?

Bonnie Brownstein is a former teacher who heads the Institute for Schools for the Future, a nonprofit educational think tank affiliated with the City University of New York. She worked with Papert in the early 1980s, training teachers in the New York City schools to use computers. Their training workshop eventually gave rise to the Computer School, an alternative junior high school in Manhattan that has been highly successful in reducing absentee rates and raising reading and math scores. Brownstein believes that computers can be used effectively in education, particularly in math and writing. ''With the computer, I've seen kids redo and redo what they write and experiment,'' she says. ''Children never used to edit or critique what they wrote because they'd have to copy it over.''

However, Brownstein agrees with Weizenbaum that any substantial improvements in the public schools will require a major restructuring of the system as it now exists. ''Computers can't teach a powerful new way of thinking in a vacuum,'' Brownstein says. ''We need more time and more money, and we need to look at the system as a whole. I mean, kids in the New York schools don't even have pencils to work with.''

Still, Brownstein gives Papert high marks for seeking new avenues of change. ''People like Papert are needed to keep stretching our thinking about what is possible,'' she says.

Other critics are not as sanguine. Weizenbaum and Hubert Dreyfus and his brother Stuart, both professors at the University of California at Berkeley, believe that Papert's approach is actually detrimental to the process of learning. They are particularly worried about his insistence that children learn how to think by programming. Papert has long believed that programming teaches children valuable cognitive skills. It isn't what they program that is so important, but rather the process of breaking problems down into subproblems and solving them, he says. By programming computers to perform almost any kind of task, children learn how to think.

Weizenbaum argues that the kind of thinking learned through programming—logical step-by-step analysis—is only one, limited variation of human thought. And, in fact, it is not the way human beings solve most of their problems in everyday life, particularly complex problems. ''Programming applies to a very narrow domain of problem solving,'' Weizenbaum maintains. ''But most human problems—whether to get married, whether to have children—are not solved that way.''

The analytical approach to problem solving is already emphasized ''too much and too soon in our schools,'' he says. Both he and the Dreyfus brothers believe that computers will merely reinforce society's reliance on such thinking—with dangerous consequences. The Dreyfuses say that Papert's approach encourages children to discount their more important intuitive thought processes in favor of a more limited analytical approach.

Even in Papert's group, a few researchers worry about the effect of computers on the mind. Edith Ackerman, a Swiss-born child psychologist who worked with Papert at Piaget's Center for Genetic Epistemology in Geneva, agrees that children exposed to computers ''will be more likely to think of their own thinking like a computer.'' But the presence of computers is a fait accompli in this society, Ackerman points out, and Papert is doing his best to turn something that could be destructive into something positive and enormously creative.

''If somebody like Papert puts all his energy and years of life into having children control computers and not be controlled by them, that to me is very good,'' Ackerman says. ''Computers are already here; we can no longer escape unless we go to a tropical forest.''

Weizenbaum has other problems with Papert's vision. Computers may indeed help children learn by experience, but ''I question the nature of the experience,'' he says. ''We live in an increasingly abstract world where much of our experiences come to us via cathode-ray tube—television. Many kids have never had the experience of raising an animal or hammering a hut together. Learning by experience is important, but I would rather it be a different kind of experience.''

Yet schools were created to teach abstract ideas not easily gleaned in the ''real world.'' And it is those largely abstract ideas used in writing, science, and mathematics that children from impoverished families need most to learn. What Papert is trying to do, his supporters say, is teach the ''basics''—but in more interesting and imaginative ways.

BATS and STATS

by Babe Cipher

Y ou are at Veterans Stadium in Philadelphia, enjoying a close game from a good seat right behind home plate. Sitting next to you, however, is a man who hardly seems to notice the taut 2-2 pitcher's duel the Phillies and Cardinals have carried into the top of the ninth. Instead, he is frantically scribbling information about each pitch onto a series of charts and graphs. The man's name is Ken Hultzapple, the Phillies' batting practice pitcher,

and he's not at the game today to enjoy himself. He's here to work.

Within a few hours, Hultzapple's jotted codes will be entered into a computer, and by tomorrow the team will have a detailed profile of the performance of every player who took the field for even a single pitch or swing. Hultzapple and his Phillies' bosses may know more about how the Cardinals played today than the Cardinals themselves.

"It ain't over 'til it's over." Yogi Berra's adage rang true in game six of the 1986 World Series, when the Mets staged one of the most statistically unlikely comebacks in baseball history. Down by two in the tenth inning, the Mets miraculously produced three runs. Third baseman Ray Knight (above) scored the run that won the game.

A Game of Numbers

Baseball is a game of numbers—floods of numbers: batting averages, earned run averages, slugging percentages, on-base percentages, errors per game, runs per season, and miles per hour. These days, in pursuit of that winning edge, teams—and fans—are scrutinizing those numbers as never before. But it's not an easy job. Because baseball is not just a game of numbers; it's also a game of randomness, of fractured stats, of broken rules, of the unpredictable happening with certain predictability. Even as the computer provides more and more ways to analyze the game, the game itself resists scrutiny.

Often as not, baseball just plain defies common sense. A mediocre hitter like Doug Griffin could do no wrong against all-time-great pitcher Jim Palmer, while slugger Boog Powell managed only 2 hits in 61 at bats against Mickey Lolich. Of all the people who might have slain the Red Sox in the 1978 American League East play-off, it was the normally light-hitting Yankee Bucky Dent who launched the game-winning homer. Tom Seaver had no-hitters broken up by such "immortals" as Jimmy Qualls—who scratched out only 30 other hits in a 63-game career—and Tarzan Wallis. In the first 81 years of World Series play, no team had ever lost the first two games in its home stadium and come back to win the series. Teams did just that in 1985 and 1986. Almost inevitably, pitchers who win the Cy Young Award one season can barely manage to buy a win the next.

The Repeat Jinx

October brings crisp days, brilliant leaves, and, of course, the play-offs and World Series. This year, as in many years past, not one of the reigning divisional champions has spent much of its season in first place. If all four fail to defend their titles, they will follow a trend that some have dubbed the repeat jinx. Since 1978 only 2 of 32 divisional winners have managed to finish first two years in a row, and one of those, the Yankees of the strike-torn 1981 season, won in a special patchwork play-off despite having only the third-best record in their division. This drought is even more amazing in light of the regularity with which teams successfully defended divisional, league, and even World Series titles in the previous eight years.

Are all these events simply accidents, rips in the usually tight statistical weave? Or do they hide some fundamental baseball truths?

Ever since the *New York Herald* ran the first primitive box scores back in 1845, people have looked to statistics to measure the abilities of their favorite players. Early game reports were modeled after those used in cricket; they measured simply the runs scored and outs totaled by each player. This formula captured the essence of winning baseball: scoring runs. Nevertheless, as the years passed, the box score swelled to include everything from walks to balks to sacrifice flies, all in an attempt to explain and quantify the quirks of the game.

Hitting Stats

As the *Herald* knew, however, runs are the coin of the realm, and it is here that any good study of the sport begins. A run is usually the culmination of a series of events. A player won't score many runs without good hitters behind

him to drive him in. Likewise, a player won't drive in many runs without people ahead of him getting on base.

But how do you start measuring the ways all these runs are created? Batting average? Maybe, but this most common of baseball stats doesn't do full justice to a player who walks a lot; more important, it doesn't weigh the extra-base hit at all, crediting the player equally, regardless of whether he smacks a single, double, triple, or home run. On-base average is better, acknowledging every time the batter reaches base, whether he hits, walks, or is hit by the pitch. But this, too, fails to take into account the magnitude of his hits. Slugging percentage does give extra-base hits a weighted value (two for a double, three for a triple, four for a homer); but if two players come up four times a game, can it really be said that one batter's home run and three outs are worth as much as the other batter's four singles, even though they both yield the same slugging figure?

Pitching and fielding statistics have similar shortcomings. A pitcher may toss a masterful game but still lose if his team doesn't score a few runs for him. Earned run average is a better measure of individual talent, but the pitcher will still suffer if his team has poor fielding range. And what is poor fielding, anyway? A shortstop may commit errors by virtue of his daring as well as by his ineptitude.

Sabermetrics

A new breed of statisticians now pores over spreadsheets and juggles variables in an attempt to correct these problems and refine our ability to measure player and team ability and predict future performance. Their tools are the computer, new statistical formulas, immense amounts of player data, and good baseball sense. They even have a title: sabermetrician, a word concocted from the initials of the Society of American Baseball Research, an organization founded in 1971 to promote the historical and statistical study of baseball. SABR now boasts 6,000 members.

Earl Weaver, the great Orioles manager, is the forefather of modern baseball analysis. Although he always maintained ''there is no such thing as a new statistic,'' he made exceptional use of the more traditional stats, hauling around stacks of dog-eared index cards that showed how each of his players performed against other teams. He could see, for example, how his ace pitcher Jim Palmer was terrorized by the Yan-

A gameful of fielding errors will adversely affect a pitcher's statistics, no matter how well he throws.

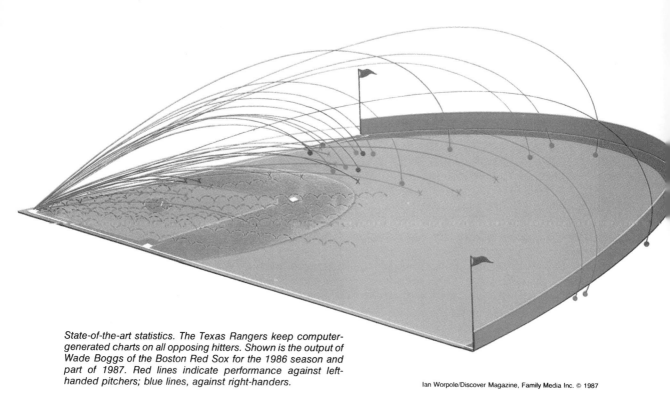

State-of-the-art statistics. The Texas Rangers keep computer-generated charts on all opposing hitters. Shown is the output of Wade Boggs of the Boston Red Sox for the 1986 season and part of 1987. Red lines indicate performance against left-handed pitchers; blue lines, against right-handers.

Ian Worpole/Discover Magazine, Family Media Inc. © 1987

kees' Graig Nettles to a .375 tune, and he knew to bring in Tippy Martinez—against whom Nettles batted barely .100—when the game was on the line. He knew that his shortstop Mark Belanger, who batted only an anemic .200 against most American League pitchers, somehow managed a fat .300 against the awesome Nolan Ryan.

Today sabermetricians and other game analysts have replaced those index cards with microchips. The Elias Sports Bureau provides computerized statistics to major league baseball as well as to the media. Many of these stats are general: say, George Brett's slugging percentage for May of 1987. Others are situational: how a player performs against a certain pitcher or with men on base. Peter Hirdt of Elias gives an example of how this information can be used: "It was early 1985, and Ron Hassey, who had just joined the Yankees, was on the bench. The Yankees were facing Charlie Hough of the Rangers. Billy Martin noticed that Hassey was hitting over .400 against Hough, so he put him into the game. Hassey responded by going 4 for 4, and after that he got a lot more playing time."

Some teams use their own computer systems to record a variety of game data. Steve

Mann and Pete Palmer of Baseball Analysis Company in Philadelphia designed a software program they dubbed BacBall, which they are offering for sale to every team in the major leagues. So far, Mann and Palmer's system is being used by the Phillies and the Braves.

"BacBall has three components," Mann says: "play-by-play, batted ball, and pitch-by-pitch. It takes two people to work it: one in the press box, who records the play-by-play and batted-ball data, and one behind the plate, who charts the pitches. The range and direction of batted balls are charted, with the field divided into nearly 200 sectors."

From such data, teams produce charts that show where batters tend to hit balls against particular pitchers. The pitch-by-pitch system is likewise very specific. The operator charts the type of pitch, its location—out of 29 alternatives—and its speed. Data from the different components can be combined to determine such variables as what type of pitch any given batter is likely to hit to a certain location.

The Texas Rangers use a similar system. Bob Garvey, who charts the information for the team, describes one of its key uses. "It probably helps most with defensive placement," he says. "If we know where the batter is likely to hit the ball, the manager can adjust our outfield accordingly.'' Other teams using computers to assist in field decisions include the Mets, Yankees, and White Sox.

The Linear-Weights System

Sabermetricians are also helping teams sharpen their offense, developing formulas that combine the best of batting average, on-base average, and slugging percentage to provide—at last—an accurate measure of not just how hard a player hits but how well he contributes to his team's run production. Sifting through reams of data from games played between 1901 and 1977, Pete Palmer began calculating how many actual runs any specific offensive event helps create. The average single, for example, results in .46 runs scored; the average home run leads to 1.4. By multiplying these numbers by the actual numbers of singles, doubles, triples, walks, hit-by-pitches, and stolen bases a player produces, adding the total and subtracting the player's outs, sabermetricians arrive at a figure for runs contributed over the course of a season

(or a career). The exact formula, presented by Palmer and writer John Thorn in their book *The Hidden Game of Baseball,* is: runs = .46 (singles) + .8 (doubles) + 1.02 (triples) + 1.4 (home runs) + .33 (walks + hit-by-pitches) + .3 (stolen bases) − .6 (caught stealing) − .25 (at bats − hits) − .5 (outs on base).

This complicated bit of tallying—which its inventors call the linear-weights system—may be the most accurate measure of run production ever devised. Thorn and Palmer tested their creation by comparing the linear-weight totals of all the players on all the teams in baseball for the past 33 years with the actual number of runs the teams scored. The two figures were remarkably close.

A similar approach can be used to calculate the number of runs prevented by a pitcher or fielder. For pitchers the sabermetricians measure how far above or below the league average the hurler's earned run average is, as well as how many innings he has worked. For fielders the data crunchers study the number of plays made successfully or unsuccessfully and adjust

With computer data banks at their disposal, today's stat keepers can provide baseball fans with virtually instantaneous updates of a player's statistics on a play-by-play basis.

this figure for position (since, for example, a shortstop is likely to get many more chances than a right fielder).

Babe Ruth Still the Best

The use of linear weights produces some surprising results. Under this system the most productive single season at the plate since the late 1950s occurred in 1961, but it was not achieved by Roger Maris, who belted 61 home runs, nor Mickey Mantle, who socked 54, but by Tiger youngster Norm Cash (though years later, rumors continue to circulate that Cash's stats were helped considerably by an illegally corked bat). In 1984 Orioles shortstop Cal Ripken had the fourth-best overall season (combining runs produced plus defensive runs saved) in history, better than seasons by anyone but Babe Ruth, who holds positions, one, two, and three.

Despite the accomplishments of the new science, sabermetrics has largely been ignored by the baseball establishment. Only a quarter of big-league teams use computer systems to aid on-field decisions. Gary Gillette, who edits the monthly journal *Sabermetric Review,* offers an explanation: "People who have spent their lives in baseball tend to distrust the ideas of people who haven't played. It's like the artist's view of the critic. "If they can't do it themselves, then what good are they?"

The Computer Edge

Some people worry that baseball will become less human if a computer is involved. But Peter Hirdt believes that the manager's job is hardly in jeopardy. "Some of the newer managers—Davey Johnson, Bobby Valentine—use computers to gain an edge, but they still make the decisions."

The biggest consumers of baseball statistics are the fans. The annual *Baseball Abstract,* written by sabermetrics czar Bill James, has introduced a generation of sports enthusiasts to the numerical cogs and balance wheels that tick just behind the face of the game. Newspapers and sportscasts are filled with an ever-growing mass of data, the proliferation of which inspired one television station to offer a satirical "Stupid Stat of the Day," which included such details as the number of times a pitcher picked up his rosin bag in the first seven innings and the number of times Keith Hernandez kicked first base over the course of a full game.

With all this information now at our fingertips, have we run out of new things to study? Has the DNA of baseball at last been unraveled? Bill James doesn't believe so. "Almost everything defies easy analysis," he says. "Defensive strategy, for instance. Does pulling the infield in really raise a player's average by a hundred points?"

Mysteries Remain

Gillette suggests a few other areas that are still open to exploration. "There is the question of clutch hitting," he says. "Do some players have the ability to hit better in critical situations, or is it an illusion due to random fluctuation? There is also a lot of controversy concerning the merits of such plays as the hit-and-run. The more questions we answer, the more there are to ask."

Most important to the fans, however, is the mysterious inability of one season's division winners to defend their titles the next season. Here even the sabermetricians are baffled. "There haven't been any dominant clubs in the '80s," says Mann. "A good deal of it is due to the fact that players simply cost more, and a team like the Yankees can't afford to buy up a lot of stars."

Adds Thorn: "There will always be teams

Statistical excess? Some baseball fans even record such trivialities as how often a player cleans his cleats.

© Rick Stewart/Focus West

DIVISIONAL CHAMPIONS SINCE 1978

NATIONAL LEAGUE EAST

Year	Team	Record	(Year after)
1978	Phillies	90–72	(84–78, fourth)
1979	Pirates	98–64	(83–79, third)
1980	Phillies	91–71	(59–48*)
1981*	Expos***	60–48	(86–76, third)
1982	Cardinals	92–70	(79–83, fourth)
1983	Phillies	90–72	(81–81, fourth)
1984	Cubs	96–65	(77–84, fourth)
1985	Cardinals	101–61	(79–82, third)
1986	Mets	108–54	(92–40, second)
1987	Cardinals	95–67	—

AMERICAN LEAGUE EAST

Year	Team	Record	(Year after)
1978	Yankees	100–63	(89–71, fourth)
1979	Orioles	102–57	(100–62, second)
1980	Yankees	103–59	(59–48*)
1981*	Yankees**	59–48	(79–83, fifth)
1982	Brewers	95–67	(87–75, fifth)
1983	Orioles	98–64	(85–77, fifth)
1984	Tigers	104–58	(84–77, third)
1985	Blue Jays	99–62	(86–76, fourth)
1986	Red Sox	95–66	(78–84, fifth)
1987	Tigers	98–64	—

NATIONAL LEAGUE WEST

Year	Team	Record	(Year after)
1978	Dodgers	95–67	(79–83, third)
1979	Reds	90–71	(89–73, third)
1980	Astros	93–70	(61–49*)
1981*	Dodgers***	63–47	(88–74, second)
1982	Braves	89–73	(88–74, second)
1983	Dodgers	91–71	(79–83, fourth)
1984	Padres	92–70	(83–79, third, tie)
1985	Dodgers	95–67	(73–89, fifth)
1986	Astros	96–66	(76–86, third)
1987	Giants	90–72	—

AMERICAN LEAGUE WEST

Year	Team	Record	(Year after)
1978	Royals	92–70	(85–77, second)
1979	Angels	88–74	(65–95, sixth)
1980	Royals	97–65	(50–53*)
1981*	A's	64–45	(68–94, fifth)
1982	Angels	93–69	(70–92, fifth)
1983	White Sox	99–63	(74–88, fifth)
1984	Royals	84–78	(91–71, first)
1985	Royals	91–71	(76–86, third, tie)
1986	Angels	92–70	(75–87, sixth)
1987	Twins	85–77	—

*Season interrupted by players' strike   **Third-best division record overall
***Second-best division record overall

that do better than statistically expected, like the Orioles of the late '70s and early '80s. Or maybe they just won because Earl Weaver was a great manager.''

Other observers theorize that the absence of dynasties like the Yankees of the 1950s or the A's of the 1970s has less to do with what happens on the field than off it. World Series winners in the 1980s have spent their off-season being feted and fed, working the banquet circuit and negotiating million-dollar product-endorsement contracts. By the time spring training has rolled around, many have been too happy, plump, and sated to chase another pennant with any real hunger. For statistical purists, however, such explanations lack the concrete appeal of sabermetric numbers.

Sabermetricians also have little luck explaining the phenomenon of the little guy doing big things. Why is it that in any game, anyone can be a star? Why did Juan Beniquez belt three of his six 1986 homers on a single summer night against the Yankees? How did manager Connie Mack know to bypass all his pitching stars and call on the aging Howard Ehmke, who had

pitched only 55 innings all year, to start the 1929 World Series? How did Ehmke manage to stymie the Cubs for nine full innings, holding the National League champions to just one run? In response to these questions, many sabermetricians just shrug. Maybe it's the wind, the weather, what the player had for breakfast. ''Much of baseball,'' says Thorn simply, ''can be reasonably attributed to chance.''

Numbers can help us understand the game. They can record what has happened, but they can't always tell us why, nor what the future may bring. No computer can predict injuries or drug addiction or clubhouse dissension. How do you measure motivation or the effect of a crushing loss? Anyone who watched the 1986 playoffs and World Series experienced the full complexity and fickleness of the game. After the series was over, two fans using a baseball board game replayed the tenth inning of game six, in which the Mets were down by two runs with two outs but came back to win. Given that setup, it took 150 rolls of the dice before a scenario appeared in which the New Yorkers came away with the victory.

EARTH SCIENCES

On October 1, 1987, southern California was jolted by an earthquake measuring 6.1 on the Richter scale. A series of aftershocks over the next few days caused still further damage.

© Bill Nation/SYGMA

REVIEW
OF THE
YEAR

EARTH SCIENCES

A major California earthquake, accelerated coastal erosion, marked changes in water levels of the Great Lakes, new information about the crustal plates, and significant fossil discoveries were the major earth science news of 1987.

EARTHQUAKES AND SEISMOLOGY

The most severe earthquake to hit the U.S. in 1987 struck the Los Angeles area October 1. The quake, centered between Whittier and Pasadena, measured 6.1 on the Richter scale. Three minutes after the initial quake, a severe aftershock of magnitude 5.3 shook the area. Before day's end, at least 16 aftershocks measuring 3.0 or greater had been recorded. Three days later the most powerful aftershock (5.5 magnitude) did still more damage. In the end, six people were killed, and damages totaled some $213 million.

The quake was at first thought to have originated from the Whittier-Elsinore fault, a vertical fracture between two crustal plates moving in opposite directions. Later studies suggested that it was generated by a deep-seated thrust-type fault where one plate rides over another.

Another earthquake jolted 16 states from Missouri to Virginia and parts of Canada on June 10. The temblor, centered near Lawrenceville,

Illinois, measured 5.0 on the Richter scale, although no casualties or major damage were reported. Three days later a second Midwest quake hit three Missouri towns along the New Madrid fault—the same area where the nation's strongest series of earthquakes was recorded in 1811.

Two major earthquakes rocked the mountains of northeastern Ecuador on March 5 and 6. The twin shocks of magnitude 7.0 were followed by hundreds of aftershocks that caused severe mud slides and flooding, leaving as many as 110,000 homeless and an estimated 1,000 dead or missing. On February 8, a 7.4 quake leveled villages on a Papua New Guinea island, leaving at least 1,000 people homeless. Strong earthquakes were also recorded in Alaska, Chile, Japan, and Nicaragua.

VOLCANOES AND VOLCANOLOGY

On January 21, Pacaya volcano, about 15 miles (24 kilometers) from Guatemala City, erupted, damaging crops and injuring 12 villagers. On October 11, oceanographers on a California-based research trip were shaken by an undersea eruption directly beneath their vessel. Loud noises accompanied the large bubbles of steam and volcanic ash that burst under the ship's hull and the explosions that shot out jets of gas and expelled gas-filled volcanic rocks. This phenomenon seems to support a hypothesis of French seismologists in Tahiti, about 1,000 miles (1,600 kilometers) to the northwest of the eruption, that the similar submarine rumblings they have recorded are indeed undersea volcanic eruptions.

Meanwhile, some volcanologists have challenged the basic concept of "hot spots"— areas of the earth that apparently remain hot for periods as long as 100 million years. This concept, based on the presence of deeply buried plumes of semimolten rock, has been used to explain linear chains of volcanic islands such as Hawaii. Hot spots also appear to account for volcanic areas such as Yellowstone. At first, hot spots were assumed to be buried deep within the earth; new evidence now suggests that they may occur at relatively shallow depths. Moreover, hot spots seem to move more than originally believed. Because hot spots apparently provide energy for seafloor spreading and continental drift, the debate may cause rethinking about certain aspects of plate tectonics and plate movement.

COASTAL EROSION

Rising sea levels caused accelerated flooding and shoreline erosion in 1987—a trend that will endanger coastal communities during the next century. In the past 100 years or so, sea level has risen 4 inches (10 centimeters) on the Pacific Coast, 6 inches (15 centimeters) on the Gulf Coast, and 12 inches (30 centimeters) on the Atlantic Coast. Alaska, on the other hand, has recorded a drop in sea level because melting glaciers have removed weight from the Alaskan landmass, enabling it to rise. Paradoxically, meltwater from these and other glaciers is contributing to the rise in sea level. The warming of the atmosphere, which causes seawater to expand, also contributes to rising global ocean levels.

THE GREAT LAKES

Rising water levels also produced problems for property owners on the shores of the Great Lakes. Heavy rainfall during the past two years raised Lakes Michigan and Erie to record levels, causing flooding, severe erosion, and great property damage. During 1987, however, Lake Michigan dropped 18 inches (46 centimeters) following an unusually dry summer and spring. But more wet years could elevate lake levels another 9 inches (23 centimeters) to 18 inches (46 centimeters) in three to four years. The fluctuating—and unpredictable—lake levels are being studied by teams of scientists from both Canada and the United States.

PALEONTOLOGY AND FOSSILS

The remains of a new type ceratopsid (horned) dinosaur, *Avaceratops lammersi,* were found in 75-million-year-old rocks in Montana. The 400-pound (181-kilogram) plant eater was about 7.5 feet (2 meters) long and almost 3 feet (1 meter) tall. A dinosaur braincase found in Alberta, Canada, that resembles that of modern birds may prove valuable in understanding the evolution of dinosaurs, birds, and mammals.

The oldest known dinosaur eggs, found in 145-million-year-old Upper Jurassic strata in western Colorado, may provide new information on the nesting habits of dinosaurs. At least six layers of nests had shells arranged in a way that suggests that certain dinosaurs preferred isolated nesting sites and used them repeatedly. Additional knowledge of nesting habits came from nests found in central Texas, some of which contained the skeletons of baby dinosaurs. In Mongolia's Gobi Desert, where the first dinosaur eggs were found in 1922, egg fragments were discovered arranged upright and packed in strawlike plant fibers—further support of a close dinosaur-bird evolutionary link.

Unusual discoveries also were associated with the preservation of material in amber (fossil resin). Although plant fragments and insects were frequently fossilized in amber, a Late Eocene (40 million years ago) frog found in the Dominican Republic became the first amphibian found encased in amber. An even more remarkable discovery was the recovery of minute samples of the prehistoric atmosphere in crushed Canadian amber dating from Cretaceous time, some 130 million years ago. The air, trapped in bubbles in hardened resin, was found to be more than 10 percent richer in oxygen than the modern atmosphere. Although not yet fully confirmed, this finding has implications for both evolutionary theory and concepts of how the earth's climate has formed and changed.

EARTH STRUCTURE AND PLATE TECTONICS

The earth's crust and upper mantle, or lithosphere, consists of several slow-moving plates. The causes and rates of plate movement, however, are not fully understood. In 1987 data from a computer model of possible plate mechanisms suggest that plates may provide their own motive force through the pull of cooling ocean plates as they sink in deep-ocean trenches. Great heat may be another mechanism. California scientists have learned that the earth's core is much hotter than originally believed: more than 12,000° F (6,650° C). The heat may seep from the core to the mantle, generating currents that shift crustal plates. Rates of movement have been monitored by means of large radio antennas that record signals from different quasars as reference points. For example, data derived from the relatively fast-moving Pacific plate reveal that the distance between Hawaii and a site near Fairbanks, Alaska, has decreased by about 2 inches (5.2 centimeters) per year, and scientists have now determined that Hawaii is moving toward Japan at the rate of 3.26 inches (8.3 centimeters) per year.

WILLIAM H. MATTHEWS III

© David Cupp/Woodfin Camp

Ski patrollers prepare to set off an avalanche. The snowpack, if left alone, could unleash later on unwary skiers.

Averting Avalanches

by Tom Callahan

At 6:00 A.M., it is still dark and snowing heavily as Taos ski patrolmen Jim Lee and Mike Kirby struggle through 4 feet (1.2 meters) of new snow along the precipitous, avalanche-prone Highline Ridge. On their backs, each carries 30 pounds (13.5 kilograms) of explosives for setting loose avalanches. Strapped to their chests are two-way radios and avalanche beacons to help other patrollers rescue them should they be swept away and buried in a slide.

At the top of an avalanche chute called Hidalgo, Lee and Kirby huddle against gusts of blowing snow to light the fuses of two 1-pound (450-gram) bombs the size of tomato cans, which they lob into the center of the chute. Before their ears stop ringing from the explosions, the mountain begins to rumble. Bingo! They've set loose an avalanche, which they hear crashing through timber 500 feet (150 meters) below. ''We've got results on Hidalgo,'' radios Lee to the ski patrol center.

At the patrol center, located atop 11,000-foot (3,350-meter) Taos Mountain, it's like war as Lee, Kirby, and a dozen other patrollers detonate charges from every ridge. The mountain shakes as though there's an earthquake, and the radio crackles as results are called in. For the next two hours, before the area is opened to recreational skiers, patrollers will release some 20 avalanches, which, if left alone, could release later in the day onto unwary skiers.

Caught in an Avalanche

At 8:30 A.M., Lee and Kirby heave their final six bombs down the treacherously steep Treschow Chute. The snow fractures, settles, and groans, but doesn't slide. The men need only glance at each other to communicate that they're in big trouble. The only way back to base is down this chute, leaving them little choice but to ski it and hope it doesn't run. Lee goes first, plowing across the slope through waist-deep powder to a tree on the far side, which he grabs with a linebacker's bear hug. Kirby follows, cutting across the chute to the safety of another tree. Halfway down, Kirby sees the trees shaking above them. "Look out! It's coming down big!" is all he has time to yell.

One hundred feet (30 meters) above, a layer of snow 4 feet (1.2 meters) thick and 50 feet (15 meters) wide has broken loose and begun to slide as a single unit, like a river of ice during spring thaw. The men grab their trees with death grips. "It hit me real hard," Lee later tells rescuers. "The snow was over my head, pounding, just whaling my face into the bark." The slide passes in less than 10 seconds, leaving Lee buried to his waist. Immediately he looks to his partner's tree. Kirby is gone.

Two years earlier, Kirby was caught in an avalanche while patrolling at Mt. Hood Meadows in Oregon. Tossed around at the top of that slide like a cork in heavy surf, Kirby was able to swim to the side and rescue himself. Not now. The weight and momentum of this avalanche is so strong, it hits like a tidal wave and tears Kirby off the tree. He can do little but let himself be swept away by the wave. When the slide grinds to a halt at the base of the chute, Kirby can't move. He's trapped in a form-fitting casket of ice. There is precious little air.

Partner Mike Lee quickly digs himself free from his tree and radios the patrol center for

In a mock avalanche emergency, a specially trained dog sniffs out and "rescues" a dummy.

help. Turning his avalanche beacon to *receive*, he skis to the base of the slide, where the snow is piled 15 feet (4.5 meters) deep, and begins a zigzag search pattern for the signal from Kirby's transceiver. In five minutes he's got something and throws himself at the snow. After 3 feet (1 meter) of furious digging, he uncovers Kirby's head. The buried patroller, almost unconscious from lack of oxygen, gasps for air, looks up at his rescuer, and croaks, "Lee, I thought you were a dead man."

At the Taos Ski Valley, where there are more than 300 avalanches during the average 131-day ski season, most ski patrollers have been caught, at one time or another, in similar avalanches. Luckily, no Taos patroller has ever died in a slide. Snow-safety workers at other ski areas have not been so lucky. According to Knox Williams, director of the Colorado Avalanche Information Center and coauthor of *The Avalanche Book,* an average of 80 American ski patrollers a year are caught in snow slides; nine have died in avalanches during the past seven years.

Capricious Killers

The fact that so many snow-safety workers die as a result of the very force they're trained to control reveals the bitter truth about avalanches. They are wildly capricious killers, as erratic and enigmatic as they are awesome. Throughout history the "white death," as it is often called, has wrought such devastation that many cultures consider it a wrathful god of destruction. A German folk riddle calls an avalanche "the monster that flies without wings, strikes without hands, and sees without eyes."

The largest and most destructive avalanches begin on steep, treeless slopes that have received large amounts of snowfall in a short period of time. At the start, there's usually a "whoomp" like a stick of dynamite detonated under a snowpack. Then—at least in the most dangerous slides, called slab avalanches—an entire layer of the snowpack, sometimes 5 to 10 feet (1.5 to 3 meters) deep and dozens of acres in surface area, breaks loose and begins its descent like a million-ton tombstone. As the slide accelerates and gathers up snow in its path, it throws clouds of snow spume hundreds of feet into the air. Barreling along at speeds of 40 to 60 miles (65 to 100 kilometers) per hour, some avalanches accelerate, rising farther, skimming along on a cushion of air and pushing before them an air blast that, according to current theory, creates a vacuum behind it that sucks the slides along even faster. Seemingly defying the laws of physics, such avalanches attain speeds in excess of 230 miles (370 kilometers) per hour, almost twice that of a free-falling sky diver! The friction created within such a slide melts some of the snow, and when the slide stops, the free water freezes, binding the avalanche debris together like concrete.

On January 10, 1962, the most destructive avalanche in history swept the slopes of 22,205-foot (6,770-meter) North Huascarán peak in the Peruvian Andes. Six villages in the slide's 10-mile (16-kilometer) path were annihilated. Four thousand people and 10,000 animals died. Eight years later the avalanche struck again, taking 18,000 lives.

Growing Death Toll

Despite the popular belief that modern technology makes avalanche disasters a thing of the past, the death toll by avalanches in the United States has been growing, doubling every 10 years. The reason, according to Knox Williams, is not due to an increase in avalanches, which always number about 100,000 a year in the United States, but to an increase in the number of skiers and climbers who are venturing into

Both photos: © James Balog/Black Star

The likelihood of an avalanche depends on the properties of the flakes that make up the snowpack. In a pit dug deep into the snow, a scientist removes a snow sample and measures its density (above). Snow samples also are analyzed for crystal structure and size using a specially designed magnifying glass (right).

© James Balog/Black Star

A ski patroller assembles rockets that will be launched into unstable snowpacks to create controlled avalanches.

most questions about avalanches with, ''It depends,'' or ''It's hard to say,'' and warns that all the scientific instruments of the computer age do little to increase the accuracy of his predictions and effectiveness of his control strategies.

Snowflake Mechanics

The difficulties of avalanche prediction and control, Rose explains, lie in the instability and mercurial nature of the snow crystal. During warm days, snow falls wet and sticky, clinging to even the steepest slopes like meringue. On cold nights, it falls dry and crystalline, running off even the beginner's hill like sugar. Forecasting which snow will hold and which will slide gets complicated when different snows layer on top of one another and then begin to settle, crystallize, and metamorphose. Sometimes the bond holding a layer of sticky surface snow to an underlying layer of unstable snow is so tenuous, the weight of a single skier can break the delicate cohesion and trigger an avalanche. Predicting such slides before they happen is an obsession with Rose, who periodically digs 5-foot (1.5-meter) snow pits at various locations around the mountain, and examines the snow layers with thermometer, scale, and magnifying glass. ''The snow is always changing,'' says Rose. ''A slope that was stable yesterday might not be that way today. We have to act like we're in enemy camp all the time.''

On avalanche-danger mornings, which occur an average of once every three days, Rose wakes at 3:45 A.M. and radios the snow-cat operators, who've been on the mountain all night compacting the slopes. If there's new snow or the old snow is unstable, Rose calls the 16 patrollers on duty that morning, and by 5:45 A.M., all are on their way up the mountain to collect their morning's supply of bombs and start their control routes. On high-hazard days the men will throw 200 pounds (90 kilograms) of explosives. That's 4,000 to 5,000 pounds (1,800 to 2,300 kilograms) of explosives used each winter.

When the slopes can't be safely bombed with hand-thrown charges, the patrollers shell them with a Korean War–vintage, 105-millimeter recoilless rifle or a compressed-nitrogen mortar called an Avalauncher. If this shelling fails to release an avalanche, the patrollers ski the slopes to check their stability. It's during such ''body-bombing'' missions that many accidents occur.

avalanche-prone areas for adventure. In an average winter, Williams estimates that 140 Americans are caught in avalanches. Sixty to 70 are wholly or partly buried. Seventeen die, and 12 more are injured.

It's the job of Taos Ski Valley's Ski Patrol to make sure that none of this winter's avalanche accidents occur at their resort. Because of Taos's notoriously steep slopes and average yearly snowfall of nearly 20 feet (6 meters), their job is not easy.

On a sunny New Mexican day, Chuck Rose, Taos Ski Valley's avalanche expert, sits in the area's snow-safety office poring over weather forecasts and minute-by-minute printouts of wind speed and direction, precipitation, relative humidity, and barometric pressure from weather stations around the mountain. From these figures, Rose is formulating the next morning's avalanche-control battle plan. At 37, Rose has ten years' experience on the Taos Ski Patrol, and knows enough about avalanches, he says, to realize how little he knows. He answers

A ski patroller hurls a hand charge into an unstable field of mountainside snow (above). In the resultant avalanche (below), the snow barrels down the slopes at 40 to 60 miles per hour. Some powerful avalanches—seemingly defying the laws of physics—have been estimated to reach speeds of up to 230 miles per hour. Such an avalanche would annihilate everything in its path.

A Range of Duties

By opening hour at 9:00 A.M., all 76 slopes on Taos Mountain have been evaluated and checked. "That's a lot of ground to cover in a short period of time," says Rose, "a lot of pressure." Inevitably, the patrollers sometimes miss a slide, and an avalanche occurs during operating hours. Then a communications network of 23 telephones located at various points around the mountain—and radios with every patroller, snow-cat operator, and lift operator—assure that rescue teams arrive at the slide area within minutes. At least one of three avalanche dogs is always on duty with its patroller handler at the top of the mountain. The dogs are trained to search an avalanche area with a disciplined zigzag pattern, and can usually sniff out a buried victim, at least in practice situations, in less than a minute. If the victim is buried too deep for the dogs to detect, rescuers organize a probe line consisting of a dozen or more people, each with 12-foot (3.6 meter) metal poles, marching a few feet apart probing the snow.

If avalanche control and rescue were the only duties ski patrollers performed, their jobs would be relatively easy. As it is, 250,000 ski tickets are sold each year at Taos, 4,500 on busy days alone. Patrollers must issue speeding tickets to reckless skiers, evacuate derailed ski lifts, monitor "off-limits" slopes, and tend to broken equipment and injuries. By 5:00 P.M., some 12 hours after their shifts begin, patrollers make a final sweep of the slopes and close the mountain. "Most days," says assistant snow-safety director Rey Deveaux, "I'm so tired I go right home, eat dinner, and hit the sack. I've got to be ready to go at 4:30 the next morning."

For their services, Taos patrolmen are paid $5.65 to $9.20 an hour, depending upon their experience. Admitted ski addicts, all love their job for the ski time it affords, and few complain about the pay. Most are single men in their mid-twenties to early forties—a burly, bearded, wild-eyed-looking crew. Each has a nickname: Eske, Jet Man, The Ayatollah, Spike, Edge, Rage, and the proverbial Mad Dog. Famous for their practical jokes, they push each other around like college boys.

A Taciturn Facade

On a recent, cloudless day when there is no early-morning avalanche-control work to do, the patrollers gather on the slope above the first chair lift. An empty soda can is produced, and a wild game of ski-hockey is played as the men

© David Cupp/Woodfin Camp

Aftermath of an avalanche: a demolished ski lift bears grim testimony to the awesome power of an avalanche.

ski down the ramp to the second chair. A ski pole catches one player below the eye and opens a nasty gash. As teammates try to stanch the blood flow, which is quickly painting the snow crimson, one patroller quips, "Someone call and see if there's a vet on the mountain."

At the morning meeting in the patrol center, which looks like a college fraternity house, with walls and rafters adorned with swimsuit-clad Amazons from *Sports Illustrated* and trophies mounted on beer cans for ski-race victories, patrol leader Mark Richardson, wearing a Donald Duck hat and garish Hawaiian shirt in honor of the Hawaiian-shirt keg party to be held that night, begins by making what appears to be a standard request. "Hey, guys, let's cool it on the hockey; we lose someone every year with that game." Groans all around.

Later in the day, when the patrollers return to the center for lunch, a tape player blares Beach Boys' tunes, and a few of the men, sitting on a bench against a sun-drenched window, hold imaginary microphones and sing along. "Girls, Girls, Girls. Wish they all could be California—Wish they all could be California . . . Girls."

Most skiers would blanch at such a scene when considering these men throwing dozens of bombs each morning and doctoring hapless skiers' broken legs. More than likely, however, no one will see them this way. When they put on their red jackets with big white crosses and exit the patrol center, they also put on a professional, almost taciturn, "Right Stuff" demeanor common to ski patrolmen around the country.

Sometimes the patroller's cool is pushed to its limits. Three years ago, during a five-day cold snap, the snow was so unstable, two or three patrollers were caught each morning in avalanches. "Guys would come in at the end of the day exhausted," says Rey Deveaux, "and they'd be laughing almost hysterically."

Understandably, most patrollers speak in philosophical or spiritual terms when talking about their relationship with the mountain, avalanches, and death. "I work this job and take the risks I do because I love the mountain," says Deveaux. "Every day the mountain is different. It keeps me alive—it's my teacher. The mountain is always there—it's my companion. On good days, when I ski a beautiful powder run, it's my therapy—my best friend. On high-hazard days, when everything's running, it's my adversary—my enemy. I can't imagine doing anything else but being on the mountain patrolling."

MASTERING THE
MICROBURST

by Richard Monastersky

On August 2, 1985, Delta Flight 191 was descending through scattered thunderstorms at 6:04 P.M. on a routine approach to the Dallas–Fort Worth Airport. At 6:06 the plane was a ball of flames, lying less than a mile (1.6 kilometers) from the runway. In the interim, Flight 191 had flown through the treacherous winds of a microburst.

Microbursts "are the largest source of air carrier death in the United States," says John McCarthy, a meteorologist at the National Center for Atmospheric Research (NCAR) in Boulder, Colorado. Over the past 12 years, this small, short-lived pattern of intense winds has been implicated in three of the most catastrophic weather-related air accidents, which were responsible for a combined total of 398 deaths.

Currently, airports are ill-equipped to detect these significant but infrequent threats to air travel. However, in the wake of these crashes, a concert of meteorologists, computer specialists, and aerodynamic engineers is developing systems to detect microbursts and warn pilots of their deadly presence.

During the summer of 1986, scientists in Huntsville, Alabama, conducted the most recent in a series of large-scale field experiments designed to learn more about microbursts. These experiments indicate that a combination of Doppler radar and computers may be effective in detecting microbursts, although the wide use of these systems is several years away.

What Is a Microburst?

A microburst is a wind pattern that descends from rain clouds during spring and summer months. When this stream of falling air, or downflow, hits the ground, the wind fans out horizontally into an outflow. In this way it resembles the spray pattern that water from a kitchen faucet makes when it hits the bottom of the sink. By producing a strong divergence of wind, the microburst outflow causes a condition known as wind shear, a quick change in the wind's speed or direction.

For airplanes on takeoff or landing, an intense wind shear can be particularly hazardous. When an airplane enters a microburst, it first runs into a head wind, which increases the

Microbursts—intense but short-lived downdrafts of air that create rapid changes in wind speed and direction—often elude detection, especially when they take the form of an innocent-looking cloud formation.

speed of the air that is rushing over the wings and gives the plane additional lift. After the plane passes through the downdraft in the center of the microburst, it is swept by a tail wind, which robs the plane of lift.

This dramatic change from head wind to tail wind poses an insidious combination of forces. A plane on a landing approach is usually at 70 to 80 percent of full power. Upon entering the head wind of a microburst, a pilot may mistake this for an ordinary head wind, and will not expect a sudden wind shift. "Then you are caught in a big surprise" when the airspeed drops dramatically and the plane begins to fall, says T. Theodore Fujita of the University of Chicago. It takes several seconds to reach full power, and by that time the plane may have lost too much altitude to pull out of its fall.

Fujita is generally credited as being the first to deduce the existence of microbursts, during an aerial survey of tornado damage in 1974. Instead of seeing a typical swirling pattern of fallen trees, he noticed hundreds of trees blown outward like the spokes of a wheel. Since then, he and the NCAR have conducted several large-scale field experiments, including the 1982 Joint Airport Weather Studies (JAWS) and the Microburst and Severe Thunderstorm (MIST) project in 1986. The aim is to understand the mechanics of the microburst event and develop ways to avert wind-shear-related air disasters.

Although the mechanics are not totally understood, says Fujita, it appears that the evaporation of raindrops is critical to the microburst formation. This evaporation cools a parcel of air, which will begin to fall as it gets heavier, thereby producing a downdraft. Humid areas like Huntsville, where the downdraft is almost always associated with rain, usually spawn the so-called wet microbursts. Dry microbursts, on the other hand, frequent more arid places like Denver, Colorado, where cloud bases are higher and the precipitation will often totally evaporate before the downdraft reaches the ground.

Few Visual Clues

These factors conspire to make the microburst a dangerously elusive phenomenon. Wet microbursts will produce a visible rain shaft, but this can often be obscured within a benign rain shaft. Conversely, without any associated precipitation, dry microbursts present almost no visual clues of their presence. Pilots and controllers hoping to spot a microburst cannot even rely on the character of the clouds for clues because both thunderheads and small, seemingly innocuous rain clouds can produce these hazardous wind shears.

From the JAWS and MIST projects, scientists have learned that microbursts are small, typically 0.6 to 1.9 miles (1 to 3 kilometers) across, and short-lived—on the order of 5 to 15 minutes. The average difference between the head wind and the tail wind is 60 miles (96 kilometers) per hour, but Fujita has documented a case with a differential in excess of 172 miles (276 kilometers) per hour.

At present, 90 airports across the United States are fitted with a Low-Level Wind Shear Alert System (LLWAS)—an array of 5 anemometers, or wind detectors, at the boundary of the airport surrounding an anemometer at the center field position. A processor compares differences in wind speed and direction, to determine if there is any shear within the LLWAS area.

However, LLWAS was installed to detect gust fronts, a different weather hazard, and aviation officials have known for several years that LLWAS cannot reliably detect microbursts. False-alarm rates are high, and for this reason, ''some pilots are very skeptical'' of these wind shear warnings, says Dan Rebhun of the Federal Aviation Administration (FAA).

Furthermore, the LLWAS array is too small and too porous—microbursts can first touch down outside the LLWAS network or even between the sensors, leaving pilots unaware of the wind shear hazard. Flight 191, for example, passed through the center of the microburst over 1.5 miles (2.4 kilometers) outside the outermost sensor. It was only several minutes after the accident that the LLWAS alarm went off, indicating that wind shear hazard was present.

The FAA is increasing the number of anemometers at the 90 airports and adding LLWAS systems to 20 others in an effort to enhance coverage, but many scientists believe that ground anemometers cannot do the job when it comes to detecting microbursts. ''It's our feeling that they may be tardy in recognizing that a microburst has occurred,'' says Jim Evans, who is

NCAR

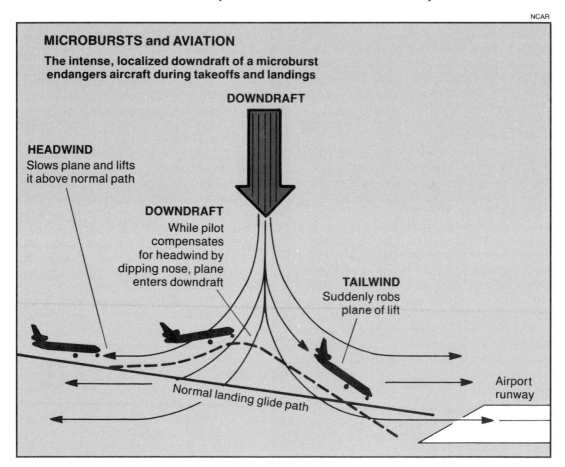

MICROBURSTS and AVIATION

The intense, localized downdraft of a microburst endangers aircraft during takeoffs and landings

DOWNDRAFT

HEADWIND
Slows plane and lifts it above normal path

DOWNDRAFT
While pilot compensates for headwind by dipping nose, plane enters downdraft

TAILWIND
Suddenly robs plane of lift

Normal landing glide path

Airport runway

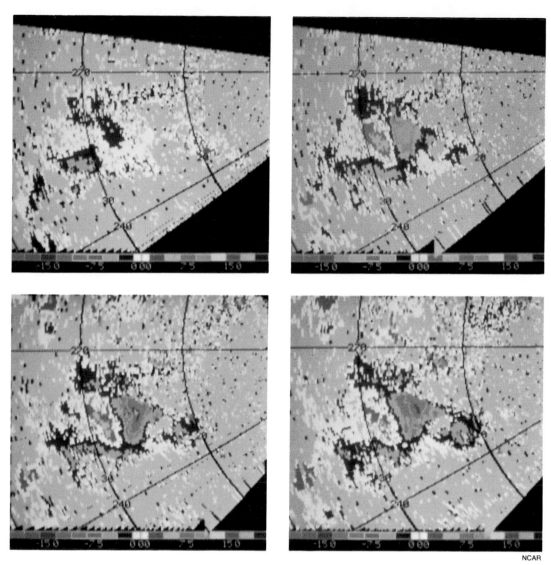

The life cycle of a microburst, documented by a seven-minute Doppler radar sequence. The microburst forms (upper left), intensifies (upper right), and reaches maximum strength (lower left) before it begins to dissipate (lower right). Black and white areas indicate winds moving toward the radar; colored areas show winds moving away.

developing a computerized detection system for predicting microburst phenomena at MIT's Lincoln Laboratory located in Lexington, Massachusetts.

The LLWAS can measure only the outflow of the microburst. It unfortunately does not have the capacity to register a wind shear warning until the difference between the central sensor and an outlying sensor is greater than 17 miles (27 kilometers) per hour. During the interim, the microburst has the opportunity to touch down and spread out before controllers have any warning of its presence.

Doppler Radar

Results from the MIST data give scientists even more cause for concern. The JAWS data indicated that it took at least 5 to 6 minutes from the time the downburst reached the ground to the time when the winds of the outburst had reached their highest and most dangerous speeds. However, from a preliminary study of the Huntsville data, Fujita is finding that "the wet microburst cases build up in a very short time, taking 2 to 3 minutes." Such a time scale does not give controllers enough time to warn pilots, says Fujita.

Doppler radar is the most reliable way of detecting microbursts. From inside the spherical radome, the Doppler radar unit emits microwaves that then bounce off raindrops. By measuring the frequency shift of the returning microwaves, Doppler radar can determine wind velocities and directions.

In an effort to gain more time, scientists are using a type of radar called Doppler radar to sense the microbursts before they reach the ground and develop an outflow. Conventional weather radar, the kind that provides the weather maps on television, measures distance. Doppler radar, on the other hand, can measure velocity as well (police use it to catch speeders). It gauges wind speed by bouncing microwaves off objects that move with the wind, such as raindrops, ice particles, and even insects.

A single Doppler radar cannot measure vertical winds, and therefore cannot directly sense the descent of the downdraft. However, through field observations and computer models, meteorologists have learned to use Doppler radar to look for indirect evidence that a downdraft is developing.

Both above and below the cloud base, wind and rain will often converge around the descending current of air, in a sense feeding into it. Another indicator of a downdraft is the rapid descent of a precipitation core. The existence of these and other precursors does not prove that a microburst is forming, but they serve as good warning signals that something may be on its way down.

In the summer of 1984, NCAR meteorologists used these precursors to provide microburst warnings for Denver's Stapleton Airport in a program called the Classify, Locate and Avoid Wind Shear (CLAWS) project. When the NCAR group spotted precursors on the radar screen, they issued an advance notice that a microburst would reach the surface within 5 minutes. Then, upon first signs of divergence at the surface, the meteorologists issued a full-scale microburst warning. On the average, they warned pilots 4 minutes before the most severe wind shear, giving the pilots enough time to avoid a hazardous encounter.

The CLAWS project demonstrated that Doppler radar can be an effective tool in microburst detection and warning. However, the project relied on expert meteorologists to continuously monitor the radar during the day—a process that is too expensive and time-consuming for widespread use. For that reason, Lincoln Laboratory is developing an automated detection algorithm, a computer program that will sift through incoming radar data for the signs of a microburst. In last summer's Huntsville experiments, researchers tested an algorithm that takes 10 seconds to detect an outflow within 6 miles (9.6 kilometers) of an airport.

Computerized Cloud Models

Although this system is reliable, notes Evans, "this initial algorithm was not tremendously intelligent because it only looked at data near the surface. It didn't use any of the data aloft. Now we have some more refined algorithms, which are undergoing initial testing, that take advantage of the fact that microbursts just don't pop up on the surface. Things happen aloft that precede development.'' These so-called expert systems are programs that seek to imitate the reasoning that meteorologists use when searching for precursors as an advance warning of a microburst. Testing of these advanced algorithms will continue this summer in Denver.

John Anderson of the University of Wisconsin in Madison is working with Lincoln Laboratory in developing what he calls ''a second-generation processing system''—computerized cloud models that can forecast a microburst before the downdraft develops. The models rely on data from Doppler radar. As the model goes through a simulation, radar data from the actual environment are used to update or correct the simulation. Such a combination can ''make a prediction for what the cloud will look like in 10 or 15 minutes,'' says Anderson.

The next stage in this research, according to Anderson, ''is figuring out what kinds of observations you need to update the model. . . . How good do the radars have to be?'' He notes that forecasting on a larger scale has been practiced for many years, but ''the idea of doing forecasts on cloud scales is really a new idea.''

In another area of research, the National Aeronautics and Space Administration's (NASA's) Langley Research Center in Hampton, Virginia, is developing airborne sensor systems. Since not all airports will receive Doppler radars in the future, ''the idea is to take your protection with you whenever you fly—sort of like a turtle with his shell,'' says NASA's Roland Bowles. They are considering equipping planes with Doppler radar on Doppler lidar, which uses laser light instead of microwaves. However, these systems as well as the forecasting models are just in their infancy.

Simulated Encounters

Ground-based Doppler radar will be reaching some airports in the near future. In 1989 the FAA plans to begin deployment of 16 Doppler radars at critical airports such as Dallas–Fort Worth, Atlanta's Hartsfield, Chicago's O'Hare, New York's Kennedy and La Guardia, Washington National, Miami, Fort Lauderdale–Hollywood, and Denver's Stapleton.

In the meantime, the FAA and airlines are seeking to arm pilots with both the knowledge and skill to handle a microburst, in the event of an encounter. In February a consortium of airplane manufacturers completed the framework for a pilot-training program involving meteorologic training and simulated microburst encounters. The FAA plans to require this training for all U.S. air carrier pilots, and implementation of the program should take a year or so. ''When that gets transferred to the pilots, then I think we're going to be in a lot better shape,'' says McCarthy, who advised the consortium.

''I don't think we're going to eliminate wind shear accidents,'' says McCarthy, ''but I think we're going to make them a 20- to 30-year phenomenon instead of a one- to two-year phenomenon.''

The visual system of a B727 aircraft flight simulator creates encounters with microbursts and other weather phenomena as part of pilot training. The FAA plans to make such instruction mandatory for all U.S. air carrier pilots.

The author boards Alvin *(above) before its descent into South Wilmington Canyon off the coast of New Jersey.* Alvin's *sampling basket (below) carries cylinders for holding mud samples.*

UNDERWATER CANYONS

by Robert Gannon

For years I had longed to dive with *Alvin*—in my mind, this was second only to a trip in the shuttle as the ultimate science/technology adventure. Now, 82 miles (130 kilometers) east of Atlantic City, New Jersey, as the only nonscientist on a scientific team, I was about to get my chance.

As part of a series of 14 dives in the area, the research team was looking at Wilmington Canyon and its neighbors, a system typical of the U.S. continental margin along the northern Atlantic coast. The objective of the expedition: to gather information that might answer the question of how such canyons were created. Our dive was to explore South Wilmington Canyon, gathering samples of the canyon walls and floor along the way.

Geological Expedition

The leader of this leg of the expedition was Bonnie McGregor, a geologist with the U.S. Geological Survey (USGS). Late into the night before the dive, she and I sat in the warm mess hall of *Atlantis II*, *Alvin*'s 210-foot (64-meter) mother ship, and talked about those canyons. They run roughly parallel, eastward from the North American continental shelf, down the continental slope (the edge of the tectonic plate) toward the deep ocean. Most of the canyons are relatively straight, but others meander, much like rivers on dry land. Some, in fact, seem to stretch out to sea from river mouths. Wilmington Canyon, for instance, runs out from an ancestral channel that leads from Delaware Bay.

That many of them look like river channels seems at first to be logical: rushing water—from, say, the Delaware River—carrying sand and mud could gouge out a sinuous path underwater the same as on dry land. But on second look, it's not the same; at the mouths of rivers, debris tends to build deltas, not cut gorges. And some underwater canyons begin 3,200 feet (1,000 meters) deep. There must be another mechanism at work—and that's the mystery.

But as the *Atlantis II* launch yoke swings the 25-foot (7.6-meter) submersible out from her stern at 8:12 this morning, my mind is not on geological theories and processes. It's on us and our craft.

I am sharing this titanium-alloy ball with two others: a scientist and a pilot. Steve Culver—a gentle-voiced Englishman with a close-cropped beard and a mind of warm steel—is a paleontologist at Old Dominion University in Norfolk, Virginia. His specialty is biostratigraphy; he figures out how mud was deposited by studying the biological life entrapped in it.

The pilot is John Salzig—cool, professional, and competent. He's only 25, and looks even younger. But no worry—this is his 19th dive. He works for Woods Hole Oceanographic Institution (operator of *Alvin* and *Atlantis II*), and holds a degree in mechanical engineering.

A Slow Descent

Suddenly the light in the capsule changes to aquamarine, and streams of bubbles swirl past my port as we enter the water. Then, shockingly, a leg kicks by. It belongs to one of the launch swimmers. He's opening a flood valve so we can sink.

By 1,640 feet (500 meters) the azure water has turned to black. Outside, it's dark as night; inside, the instruments bathe the cabin in soft reds and dapples of orange. Readouts on small CRTs show our depth (from water pressure),

distance from the bottom (from sonar), time, and heading.

The low light gives Salzig a mystical sheen as he squats, half kneeling, on a foot-high wooden box before his forward porthole. He's not steering now, just coasting as he runs systems checks.

Close Quarters

Culver and I are scrunched together, lying on our sides, legs by necessity intertwined. We each have our own port—a saucer-size, truncated cone of clear plastic panels 4.5 inches (11.5 centimeters) thick. Bottom pressure will deflect it inward 1/32 inch (0.8 millimeter).

Above us a lithium-hydroxide scrubber sucks carbon dioxide from the atmosphere while oxygen cylinders, at 1.6 quarts (1.5 liters) a minute, slowly vent their contents. The scrubber will gain 2 pounds (0.9 kilogram) during the trip. Elsewhere: snaps, beeps, and clicks as Salzig tests the gear. Every five seconds a tracker pings our position, recorded in the ship above. And echoing is heard from somewhere in the distance—the haunting song of dolphins.

At 3,300 feet (1,000 meters) now, far deeper than I've ever been before, a surprising thought: I'm not the faintest bit afraid. I anticipated at least a touch of claustrophobia (one of the ship's crew said if the sphere split, we'd be a foot high and speak with a squeak), but I probe my feelings and find not a sliver of fear.

The reason, I guess, is that the vessel is so stable I hardly believe we're sinking. Further, yesterday's orientation was designed to reassure. We sat huddled in *Alvin*—cradled on *Atlantis II*'s deck—while another pilot talked about the trip and laid out the rules: "Wear no deodorant; it may foul the air cleaner. Urinate in your personal HERE [Human Element Range Extender] flask. Leave your shoes topside." Nobody, so he told us, has ever panicked in the deep—though a few have chickened out before they were launched.

"This is *Alvin*. Fifteen hundred meters." A ghostly echo follows exactly two seconds later, Salzig's voice reflecting from the surface. A voice answers from far, far away: "Roger, *Alvin*." We continue to sink.

Canyon Scouring

The canyon project, funded by the National Oceanic and Atmospheric Administration (NOAA), the National Science Foundation, and the USGS, was jointly organized and directed

Leg room is at a premium in Alvin's cramped crew area. Passengers also must endure relatively cold temperatures (about 50° F) inside the submersible, since a heater would quickly drain the batteries.

by McGregor and William Stubblefield, chief scientist for the NOAA's Undersea Research Program.

Preliminary research was laid in 1980, when McGregor mapped the Atlantic continental margin off New Jersey with a new deep-towed sonar system. As her ship cruised back and forth in a grid, two side-scanning sonar units, towed 1 mile (1.6 kilometers) or so above the seafloor, recorded the contours.

Later, Stubblefield made three dives into the Wilmington Canyon, and he found a channel winding down a gentle 1-degree-gradient valley edged by gullied canyon walls strikingly like the South Dakota Badlands. What he found convinced him that some process similar to that on land scoured out the canyons. But just what, remained elusive.

He and McGregor decided to assemble a team to explore further. "We needed people with a variety of skills," says McGregor. "Bill is a sedimentologist, and I'm a geophysicist, but we needed a paleontologist, an isotope geologist, and a fluid hydrodynamicist to model the canyon system. We wanted to find out how the scouring material moves, how often it moves, how large the flow is."

Culver and I are crumpled on a carpeted wooden floor a few inches up from the bottom of the ball. I notice that where the hull is exposed, the 2-inch (5-centimeter)-thick metal is sweating. By the time the trip ends, the bottom of the sphere will hold more than 2 inches (5 centimeters) of water—almost all of it condensed from our lungs.

The air is getting cold already. The water outside is just above freezing, and soon the temperature in here will settle near 50° F (10° C). A heater would be too expensive in terms of electricity. It would drain our batteries (72 kilowatt-hours of capacity) so quickly that bottom time would be cut drastically. So we're dressed in two sweaters, two pairs of socks, and long underwear.

Practical Applications

This is not a simple pleasure trip for any of us. Divide the number of dives into the cost of the total expedition, and you'd find that my seat for these few hours is worth about $31,000.

Our mission is easy: guided by the ship, we'll drop to the relatively flat floor of the mile-wide canyon, then traverse 330 feet (100 meters) or so directly north to the canyon's wall. Then we'll edge up it until we run low on power. Every so often we'll stop and, using Alvin's manipulator arms, take small core samples. The arms will simply push open-ended cylinders into the mud; when withdrawn, spring-loaded ends will flip shut.

The prime objective of the project is pure science—to gather data leading to an understanding of how the gorges form. But the research has practical aspects as well:

• Oil companies, looking toward the time when they may have to drill this far out, want to know as much as possible about geology. (Already, Shell Oil Company has drilled a few exploratory holes some 15 miles [24 kilometers] from here.) "A canyon floor is an ideal place to drill," says McGregor, "because the canyon has nicely removed several hundred meters of material for you. But you want to know how active the area is, because a slump or slide or unexpected current could cause problems."

• Communication companies want to understand seafloor processes, too, for even in this age of satellites, underwater cables remain highly useful.

• Ocean canyons are looked on by many as ideal waste-disposal areas—especially if they periodically flush themselves out. But do they? How often? How?

"O.K.—here we are," says Salzig. My CRT says that we're hovering 100 feet (30 meters) from the bottom. I look out. Nothing.

To halt our descent, Salzig has released a 237-pound (107-kilogram) weight. He wants to take the last bit easy, so we won't get stuck in the mud. We edge down another 5 feet (1.5 meters), and he releases another 237 pounds (weight varies with occupants), then adjusts the trim by pumping water into the ballast tanks. To ascend, he'll loose a 950-pound (430-kilogram) weight. I flip on my thallium-iodide observation light. Down below, barely visible, stretches a hint of gray-brown bottom.

And then, at 9:59 A.M., we edge down and land in a little puff of mud. The temperature is 37.6° F (3.125° C); depth, 7,770 feet (2,368 meters); pressure, 3,550 pounds per square inch (10,390 kilograms per square centimeter). I look at the surface of my window to see if it's bulging. Can't tell.

Projects Under Way

Up in the ship, meanwhile, members of the scientific team are working on their individual projects:

McGregor—calm, organized, running the whole operation apparently with no need of sleep—is keeping track of us. She's in the top-deck tracking room, watching our pings dot along a chart.

She's also studying reports of the previous dives—trying to work out the grand picture of how canyons form. The working hypothesis developed by her and Stubblefield is that canyon formation probably begins when a block of ma-terial on the continental slope sloughs off, then slowly erodes toward the land. But the question remains: Why the erosion?

Henry Pantin, a sedimentologist with the British Geological Survey, sits in the corner of the map room studying last night's Sea Beam charts. Each night, the ship steams back and forth, contour-mapping the seafloor by projecting 16 beams of 12-kilohertz sound from a hull array to the seafloor, and feeding the reflections into a computer that spews forth a continuous 11-inch (28-centimeter)-wide plot of the bottom. Pantin is trying to correlate the maps with the grain size and arrangement found in the day's core material. The kind and contours of mud and sand have given him clues as to how the bottom was formed.

So far, he believes that most of the canyons were developed by mass wastage: "When the edge of a canyon several miles long suddenly becomes unstable and collapses like a sodden hillside, it oozes away like the toe of a glacier," says Pantin.

But some canyons, particularly those that meander, may have been formed during the last ice age, when the sea level fell, the continental shelf narrowed, and mouths of rivers moved closer to the continental slope. "In times of flood, and because the rivers were laden with glacial rock dust and other matter," he says, "the outflow would not only deposit sediment but would excavate underwater canyons as well."

Charlotte Brunner—quiet, unassuming, waiflike (and acknowledged to be the best underwater navigator among the scientists)—is a paleontologist with the University of California at Berkeley. She's in the mud lab now, pawing through bottom cores collected in yesterday's dive.

Already she's discovered an interesting fact: most of the surface silt is bioturbated—burrowed and churned by organisms and composed primarily of fecal matter. According to Brunner: "The mud is mostly mineral grains and plankton shells, but it's accumulated slowly enough to have been swallowed and excreted so many times by bottom creatures that it shows almost no structure. The critters here are so active and abundant that they obliterate any current layering within months, maybe less."

The remains of organisms that she finds will tell her, she hopes, the depth of water in which they were deposited, and perhaps the time as well.

Charles Nittrouer of North Carolina State University, tucked off in a tiny lab of his own, is X-raying slices of mud with a portable veterinary unit. Mustache twitching, he, too, is looking at the sedimentary structure, and is also finding little layering.

Steven Kuehl, meanwhile, is slicing larger samples to send back home. Last night he dropped overboard three 5-foot (1.5-meter), 1,200-pound (544-kilogram) tethered box corers. When they smacked the bottom, they stuffed themselves with mud. Now Kuehl is packaging the samples for study back at his University of South Carolina lab. There he'll check for lead-210 and cesium, and will date them isotopically to determine when they accumulated.

Nearly Lifeless Landscape

Alvin is sitting on a flat, undulating plain now. The scene is lifeless except for a few sea urchins, one long-armed starfish, and an occasional hump with a hole on top. This world is nearly colorless—just shades of browns and grays.

Culver, I notice, isn't looking through his porthole. He's staring at the sonar screen. "Where's the bloody wall?" he asks Salzig. "This sonar working O.K.? Guess we're farther south than we should be."

We set off north, about 1 knot. *Alvin* is capable of at least 1½, but at that speed it uses too much electricity.

As we rise over a hummock, a giant crayfishlike creature ambles by, surrounded by fish the size of pencils. Salzig is steering mostly with a little joystick; suddenly it strikes me what this is really all about: I'm in a giant video game.

Now, under Culver's direction, Salzig sets us down and, working manipulators like an isotope technician, he rams out a 1-foot (0.3-meter)-long core and drops the cylinder into one of the wire baskets protruding from *Alvin*'s chest.

Off the side, barely visible, lies a 15 foot (4.6-meter)-high slab, oddly out of place on this plain. Where did it come from? How did it get there? We take a core from it that may help provide answers.

We pass over a field strewn with shrimp molts, then a series of odd striations running parallel to us, over a stumbling, spidery thing the size of a manhole cover, over a bouquet of anemones and washtub-size sponges.

A 3-foot (1-meter)-long fish, a rattail, flashes into view and stares into my port with a startling white reflective eye. Or is everything down here blind? Another rattail zips into view, nips at a 5-inch (12.7-centimeter) slug, and speeds off on its side.

"That current is getting strong," says Salzig. "That's really strange here." The current—that's why we ended up so far from the wall.

We stop once again to take a core. Later, back on the ship, Culver will stay up all night sifting through samples. He'll discover an acorn-size terebratulid brachiopod in the muck—a common creature off the coast of Japan and New Zealand, but rare elsewhere.

Fascinated Concentration

Again it occurs to me that I have no fear, that I don't believe there's nearly 1.5 miles (2.5 kilometers) of water overhead. I drift into a primordial reverie of fascinated concentration—and then suddenly it's broken. We pass over a bile-green plastic garbage bag lying on the sand, a rag, then a soda bottle, like a series of insults. They're all from passing ships, explains Culver. Five minutes later we slide over a black telephone cable thick as a knockwurst. We're a million miles from anywhere, and still civilization intrudes.

And then a further shock to my complacency. Salzig, hands on the controls, hunched forward, squints and speaks: "Uh, oh. It's not behaving."

I don't want to hear that. Suddenly I feel something the size of a meadow mouse turn over in my stomach. It's called fear. Thoughts flash—of air supply, of water pressure, of wills, of vulnerability. . . .

And then, just as suddenly, the feeling's gone. "One of the manipulators hasn't the strength it should," says Salzig. I sigh aloud, surprising myself with the volume.

The truth is, *Alvin,* nearly a quarter of a century old, is safe. The hull is designed to operate more than twice as deep as we are. Our dive is number 1,750, and there has not been a major failure yet. All critical systems—battery, communications, atmospheric—are redundant. The batteries can be dropped to reduce weight, and the arms can be discarded as well. And if all else fails, we can simply blast the sphere loose. It's never been tried, but speculation is that it would turn over and over and rocket some three stories into the atmosphere.

At a depth of 7,550 feet the north wall of South Wilmington Canyon (right) gives little indication of how it formed. But from mud samples taken during the expedition, scientists discovered biological remains dating back to the Ice Age. At such great depths the undersea world is nearly lifeless, except for occasional starfish, sea urchins, and pycnogonids (below)—sea spiders the size of manhole covers.

Courtesy Stephen J. Culver

Woods Hole Oceanographic Institution

Giant Eddies

We ease now over a stretch of flatland dotted with funnels. But they seem to be filling in. And sea urchins, worm tubes, trails of bottom dwellers, brittle stars, and the slugs all seem dusty, muted as though by a sprinkle of snow.

Now at 7,860 feet (2,396 meters), I notice that the water is becoming hazy, then turbid. "That current is amazing," says Salzig, "and it's building. Just look at the animals." The vehicle stops again to get another core, and now I see: the starfish and other bottom fauna are hanging on for dear life while rivulets of muddy sand stream southward.

"There's the wall!" says Culver, looking at the sonar. "Maybe 200 meters."

We rise up again, and immediately swing sideways, even at full power. "I've never seen such a current," says Salzig. "I can't move forward." He straightens *Alvin* out, but the craft swivels again. "O.K.—we'll try tacking." Like a sailboat, we slowly zigzag northward, the turbidity increasing, the vessel rocking.

We land to take stock and, in the glare of the searchlights, look at the bottom. There are no funnels now, no trails; all are silted over. The plants are waving downstream like flags. A fish passes, swimming against the current—backward. And the sea urchins, one by one, let go of the canyon floor to cartwheel out of sight.

Somehow we've happened into an exceedingly rare occurrence: an underwater sandstorm, a current never before recorded in this part of the ocean. Although the exact cause is still a mystery, the most likely explanation is an eddy current. For at least a century, oceanographers have known that such major currents as the Gulf Stream spin off giant eddies or whirlpools.

Although most of the time such deepwater eddies simply stir the bottom silt a bit, occasionally an eddy will have the strength to swirl up enough mud to make the water turbid. This is called a benthic storm, and *Alvin* probably experienced one induced by the Gulf Stream some 315 feet (96 meters) to the east.

We rise again, but find ourselves, at full power, moving backward. Salzig works his joystick and thrusters, trying to keep a heading, while outside there's only swirling dust. Through the silt the floodlights suddenly illuminate two parallel tracks in front of us, starkly out of place. Then I realize that they're *Alvin*'s scrape marks, for we're being dragged backward. As we ease upward again, the vessel lurches, and a front corner bangs the bottom. (Later we'll find we've ruined one of the strobe lights.)

Salzig gives up. The wall is only 500 feet (150 meters) away, but we're too low on power to fight anymore. At 2:42: "*Atlantis II: Alvin*— our depth, 2,383 meters. Request permission to surface." Permission, I'm glad to report, was granted.

Pioneering *MIDDLE EARTH*
by Bill Lawren

The voyage began in the center of a dormant volcano. Plunging down through the wild and savage staircase of the crater, the travelers descended until they reached the very core of the planet, where they discovered another world: a huge, dark ocean whose shores percolated with life. Giant reptiles. Furry mastodons. A race of pale Neanderthals. Eventually, thrust back to the surface by a violent volcanic eruption, the voyagers returned to find their faculties and perceptions intact with one curious exception. No matter what direction they faced, the needle on their compass pointed north.

This adventure, the product of the extraordinary mind of Jules Verne, echoes the mythic imagination of the human race. Ever since the first *Homo sapiens* fled the eruptions of Kili-

manjaro and the earthquakes of the Great Rift Valley, we have been fascinated by the world down under. The mythological tales of Hades and Vulcan, of Sinai and Pele, even of Dante's fiery inferno, can in some ways be read as our attempt to shed light on the nature of the dark underground. But until this century, even the most scientific attempts to describe the Earth's interior have been only a step removed from the fantasies of the poets. The 18th-century scientist John Cleve Symmes, for example, saw the whole Earth as an immense doughnut, with large holes at or near both the North and South poles. In the 19th century the "doughnut" theory gave way to the "egg," in which the Earth is seen as a huge, undifferentiated ball of molten liquid surrounded by a relatively thin (50-mile or 80-kilometer), solid "shell."

The "Golf Ball" Theory

In the beginning of our own era, when the study of earthquake-generated seismic waves began to give a somewhat sharper picture of middle Earth, the "egg" was replaced by a "golf ball." In this picture the 8,000-mile (13,000-kilometer)-diameter inner Earth is seen as a descending series of spherical zones. First comes the crust, with its variegated rocks and sediments and its pockets of oil, gas, and volcanic magma. The crust stretches downward to a depth of about 20 to 35 miles (30 to 60 kilometers). Next comes the mantle, almost 2,200 miles (3,500 kilometers) of compressed rock, forged by heat and pressure into hard and stable crystal. After the mantle, the next 1,000 miles (1,600 kilometers) belong to the outer core, a roiling inferno composed entirely of molten iron compounds. At the center of everything is the heart of the Earth: about 800 miles (1,300 kilometers) of iron that, despite its stellar temperature, has been squeezed by unimaginable pressures into a superhot, solid ball.

But even the golf-ball picture was accurate only in outline. It gave the impression, first of all, that the zones were relatively uniform features, with smooth, precise boundaries dividing one zone from another. It yielded what turned out to be a massively mistaken estimate of temperatures in the core. It only partially answered important questions about the behavior of the Earth's magnetic field, which is generated along the boundary between the core and the mantle. And it failed to resolve one of the hottest of the many controversies that have enlivened the modern study of the ancient Earth: To what degree do forces generated deep in the guts of the Earth drive the majestic movements—from the grand and gradual waltz of the continents to the explosive tremors of earthquakes and volcanoes—that in turn determine the nature and distribution of life itself?

Obviously, a clearer picture was needed. Lately a new group of scientific adventurers has been attempting to plumb the depths of inner Earth as never before, using new tools and techniques to travel—in a figurative sense, at least—all the way down to the planet's core. They are drilling, mapping, and measuring the interior with such skill that the deep underworld is finally beginning to reveal some of its most important secrets. In at least one case, a group of explorers have begun a literal descent, looking deeper with their own eyes into the planet's heart than anyone since Orpheus.

Hot Spots

One of these scientists is Harmon Craig of the Scripps Institute of Oceanography in La Jolla, California. The proper scientific name for what Craig does is geochemistry, but it may be just as accurate to call him a helium prospector. Craig, a big, graying man whose avuncular smile masks a hard-nosed scientist with a reputation for almost always getting what he wants, discovered helium-3 20 years ago. Most of what remains of the Earth's stores of this rare isotope, which was formed during the birth of the solar system, is locked deep in the interior, most of it inaccessible. But at certain places along the seams of the Earth—places where the boundaries of the great continental plates crack the crust or where volcanic pipes known as hot spots punch their way up through the ocean floor—the gaseous stew that bubbles up contains much larger proportions of helium-3 than are found elsewhere. At those places, says Craig's colleague David Hilton, "you know you're looking at material that has come up from the mantle itself."

Craig went searching for hot spots and found one at Loihi, a volcanic crack in the ocean floor about 30 miles (50 kilometers) off Hawaii. Preliminary sampling of the water around Loihi indicated that it contained the highest helium-3 levels found anywhere on Earth. Theoretically, Craig knew what this meant: the Loihi vent plunged deeper into the Earth than any oceanic site yet examined.

A 3,000-foot (900-meter) descent to Loihi in *Alvin* revealed a glowing crack in the ocean floor, surrounded by bright red "rust"-covered terraces of basalt rock. Shimmering, champagne-like water bubbled out of the vent—water hot enough to rise, but "so stuffed with carbon dioxide," according to Hilton, "that it actually flowed down." Clinging to the sides of the vent were billowing white plumes of exotic, gas-eating bacteria. All in all, says Craig, "it was like coming upon a fairy castle or a beautiful abstract painting by Miró. . . ."

To Craig, Hilton, and colleagues, the depth of this window holds great significance. Helium-3 levels at Loihi and other hot spots have indeed proved to be much higher than they are along such mid-ocean ridges as the East Pacific Rise, indicating that vents like Loihi do indeed plunge much deeper into the mantle than do the rises. In fact, Craig estimates that the Loihi vent may penetrate as far as 8 miles (13 kilometers) into the lower mantle. The differ-

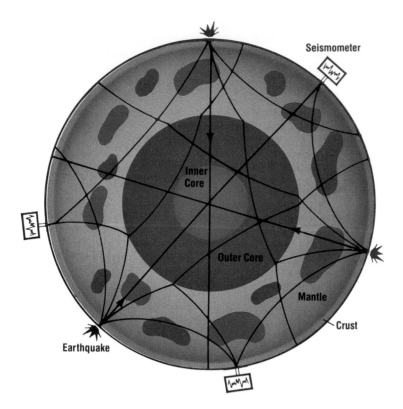

Seismometer

Inner Core

Outer Core

Mantle

Crust

Earthquake

The Earth is composed of three concentric shells: the crust, the mantle, and the core (which itself consists of a liquid outer shell surrounding a solid iron core). Each shell transmits seismic (earthquake) waves at different velocities. Using a technique called seismic tomography, geophysicists can roughly map the Earth's interior by measuring the time it takes seismic waves generated in one part of the world to reach a seismometer located elsewhere. Higher seismic-wave velocities indicate cooler rock (blue masses); slower velocities indicate warmer rock (red masses). Since warmer rock—like warmer air—tends to rise, scientists can get an idea of the flow of rock in the Earth's interior.

ences in helium-3 levels at the two kinds of sites also form part of the evidence that has led some geologists to revise the older golf-ball picture of inner Earth. The mantle, they now believe, is not an isolated and uniform zone, but in fact is layered into a number of subregions, each of them bumpy, asymmetrical boundaries, but all of them in "communication" with and fed by the core below. Despite its peaceful, almost ethereal appearance, then, the Loihi vent makes a strong argument for the idea of an Earth even more integrated and dynamic than anyone ever supposed.

Digging Holes

For all its drama, though, and for all the unworldly beauty of its vista, Craig's trip to Loihi was still primarily a surface excursion, a look into the Earth's interior from the top down. To actually reach down and touch the depths, scientists rely on an updated, high-tech version of one of the most primitive enterprises in the history of human engineering: the hole.

Miners, of course, have been digging holes into the Earth's crust for thousands of years, and petroleum companies for the past hundred. But drilling for scientific purposes did not really begin until the late 1960s, when the interna-

tional project JOIDES (Joint Oceanographic Institutions for Deep Earth Sampling) began a systematic series of drillings into the ocean floor, drillings that continue to this day and that have been instrumental in validating plate tectonics, the modern theory about how the Earth's landmasses shift and move.

To find the Big Bertha of contemporary drill holes, one must travel to the Soviet Union. There, beneath the ancient rock of the Kola Peninsula, which lies near the Finnish border north of the Arctic Circle, Russian scientists have been drilling since 1970. By 1984 the hole had reached a depth of almost 7 miles (11 kilometers), passing through deposits of iron, copper, zinc, titanium, and nickel. American geologist Robert Andrews, who visited the Kola Superdeep hole in 1984, calls it "a major breakthrough in terms of drilling to great depths and bringing back samples. They've achieved what no one else in the world has done."

Although the Russian discovery of deep deposits of valuable ores was interesting, what really grabbed the attention of geologists was the finding, at a depth of about 15,000 feet (4,600 meters), of what Soviet geologist Y. A. Kozlovsky called "surprising, copious flows of hot, highly mineralized water."

Puzzling Pores

The find was unexpected because standard geological wisdom holds that water cannot reach such depths because the tremendous prevailing pressures (more than 1,100 times atmospheric pressure) should crush the resident rocks together so tightly that no "pores" could exist to allow water to penetrate.

Proof that pores did indeed exist set geologists buzzing. Since 1979 a maverick Cornell University astrophysicist named Thomas Gold had been claiming that there was enough natural gas (specifically methane) locked deep in the Earth's interior to solve the world's energy problems ad infinitum. The claim brought forth a chorus of scoffing from the world's geologists, who immediately wanted to know how this methane could possibly penetrate the tightly packed rock of the upper mantle and lower crust. "Pores," Gold replied bluntly. He then went on to describe in great theoretical detail how upwelling fluids and gases could create just the kind of porous layers that the Soviets subsequently found in the Kola hole.

The Russian discovery caught the eye of other researchers, and in 1986 the Swedish government decided to drill at a site in the Siljan Ring, where the impact of a huge meteorite that hit 360 million years ago was thought to have caused deep fractures in the ancient granite rocks. Such fracturing, Gold thought, might create pores that would trap and hold upwelling methane gas.

In March 1987, as the drill bit through the Siljan rock to almost 20,000 feet (6,000 meters), technicians at the site noticed something startling: the "mud" piped down to lubricate the drill bit suddenly began to disappear at a very fast rate. According to Paul Wescost, a geologist with the Gas Research Institute (GRI), the best explanation for the fluid's disappearance was that it had escaped into a zone of porous rock, just the sort of porous rock that Gold had envisioned. At this writing, it remains unclear whether these pores hold a commercially viable amount of methane. Even if the Siljan hole doesn't rescue the world from its energy problems, there is little doubt that findings at both Kola and Siljan have given deep-hole drilling a tremendous boost. In West Germany, geologists are planning to sink an ultradeep hole in northern Bavaria, a hole that may eventually reach as deep as 10 miles (16 kilometers). In the United States a three-year-old consortium of universities known as DO-

© Sovfoto/Tass

In the Soviet Union, scientists drilling into the Earth's interior were surprised to find water 3 miles down.

SECC (Deep Observation and Sampling of the Earth's Continental Crust) is drilling a 16,000-foot (4,900-meter) hole in southern California's Cajon Pass, near the line of the San Andreas Fault. The "prime objective," says DOSECC's Robert Andrews, is to get an accurate model of the fault, to aid in earthquake prediction. In the next few years, DOSECC will begin to sink a series of deep and ultradeep holes, one of which, on the island of Hawaii, could become the first in history to penetrate all the way through the crust and actually reach the upper mantle.

With present technology, researchers should be able to reach depths of more than 10 miles (16 kilometers). "Nobody's talking about going any deeper except Jules Verne," says Andrews, "and he's already done it."

High-Tech Imaging

While the hole drillers may be limited for some years to those ten miles, other scientists are reaching, by proxy, at least, much farther—in some cases as far down as 2,000 miles (3,200 kilometers), all the way down to the boundary between the mantle and the core itself. As one way of plumbing these hitherto unreachable depths, researchers have borrowed a high-tech tool from modern medicine: the computerized axial tomography (CAT) scan. By using CAT scans, it's possible to peer into the heart of the Earth in much the same way that neurologists examine the human brain.

To stretch the analogy a bit, the geologists' version of CAT scanning, called seismic tomography, is a bit like analyzing a human brain caught in the act of suffering a series of violent seizures. In the geologic case, though, the "seizures" are earthquakes. Every earthquake sends out its own shock waves, waves that can literally travel all the way through portions of the inner Earth. As they move, the waves tend to slow down or speed up depending on the temperature and density of the interior regions through which they pass. The changing paths of the waves are registered by a worldwide network of seismic detectors. By collating large numbers of these wave paths and subjecting them to computer analysis, geoscientists can now paint a portrait of inner Earth in sharper relief than has ever been possible.

The emerging picture is one of an interior that is almost as lumpy, bumpy, and generally asymmetrical as the surface on which we live. At MIT, Thomas Jordan and Stuart Sipkin (now with the U.S. Geological Survey) used seismic tomography to show that ancient cores of continents (called cratons) actually have their beginnings deep in the mantle. Massive "roots" that extend as far down as 250 miles (400 kilometers) connect the continents to the deep interior. At Caltech, Robert Clayton, a former oil prospector who still has a wiry, cowboy look, scanned all the way down to the core-mantle boundary, 2,000 miles (3,200 kilometers) below the Gulf of Alaska, where he found what appears to be a peak of interior elevation. Because scanning techniques are crude at best, Clayton can say only that the peak appears to rise as high as 180,000 feet (55,000 meters). If this peak actually represents a subsurface mountain (Clayton's techniques do not reveal the extent and angle of the slopes), it would be some six times higher than Mount Everest.

Meanwhile, MIT's Jordan has found enormous features, some of them thousands of miles across, at the core-mantle boundary. These huge anomalies, he thinks, may represent massive interior "continents" of floating slag.

Magnetic Field Source

While all this undoubtedly spells death for the golf-ball model of inner Earth, with its pat but inaccurate smoothness and uniformity, the map is still incomplete. During the next few years, as a consortium of universities called IRIS (Incorporated Research Institutions for Seismology) replaces outdated earthquake detectors and extends the existing international network by installing new ones, the resulting increase in data should help fill in a good deal of the missing detail. In the meantime, Harvard's Jeremy Bloxham is busy drawing and interpreting a map of a different kind: one that reaches deep into the heart of the planet to trace the very source of the Earth's magnetic field.

Geoscientists have long believed that the magnetic field is generated by the roiling motions of the molten iron in the Earth's outer core. Over time, as the motion eddies and shifts, the direction of the field shifts with it; and every million years or so (on average), it suddenly reverses entirely. Magnetic north suddenly becomes magnetic south. During the past several years, Bloxham and his colleague David Gubbins have been combining 18th-century sailors' measurements of the magnetic field with the much more detailed data gathered by modern-day satellites. "We're beginning," Bloxham says, "to get a picture of what the field really looks like."

To the researchers' surprise, that picture has turned out to include several pairs of huge "core spots" at the core-mantle boundary, some 2,000 miles (3,200 kilometers) below the surface. (Bloxham estimates that one such pair of spots, located under South Africa, may be up to 1,200 miles—1,900 kilometers—across.) These magnetic anomalies, they say, are "terrestrial analogues to sunspots." Significantly, Bloxham's calculations show that the spots, in which the direction of the normal surrounding magnetic field is reversed, appear to have grown by more than 10 percent during the past 150 years.

"If the process continues," he says, "in about 1,500 to 2,000 years, we'll be in the middle of a planetary reversal of the magnetic field."

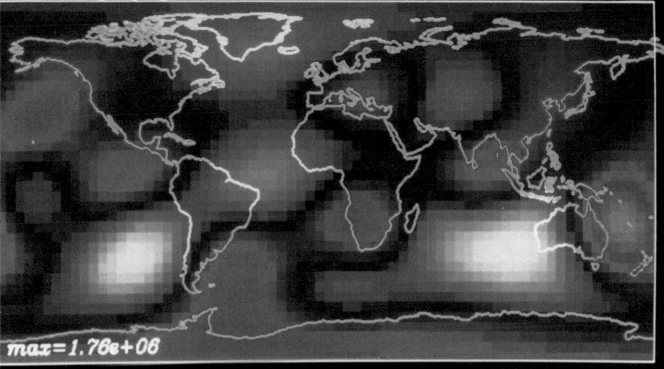

max=1.78e+06

Seismo/Caltech

By superimposing the continents over a computerized tomograph of the Earth, geophysicists can gauge the temperatures inside the planet in relation to the land masses. Cold areas show blue, mild areas purple, and hot areas red.

Such a reversal would be very disruptive, if not downright hazardous, to say the least, to life on Earth. In the first place, Bloxham says, there would be a period of what he calls "navigational chaos: a few hundred years, and possibly quite a bit longer, when compass needles would be pointing all over the place." Of course, alternative methods of navigation would allow business to go on as usual, but hikers and recreational sailors who rely on compasses would find them useless. In addition, other scientists have pointed out that the magnetic field is one of the important forces that act to shield us from incoming radiation, especially cosmic rays. A reversal of the field, they warn, could lead to a "dangerous disruption" of that shielding effect, with consequences that could include great increases in mutations as well as a skyrocketing cancer rate.

Laboratory Simulation

Bloxham's uncomfortable forecast is the product of a figurative journey that took him to the outer boundaries of the core of the Earth. Other researchers have gone still farther, using advanced machinery and techniques to simulate in the laboratories the fire and force of the core itself. The tool of this unique trade might have excited the admiration of Thor: it combines an infrared laser beam with a vise made of gem-quality diamonds. Using this "diamond anvil," geophysicists can for the first time re-create the stellar temperatures and incredible pressures of the heart of the Earth.

At the University of California, Berkeley, geophysicist Raymond Jeanloz and his colleagues have used the new technology hundreds of times. Their basic technique, called "cook and look," is to place certain materials in the anvil, clamp them down between the diamond points, turn up the pressure to the desired level (amazingly, this is done by the simple turning of a screw), then heat the pressurized matter with the laser beam.

The "guinea pig" material for many of Jeanloz's baking sessions has been magnesium silicate, which is known to transform under great pressure to a crystalline structure called perovskite. Earlier experiments had shown that perovskites, in general, are the preferred form that minerals take under the pressures found in the upper mantle, but until very recently, no one could re-create the even-greater pressures necessary to show that the same was true farther down. But in the past few years, improvements in the alignment of the diamond clamps allowed Jeanloz and his colleagues to reach the pressures of the lower mantle: pressures equivalent to those produced by 240,000 to as much as 1.3 million times atmospheric pressure. At those pressures, they found, magnesium silicate did indeed transform to stable perovskite crystals. Estimating that this magnesium silicate perovskite makes up 70 to 90 percent of the composition of the lower mantle, ''we concluded,'' Jeanloz says, ''that it is the most abundant mineral on Earth.''

From there, Jeanloz and other researchers went to turn the pressure up to what he calls ''the hairy edge of believability,'' all the way to 3 million times atmospheric pressure—just half a million short of those that prevail at the edge of the inner core (that's where the solid-iron center meets the outer core's molten iron). With corelike iron oxides between the diamond clamps, the researchers then turned the laser heat up until the iron began to melt. At that point, Jeanloz says, the temperature—about 6,300° Kelvin (10,900° F or 6,050° C)—was equivalent to that at the boundary between the inner and outer cores. By extrapolation he arrived at the temperature at the very center of the core: about 12,000° F (6,650° C)—more than 4,000° F (2,200° C) hotter than anyone had ever thought, and hotter, incredibly enough, than the surface of the sun.

A Remodeled Future?

The body of Jeanloz's work has applications and implications that go far beyond mere temperature taking. The perovskites created in the anvil are similar in structure and composition to the recently discovered class of superconducting materials that promise to revolutionize everything from data processing to mass transportation. Jeanloz suggests that the anvil process may help to stabilize such materials. In the course of his experiments, Jeanloz has found that inner-

Samples from drilling sites have revealed deposits of metals and natural gas locked deep beneath the Earth's surface.

Longyear

Earth levels of temperature and pressure change the way materials bond, which could give rise to what he calls "a new kind of chemistry," including "miracle materials" that might be harder than diamonds.

If Jeanloz's study of inner Earth promises to lead the way to a remodeled future, that remodeling will be aided even further by other new applications of today's geoscience. Tomorrow's prospectors, for example, may read seismic tomographs the way yesterday's read treasure maps. "Things that happen in the interior," explains Caltech's Donald Anderson, "are ultimately responsible for the formation of hydrothermal regions where we find concentrations of minerals. So the better we understand where these things are and how deep they extend, the better we'll be able to predict places that might have mineral deposits where we haven't looked before." That sort of understanding should be further enhanced by drill-hole technology: in fact, a current hole being sunk in Colorado's Creede Mining District is being drilled underneath known gold and lead deposits. This may reveal the inner-Earth "incubators" where those deposits are actually born.

Energy prospecting also stands to gain much from this new geology. Some oil companies, notably Gulf and Amoco, are using a localized version of seismic tomography to search for oil; and Amoco, at least, reports that the technique has successfully verified the existence of some new deposits. Caltech scientists have also used seismic tomography to locate a previously hidden magma chamber beneath southern California's Owens Valley. That chamber and others like it may in turn prove to be valuable sources of exploitable hydrothermal energy. And if Thomas Gold is proved right by findings at the Siljan hole, if in fact inner Earth holds vast stores of untapped methane, global energy problems could go the way of the dinosaurs that spawned them.

Catastrophe Prevention

At the same time, current probings of middle Earth may one day provide information that will help to combat two previously unassailable enemies: volcanic eruptions and earthquakes. DOSECC's Cajon Pass drill hole, for example, will help scientists understand the nature of the stresses and pressures near the San Andreas Fault by providing information that may eventually make long-range earthquake prediction a

reality. There is even a tantalizing suggestion that detailed profiles of fault lines could someday help scientists not only predict but prevent earthquakes or at least diminish their intensity to relatively harmless levels. Past experiments have shown that reducing underground fluid pressure by actually pumping fluids out of faults can decrease the frequency and strength of earthquakes. Although the idea has lost much of its currency because of political factors—local governments in earthquake zones have shown little enthusiasm for offering their territories as test sites—the notion, according to C. Barry Raleigh, director of the LaMont-Doherty Geological Observatory in Palisades, New York, is at least "theoretically possible" and should not be dismissed out of hand.

Oil and mineral prospecting, exotic new chemistries, catastrophe prevention—these are some of the possible near-term rewards that may arise from the contemporary scientific journey to the center of the Earth. But there are interesting prospects for the more distant future as well. The sounding of Bloxham's alarm for an impending reversal of the magnetic field (in geological time, after all, 2,000 years is shorter than an eye blink) may help us prepare for the inconveniences and outright dangers that would accompany such a reversal. Beyond that, David Hilton speaks of using data from isotope analysis at sites like Loihi to predict the composition of the atmosphere eons from now, surely a vital enterprise in the calculation of the future of life on Earth.

Geological Reprieve

In fact, today's geoscience may well be in the process of giving the Earth a new lease on life. Although this is still controversial, Jeanloz's new calculations of core temperatures seem to favor an "oil on water" model of the whole Earth, in which the various zones are sharply separated from one another and thus "communicate," or intermix fluids, very little. In this model, Jeanloz explains, "the upper layers would act like a blanket to contain the heat of the lower layers. This would mean that the Earth would retain its heat for a much longer time period than we had previously believed." So instead of being in the process of cooling down, he says, "the Earth may be as vigorous as ever; and its ultimate geological demise, instead of taking place billions of years from now, wouldn't take place for tens of billions of years."

In June 1987 a hydroelectric plant in Paterson, New Jersey, was returned to service after 20 years of dormancy. The plant, which will supply one-third of Paterson's electricity needs, harnesses the power created by a 70-foot drop in the Passaic River (background). The Department of Energy has encouraged such refurbishment programs as a relatively low-cost way of meeting the nation's future energy needs.

© William E. Sauro/NYT Pictures

REVIEW OF THE YEAR

ENERGY

Superconductivity—the ability of some materials to carry electricity without any loss of energy—was the headline news in energy. With the discovery of new superconductors, scientists began predicting exciting applications for the future: high-speed electric trains suspended on a cushion of air by powerful magnets, loss-free electricity transmission lines, and high-efficiency electricity-generating plants that would be smaller and more powerful than any now in existence.

OIL

In spite of increasing strife in the Persian Gulf, oil prices stabilized in 1987, and supplies were plentiful throughout the world. In the U.S., the increasing reliance on imported oil prompted renewed warnings that another oil crisis may be looming in the near future.

Prices ranged from $34 per barrel in 1982 to less than $9 in 1986, but leveled off in early 1987 and hovered in the $20 range throughout most of the year. Following the failure of the Organization of Petroleum Exporting Countries (OPEC) to reach any new price or production agreements at its December 1987 meeting, oil prices plummeted below $15, but rebounded to approximately $17 a barrel by year's end.

The abundance and relative low price of oil helped bring about a 2.1 percent increase in consumption in the U.S., to 16.4 million barrels per day. Coupled with a 6.1 percent decline in domestic production, the result has been a substantial increase—28 percent—in oil imports. The U.S. now relies on foreign sources for 38 percent of its supplies; this in comparison to 27 percent in 1986, and 35 percent in 1973, when the Arab oil embargoes sent the U.S. economy into a tailspin.

Imports averaged nearly 6 million barrels a day in 1987, less than the record 8.5 million barrels a day in 1977, but substantially higher than the 1985 low of 4.3 million barrels. The U.S. Department of Energy (DOE) predicts imports may reach 8 million to 10 million barrels a day by the mid-1990s.

NATURAL GAS

The demand for natural gas, currently at approximately 17 trillion cubic feet (476 billion cubic meters) per year, is expected to increase only slightly through the rest of the century. With domestic production expected to drop during this period, the shortfall will be made up by imports, mostly from Canada via pipelines.

Meanwhile, after nearly four years of decline, prices for natural gas began rising in late 1987 in the expectation that several changes in federal regulations could lead to shortages. The relatively low price of oil, however, kept natural-gas prices from rising as high as had been feared, and the shortages did not materialize.

NUCLEAR POWER

Nuclear power supplied a record 18 percent of the electricity used in the U.S. in 1987, an increase of 14 percent over 1986. Nuclear power now supplies more electricity than any other fuel source except coal. By the end of 1987, more than 110 nuclear plants were licensed in the U.S., and more than 400 worldwide.

In the U.S., public acceptance of nuclear power has remained relatively strong, with two-thirds of those surveyed saying they think nuclear energy is a good or realistic choice as an energy source for large-scale use, and three-quarters citing nuclear power as an important energy source for meeting future needs.

The waste-disposal issue continued to create controversy as federal authorities moved toward the selection of the first national site for the disposal of used nuclear fuel. At the end of 1987, Congress directed DOE to proceed with site development at Yucca Mountain in Nevada, to suspend efforts to locate a second site, and to begin development of a centralized temporary storage facility.

ELECTRICITY

In several parts of the country, voltage reductions, commonly called "brownouts," were imposed several times during the summer when unusually hot weather created extremely heavy demand for electricity, threatening to overtax available supplies. In the northeastern U.S., there were warnings that if the region's economy continues to grow as predicted, there could be serious shortfalls in energy supply by the early 1990s.

Because of the cost and other uncertainties involved in building large electricity-generating plants, utilities sought other ways of increasing supplies of electricity. These included refurbishing retired generating units and returning them to service, negotiating agreements with Canada to purchase some of its abundant hydroelectric power, and increasing the efficiency of existing power plants.

ALTERNATIVE ENERGY

With the decline in oil prices and the projections for plentiful supplies for years to come, there was decreased emphasis in the U.S. and Europe on developing alternative sources of energy. For example, the U.S. provided $150 million in 1980 for solar research; in 1987 this was cut to $43 million. By contrast, in Japan the government provided $816 million in 1987 for solar and other alternative-energy-technology research.

In the Soviet Union, plans are under way to develop huge orbiting solar satellites to beam light energy back to Earth. A prototype, possibly ready in the early 1990s, would reflect sunlight back to Earth to light up cities or farms. Similar programs under consideration in the U.S. were abandoned because of possible cost ($500 billion to $800 billion) and environmental effects.

Solar researchers at Stanford University developed an experimental photoelectrochemical cell that is 15 percent efficient in converting solar energy into electricity. Although this is somewhat lower than the 21 percent efficiency of existing photovoltaic cells, it holds promise for the future.

The cost of photovoltaic cells has come down from more than $1,000 per watt to approximately $9, greatly increasing their potential applications. In Austin, Texas, for example, a 300-kilowatt photovoltaic system has been installed to help meet peak demands. It can supply as many as 200 homes.

By the end of the decade, photovoltaic cells may cost less than $3 per watt and be more than 30 percent efficient. Some scientists predict that by the year 2000, solar cells may be producing electricity at efficiencies as high as 80 percent.

As part of its Strategic Defense Initiative (SDI, or "Star Wars"), the U.S. Department of Defense has begun development of a giant, superconducting magnetic-energy coil that would store large amounts of electricity with more than 95 percent efficiency. The coil, about the size of a football field, would be attached to the civilian electricity grid and could either draw or supply electricity to help even out the fluctuations in supply and demand. If needed for defense purposes, however, the coil could instantly power laser and other weapons.

ANTHONY J. CASTAGNO

U.S. Navy vessels escort tankers through the volatile Persian Gulf to help maintain the flow of oil to the West.

© Peter Menzel

Off and running: sun-powered vehicles embark on the World Solar Challenge, a 1,950-mile race across Australia.

Running on SUNSHINE

by Jeffrey H. Hacker

Poised in the starting area, in shimmering waves of heat that rise from the asphalt, a succession of strange mechanical creatures await the go-ahead. Hundreds of spectators line the road, all straining for a better view of the sleek, squat, other-worldly-looking vehicles. Race crews make the final adjustments and give thumbs-up signals to the drivers. One by one, the cars glide past the starting line. There is no roaring of engines, only a quiet electric buzz and the gentle whirring of drive chains.

To science-fiction buffs, the scene may have suggested a soapbox derby in the year 2187. To 24 teams of drivers and engineers, the event was the World Solar Challenge, a 1,950-mile (3,140-kilometer) race across Australia in solar-powered cars. The year was 1987.

Billed as the first transcontinental road race for cars that run on sunshine, the competition attracted entries from seven countries—Australia, the United States, Japan, West Germany, Denmark, Switzerland, and Pakistan. Teams ranged from local high schools to colleges and universities to such giant corporations as General Motors (GM), Ford Motor of Australia, and Mitsubishi. The 10 to 12 top entries represented the most advanced solar cars ever built.

The World Solar Challenge was the brainchild of Hans Tholstrup, a Danish-Australian adventurer who had led the first solar-powered crossing of Australia from Sydney to Perth in 1983. The 1987 race, beginning on November 1, would cross the sunbaked Australian outback north to south, from Darwin to Adelaide. Tholstrup's purpose in organizing the race was to stimulate progress in alternate-energy technology. By the time the event was over, it was clear that both the cars and the technology had come a long way.

Design Specs

The rules of the competition gave entrants considerable design freedom. The key component of each car was its solar panel, an array of photovoltaic cells to collect the rays of the sun, convert them into electricity, and power an electric motor. The maximum "footprint" of the solar collector (its area measured from directly overhead) was 86 square feet (8 square meters); the vehicle itself could be no more than 6.6 feet (2 meters) high. Within these constraints, the solar panel could be vertical, horizontal, arched, or contoured to the body of the car. As a consequence, the scaly layers of silicon that covered the 24 race entries came in a wide variety of shapes that gave strange new meanings to the word *sunroof*.

With 7,200 photovoltaic cells at its disposal, GM's Sunraycer can accelerate from zero to 60 in 24 seconds.

The rules of the race also allowed each car to carry a storage battery, providing extra power through cloudy periods and up hills. The electricity stored in the battery had to originate from the solar panels. Before and after each day of racing—which lasted from 8:00 A.M. to 5:00 P.M.—the cars were allowed two hours of sunlight to recharge their batteries.

For road safety, all vehicles had to be equipped with adequate braking systems, highway lights, and seat belts. Finally, every car had to prove its stability in winds up to 40 miles (64 kilometers) per hour. One of the greatest hazards on the 1,950-mile journey would be the turbulence created by the giant "road trains"—triple-trailer trucks—that barrel along Australian highways.

The Leader of the Pack

The most ambitious, sophisticated, and efficient entry in the World Solar Challenge was a flat, crescent-shaped, buglike vehicle called *Sunraycer*. Built by General Motors at a cost reported to exceed $3 million, *Sunraycer* combined advanced solar technology and aerodynamic design to achieve speeds of up to 45 miles (72 kilometers) per hour using solar power alone. In prerace tests to determine the starting order, *Sunraycer* won the pole position with a speed of 70 miles (113 kilometers) per hour. According to a project engineer, the car could accelerate from zero to 60 miles (97 kilometers) per hour in 24 seconds.

Sunraycer's body—measuring 19.7 feet (6 meters) long, 6.6 feet (2 meters) wide, and 3.3 feet (1 meter) high—was made of a lightweight, honeycombed composite material covering a frame of welded aluminum tubing. The total weight of the vehicle, including the solar panel, motor, battery, and other components, was 390 pounds (177 kilograms). Its streamlined shape was designed with the help of a computer and tested in wind tunnels to maximize aerodynamics. *Sunraycer* was said to have the lowest air resistance, or drag coefficient, ever recorded for a land vehicle.

Sunraycer's source of power was an array of 7,200 photovoltaic cells developed by Spectrolab (a subsidiary of GM's Hughes Aircraft Company) for communications satellites in space. These high-efficiency cells can convert 16.5 percent of absorbed solar energy into electricity, compared with 2 to 3 percent for more conventional solar cells. Each one was 2.5 inches (6.4 centimeters) long and about the

The arched solar panel of the alien-looking Mana La *(above) was designed to exploit wind energy as well as sunlight. The Ford of Australia entry, shown at left having its battery recharged, was equipped with a tiltable solar panel to maximize exposure to the sun's rays.*

Both photos: © Peter Menzel/Wheeler Pictures

thickness of a business card. Arranged in 20 rows of 360 cells each, the solar panel was contoured to the shape of the vehicle, covering much of the front end. Under the noontime sun of the Australian desert, it generated about 1,000 watts of electricity at 150 volts—about the amount consumed by an ordinary electric hair dryer.

To make the most efficient use of this power, *Sunraycer* was equipped with a lightweight electric motor, custom-built by GM Research Labs. Made of a high-strength magnetic material called Magnequench, the motor delivered 2 horsepower and operated at 92 percent efficiency (losing only 8 percent of electrical power); most other direct-current electric motors operate at about 75 percent efficiency.

Another innovative component of the GM entry was its specially developed silver-zinc storage battery. Made up of 68 rechargeable cells, the battery weighed only 60 pounds (27 kilograms), yet provided the jolt of power needed for climbing and quick acceleration. The battery could be recharged in two ways: from sunlight absorbed by the solar panels, and from a feature of the braking system that fed electricity to the battery whenever the driver took his foot off the accelerator (turning the drive motor into a generator).

Sunraycer's other special features included custom-designed suspension, steering, and braking systems; aerodynamically altered bicycle wheels; and a thin coat of gold over the canopy to reduce heat inside the cockpit.

All in all, the GM entry represented the cutting edge of high-efficiency, lightweight, aerodynamic, solar-powered automotive technology. ''We look at this thing as a really interesting scientific effort,'' said an engineer at GM Hughes Electronics. ''Our motivation is to push along some technologies that we think are important to the future.''

Ping-Pong Tables, Sunbonnets, and Marsupials

Sunraycer was by no means the only entry to bring technological and design innovation to the World Solar Challenge. Not every team had the budget of GM, but every vehicle represented months or years of enthusiastic effort. And every car was unique.

The Ford of Australia team took a somewhat different—and riskier—approach than the GM team. The body of the Ford car was slim and cigar-shaped, with front and rear axles extending several feet on each side. The key feature, however, was a flat, overhead solar panel about the size of a Ping-Pong table. For maximum exposure to the sun's rays, the panel could be tilted at severe angles to the right or left. The risk of this design was a sacrifice of stability for power. But when the driver proved capable of controlling the car in turbulent highway conditions, the Ford team was optimistic.

Perhaps the strangest-looking entry was sponsored by John Paul Mitchell, a hair-care magnate who operates solar-powered organic farms in Hawaii. Mitchell's car, the *Mana La* (Hawaiian for ''power of the sun''), was designed to supplement solar power with the thrust of the wind. The *Mana La*'s solar panel, supported by a pair of vertical airfoils, arched over the torpedo-shaped fuselage like a sunbonnet. In addition to absorbing the sun's rays, the panel could act as a sail. In one test run, the *Mana La* reached 30 miles (48 kilometers) per hour on wind power alone.

Several other entrants proved popular with race followers. An Australian adventurer named Dick Smith, who once jumped over 17 parked motorcycles in a double-decker bus, sponsored a crowd favorite called *Team Marsupial*. A West German engineer transported his vehicle in three suitcases, assembled it at the airport, and drove himself to the starting site. And three college students from Pakistan spent $5,600 to build and race their own modest entry, the *Solar Samba*.

Across the Outback

The 1,950-mile road from Darwin to Adelaide passes through some of the most rugged and varied terrain on the Australian continent—sweltering deserts, barren plateaus, steep mountains, and thick forestlands. As all 24 teams were well aware, the speed of the cars would be

Australia's Team Marsupial *solar car finished second despite several stops to change its bicycle-size tires.*

less important than their durability and reliability. No one expected an incident-free journey, and indeed, there were mishaps every step of the way. In fact, a 25th entry, from the Massachusetts Institute of Technology (MIT), caught fire during a test run the day before the race even started. The driver escaped without injury, but the entry had to be scratched.

From Day One, it was clear that GM's *Sunraycer* was in a class by itself. The GM strategy was to open a big lead by using battery power for the first 15 minutes of the race, and then dropping down to the optimal level for road and weather conditions. Finding this optimal level would be important for every vehicle, given the limited power that could be stored in the onboard batteries. *Sunraycer* had a major advantage in this regard, as it was followed every step of the way by a van equipped with special monitoring equipment. Technicians inside the van tracked the data continuously and advised the driver on how to conserve power.

By the end of the first day, *Sunraycer* had opened a 68-mile (109-kilometer) lead over the second-place Swiss entry, the *Spirit of Biel*. Ford of Australia was third, followed by *Mana La*—which had been forced to stop early because of a depleted battery—and the rest of the pack far behind. After camping out for the night and recharging their batteries at sunup, the teams were back on the road at 8:00 A.M.

The next several days gave further proof of *Sunraycer*'s superiority. Under a blazing sun that sent temperatures soaring to about 100° F (38° C), the GM vehicle hummed along, extending its lead with every mile. One by one, other cars faltered and dropped out. When the skies darkened and a major storm broke out, GM's race strategy also proved advantageous. While *Sunraycer* was running miles ahead of the storm, the remaining cars were catching the brunt of it. Hailstones broke several solar cells on the Ford car. The Swiss team ran into flash flooding and had to float its car on tire tubes. Another vehicle was flipped over on its top by the strong winds. Meanwhile, *Sunraycer*'s only problems throughout the whole race were three flat tires.

Of the 24 solar cars that started out in Darwin, only six made it to Adelaide. *Sunraycer* completed the trek in five-and-a-half days, some 600 miles (966 kilometers) ahead of its closest challenger. GM's sleek solar champion had covered the distance at an amazing average speed of nearly 42 miles (68 kilometers) per hour. The second-place finisher, Ford of Australia, arrived two-and-a-half days later. The Swiss team came in a close third, trailing Ford by two-and-a-half hours. And *Team Marsupial* arrived in another day-and-a-half. Although the race officially ended five days after the first vehicle crossed the finish line, other entries were still pushing on. About a month after the start of the race, two more solar cars pulled into Adelaide.

Benefits and Applications

Despite the technological progress sparked by the World Solar Challenge, most experts agree that the days of the sun-powered family car are still a long way off. For one thing, the high cost of the equipment—especially the superefficient solar panels—would make commercial production economically unfeasible. And while the various engineering teams did solve some basic technical problems, the development of a safe, practical, and reliable solar car remains very much in the experimental stage. Important technological breakthroughs still are needed.

Nevertheless, the research and development that went into the solar race cars did yield practical innovations that may soon find their way into the family station wagon. Already in the works are a solar charging system for reenergizing a battery during long periods of idleness, and a solar-powered ventilation system for pulling air through the car on hot days. GM is especially optimistic about the future of its high-efficiency Magnequench motor.

"The cutting-edge technology that we and our colleagues developed and poured into that Australia race," said a GM spokesman, "will help us build better cars and devices."

Farther down the road, say some automakers, the possibility of widespread shortages of conventional fuel may make solar power the automotive technology of choice, perhaps necessity. In another realm, space scientists foresee a day when solar-electric vehicles will be used to explore the terrains of other planets.

And so, for everyone involved, the World Solar Challenge was more than an adventure in long-distance racing. As intended by organizer Hans Tholstrup, it sparked a spirit of innovation in alternate-energy technology. For a few major automakers, it yielded some practical benefits for commercial car production. And, by demonstrating the long-distance capability of solar-powered cars, it may have indeed brought science fiction one step closer to reality.

COPING
with BLACKOUTS

by Michael Parfit

Noreen Wick was accustomed to crisis. After all, she had raised 10 children. So when the lights went out at 8:24 P.M. on the stormy night of Valentine's Day, while she was getting ready to do some knitting, she calmly got out two candles and took her two daughters who remained at home into the dining room. Sitting down with the knitting to wait, she told herself she would not let herself become edgy—but the power company, she hoped, would soon have the lights back on.

The whole neighborhood was dark. The lights were out for about 800 people who lived around the adjoining city limits of the California suburbs of Sunland and Tujunga, which share a slope on the edge of Los Angeles' San Fernando Valley. Plainview Avenue, Mt. Gleason Avenue, part of Tujunga Canyon Boulevard, and up in the hills along Alpine Way—the area seemed to have dropped out of existence.

In a way, that was true. Electricity has become so central to American life that when it disappears, the darkness seems alien and dangerous. Blackout! In stranded elevators, in

Historic blackout: America's dependence on electricity became alarmingly evident in 1965 when New York City, usually aglow with lights (above), suddenly found the full moon its only source of illumination (above right).

blinded movie theaters, in subways, in shadowy offices where all you can hear is the sigh of millions of bytes of information dying out of computer chips, and in neighborhoods like Noreen Wick's, a blackout is scarier than lightning; and when it hits, suddenly the power company is the most important force in the world.

Blackouts hit Americans so hard that they are automatic news, like tornadoes or earthquakes. Thus, there was a sense of disbelief when the 1965 blackout darkened the Northeast, leaving New York City bathed only in moonlight. A blackout teaches a society about itself: in 1965 *The New Yorker* magazine found such peace and camaraderie in the streets during the blackout that it said "this was not a disaster but merely some festival of inconvenience." That blackout showed, too, how much electric-powered diversions occupy time and interest; without them, people turned to more old-fashioned activities, and nine months later, hospitals were inundated with new babies. But when the next great blackout hit the city, in 1977, the mood was less benign, and looting was so bad that Mayor Beame talked about a "night of terror." An article later observed that the blackout had given "a sneak preview of economic and social changes that . . . would not have become visible for several more years."

Energy Control Center

In Noreen Wick's neighborhood, it was wind that knocked out the power. A storm that had beaten northern California to a soggy pulp hit Los Angeles that evening. At 8:24 P.M., years of withstanding the tension of wires and the pull of wind finally became too much for an old crossarm on a pole that stood at the corner of Hillrose Street and Oro Vista Avenue in Sunland. The crossarm's north side snapped off. The three 4.8-kilovolt (kV) wires it carried flailed suddenly, sagged, and twisted together. A flash lit the street. It was observed with some shock by two couples who were standing in the rain a block south, trying to jump-start a car.

When there's a short in a house, a fuse or a circuit breaker blows. It is the same in a power system; it's just that the breakers stand 10 feet (3 meters) high and are filled with thousands of gallons of oil to smother the spark. Down on Foothill Avenue, at Distributing Station 72, a big circuit breaker tripped open inside its tub. That was the moment at which Noreen Wick started looking for her candles. It was also the moment at which a message passed swiftly to the heart of the Los Angeles power system.

Some distance from Sunland, at a location that shall remain secret (power companies are nervous about sabotage), the message immedi-

ately appeared on a computer screen. The computer was inside a huge, windowless blockhouse of a building that stands hidden in hills. Its glass doors are mirrored and blank. Inside is a little window for the presentation of ID cards. A warning sign reads "Sulfuric Acid." A casual visitor gets the impression that if his face doesn't measure up, he will be dissolved on the spot.

This place is ECC—the Energy Control Center for the Los Angeles Department of Water and Power (LADWP), the power company that serves Sunland-Tujunga and all of Los Angeles. Inside ECC is a huge round room that looks like the heart of the Strategic Air Command. Its curved steel wall is covered with diagrams of the Los Angeles electrical distribution system and the sources of electricity.

ECC, like control rooms all over the country, is LADWP's hub. ECC sees all and knows all, at least when the computers work. (On the rare occasions when computers break down, each screen is filled with a picture of a man hitting an alligator with a stick.) The idea, says Fred LeBlanc, an ECC senior load dispatcher and training officer, is that "you can walk into the room and have an instant overview of how much trouble you're in." For laypeople, getting an overview of how blackouts happen and are fixed takes a little longer. You have to start with an understanding of how a modern electrical power system works.

During blackouts, power-company operators take calls from which utilities pinpoint the outage source.

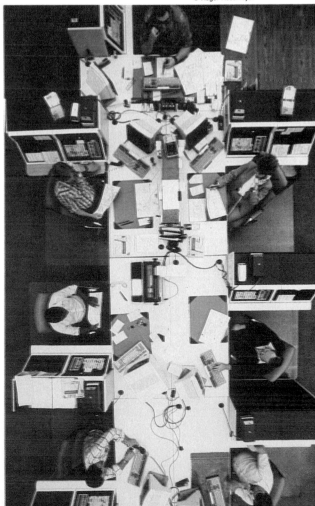

Metaphorical Flowchart

The system begins at generating stations—the burning of coal, oil, or gas; nuclear fission; falling water; the heat of the sun; the force of the wind—whatever can make a dynamo whirl. From there the power is fed into transmission lines—"steel soldiers of progress marching across the land," says one power company executive. Transmission lines carry electricity hundreds of miles to what are called receiving stations. The receiving stations turn over the power into the streets. In the power business, "transmission" and "distribution" describe parts of the system that are as related yet distinct as two Scottish clans.

In trying to explain how to think of transmission and distribution, power company people struggle for comparisons: "Metaphors," one says, "are a highly prized entity." One image that leaps to mind is the corporate organization flowchart. The wall at ECC looks a bit like one, so maybe that's apt. The power company is the chairman of the board; at the desk of each vice president is a generating station. Transmission lines are the department heads, passing high-voltage authority on down the line. After transmissions, you get into the distribution section, a kind of blue-collar district, the place where the real work is done. Here the chart branches out, with the voltage dropping all the way. The line that gets to Noreen Wick's house is the mail-room clerk. In Los Angeles each mail-room clerk, a 4.8-kV wire called a distribution feeder, handles about 800 people.

It's more complicated than that, of course. Distribution systems vary. In Los Angeles, distribution lines run radially out from distribution stations like spokes from a wheel; in most Eastern cities the system forms more of a net. And the line at the house is not as isolated as the mail-room clerk; there is almost always more than one way for the power to come down the street, so at that end of the operation, it's more like a secretarial pool.

The upper end of the system is complex, too. There isn't just one power company and a handful of generators. In the area covered by the North American Electric Reliability Council, which includes Mexico, the United States, and Canada, demand peaked at 506 gigawatts (506 billion watts) in the summer of 1985; this was generated by thousands of power plants, most of which were connected to each other. LADWP, like most of the nation's 3,400 power companies, is tied in to a huge power grid called an interconnection. Four major grids cover North America: the Hydro-Quebec system; the Eastern Interconnection, which serves most of the rest

At Los Angeles's Energy Control Center, computers monitor the city's electricity distribution, diagrammed on the wall.

of the continent east of the Rockies; the Texas Interconnection; and the Western Interconnection. Los Angeles is part of the Western grid, a network of lines that taps generators extending from Mexico to Canada.

In comparing the corporate organization chart with the interconnection system, you cannot say that each collection of linked generators and transmission lines that makes up a power company is like a subsidiary company under one grid command. Rather, to adapt the metaphor, each power company in the grid is more like a member of Congress: individualistic unto itself, but dependent on its colleagues to get things done.

"The grid system takes advantage of what we call diversity," says Kenneth S. Miyoshi, assistant chief electrical engineer for LADWP. The downside is that what affects somebody else also affects you. "We once got a call from someone in L.A. whose computer had burped," recalls Wayne Bente, an LADWP trouble dispatcher. "Turned out the Anaconda line in Montana had been hit by lightning."

One of the main reasons for this linking of lines is to permit what are called economy exchanges—the dealing of power back and forth through the system. In the spring and summer, for instance, southern California utilities are able to buy surplus dam-generated power from the Northwest instead of running their expensive oil-fired plants. Later, when the rivers are down, the flow of electricity might go the other way.

Distant Power Origins

Thus, the power from which Noreen Wick had been abruptly disconnected in Tujunga, California, may have been coming from as far away as The Dalles, Oregon. Lights on ECC's wall showed that, at that moment, a massive 2,000-megawatt converter station in that Oregon town was sending 1,490 megawatts of electricity to Los Angeles. The station was changing AC to DC in its vast halls of mercury-arc and thyristor valves. The electricity, generated by dams on the Columbia River, was coursing down a unique wire: an 850-mile (1,360-kilometer)-long, million-volt DC transmission line.

The two sides of power systems—transmission and distribution—have different kinds of blackouts. The ones you hear about on the news are usually kinks in the transmission grid, as was the case with the 1977 New York blackout. These failures often affect lots of people and can be exacerbated by the linked nature of the grid. But transmission outages are usually caused by only one or two major problems, so

Power flows from generating stations to receiving stations, distributing stations, and, finally, neighborhoods.

Walter Dorwin Teague Associates, Inc.

once they're fixed, everybody gets brought back to light.

Because of their scope, transmission outages often occur with ponderous deliberation. Alternating current in North America is generated and transmitted at a uniform 60 cycles per second, and protective equipment is set to cut power if that cycle slows. So if there's a big short somewhere, and the generators start dragging as they try to keep up with the drain, certain parts of the system are preset to shut down. Like a wet duck trying to fly, the system shakes free of a burden that has suddenly become too much.

This is called load shedding. In the LADWP system, load shedding begins when the frequency slows to 59.1 cycles per second. "If it gets down to 57, we're in big trouble," says Fred LeBlanc. "If it gets down to 55 hertz, it's going to be a blackout." This is why the 1965 Northeast blackout reached New York City not with a bang but a whisper, with dimming bulbs and slowing escalators, as if the whole world were running down.

The Local Outage

The other kind of blackout is the one most people go through occasionally—the local outage, or damage to the distribution system. Since this usually means a broken pole or line, each distribution problem is small. Sometimes, however, problems in the distribution system can be as massive as those caused by a transmission failure. In 1985, during Hurricane Gloria, for instance, two-thirds of Long Island was blacked out when much of the distribution system was savaged by wind. An individual distribution outage can be fixed much more easily than the wreck of a transmission line, but in a situation like Gloria, in which the countryside was strewn with broken wires, people may be without power for days.

A distribution blackout is not likely to announce itself by dimming lights first: it is more likely to plunge you into darkness. The lights may then flash a couple of times because, on many systems, circuit breakers are set to try to reconnect shorted lines once or twice at half-minute intervals. That way, if a short was caused merely by a momentary brush of a tree branch, power can be quickly restored. Your own lights are like a heart monitor for the whole system: if somebody else has a blackout, undamaged circuits may dip when the circuit breaker tries its recovery.

Setting Priorities

In the transmission system, priorities are set for both automatic load shedding—what happens when the cycles slow—and for times when large areas must be dropped by hand, which might happen if there were an hour or more of warning (if, for instance, a generating plant started to die). When loads are shed automatically, the system first drops off pumps that store water in its reservoirs. Next to go are residential chunks. The last islands of power are the areas critical to the city—the center of downtown, for instance, where police and city officials are headquartered, and major industrial areas.

The manual load-shedding procedure is similar, and is outlined in several red books called *Emergency and Disaster Procedures,* which are confidential. Under manual load shedding, which can be more finely tuned, the power company can cut power to relatively small areas; this helps to avoid the looting chaos that hit New York in 1977. As usual, residential areas are the first to go black.

At the distribution end, outages can't be controlled as easily, but priorities are set for who gets the repairman first. Again, homes are at the end of the list. LADWP uses a system of four letters: A, B, C, and X. When a customer is hooked up to the system, it is given a priority: "A" customers are hospitals, police departments, airports, and people with life-support systems; other utilities and certain industries are "B"; other industries and offices are "C." Everybody else is "X."

Of course, if someone's home happens to be on the same distribution line as a hospital, that home will get the benefit of the hospital's priority. But that's not something you're likely to know; to keep the setting of priorities from becoming political disputes, companies keep them confidential.

For Tom Barricklow at the Electric Trouble Center, the calls that come in to the switchboard there are also given priorities. Here the criteria are how much information a call contains and how significant an outage it indicates. If you call and say your own lights are out, that's an "E" call. If it's a business, that gets you a "D." If your neighbors' lights are out as well, you also get a "D." That doesn't mean nobody will attend to the problem, just that other things get more immediate attention. The "A" call is special.

Ed Silvestri lives near the corner of Hillrose and Oro Vista. At 8:24 he had been looking

Los Angeles receives a portion of its electricity from a giant station at The Dalles, Oregon, some 900 miles away.

out the window and saw the flash. He didn't hear the noise of the short, the harsh grunt and roar that linemen call the "bellow" of electrical fire. But he saw wires hanging loose and sparking. "It was kind of funny," he said much later, "because we hadn't lost any power. But we called anyway." This was the "A" call. Sixteen more would come in reporting lights out in Sunland-Tujunga, but this one nailed the trouble to the map.

The switchboard operator typed what Silvestri told her into the computer, and moments later the printout was in Barricklow's hand. "Wires down," it said. "Pole to pole. Explosion/flash. Sparks; hanging over street." Now he had something he could work with.

"It helps to know geographically what you're thinking about," he said later. "It also helps to have worked here for 22 years." He got out the map of circuit 72-4. The line left the distributing station, made a turn at Hillrose and Oro Vista, but didn't begin serving customers until it got up past Woodward Avenue. That's why Silvestri still had lights.

The map also helped Barricklow decide priorities. There was a green sticker on it with the words "Critical Feeder." He saw why: the circuit fed power to a main water-supply pump and a main sewer pump. If he had had one patrolman and two circuits to fix, he would have picked this one first. Barricklow also checked a

Applying molten lead to a cable splice is one job this trainee may someday perform atop a utility pole.

Weather is a frequent blackout culprit. Each storm presents unique hazards to personnel seeking to restore power.

book that listed all patients with life-support systems in their homes, referenced by circuit number. If a life-support system had been shown on 72-4, he says, "I would have jumped up and called the home and said, 'What's your tolerance? We can hook you up with a generator if you need it.' "

Many hospitals and police stations have their own backup generators, but blackouts still sometimes darken operating rooms. When Austin, Texas, was blacked out in 1983, Dr. Gerald Baugh was operating on a patient who had a pacemaker. Baugh couldn't wait for a generator to arrive. He traded the overhead light for a flashlight, and while someone kept a life-support system going by hand, he completed the operation.

Help on the Way

In Tujunga no such crisis was under way. So Barricklow picked up the phone, flipped a switch to connect it to the radio, pushed a button with his foot to transmit, and called into the field. The patrolmen he reached were Al Garrison, in one van, and Michael (Mickey) Flynn, in another. By 8:40 both were on their way to Hillrose and Oro Vista. Noreen Wick had been sitting in the candlelight, knitting, for seven minutes. How long her house would remain dark would be determined now by what Flynn and Garrison found.

The two patrolmen, each with a helper, got there before 9:00. Their vans crept around the corner as the men looked for the break, their spotlights sending columns of glitter through the heavy rain. "You go out in the middle of the night," a former lineman once said, "in driving rain, and you don't know what you're walking into." When Flynn's light settled on the broken crossarm, he knew—and he couldn't fix it.

It was Flynn's 31st birthday. He is a calm and articulate man who likes his job. "You work your way into trouble," he says. "You're your own boss out here." Like most of his fellow patrolmen, he put in a three-year apprenticeship before becoming a journeyman lineman and cable-splicer. (Lines are above ground; cables are below.) He faces as much danger as a fireman, but is unperturbed that the public doesn't recognize the risks of the job. As one former lineman has said, "They're dealing with three hazards out there: height, electricity, and the weather. Policemen get to retire after 20 years. Linemen have to work until they're 65." Yet the children of linemen frequently become linemen. LADWP is full of second-generation talent.

It didn't take Flynn and Garrison long to recognize that it would take a full repair crew several hours to get that crossarm fixed. They got out into the rain to discuss it. Fortunately, there were other options.

Alternate Power Routes

Most power systems have built-in redundancies. Even the vast power-grid transmission lines that string across the country from Canada to California or from Ohio to New York are planned so that the power carried by one line can be transferred to another if the first line fails. The same principle applies to distribution lines: they crisscross a neighborhood in such a way that alternate power routes can be used. The circuit map looks like a maze, with many hallways and a lot of doors, but at any one time that smart mouse, electricity, can get to your house only one way. If that way gets blocked, you just open a couple of doors, and the mouse finds another route.

Studying the circuit map, Flynn and Garrison saw that they could open the doors to the neighboring circuits 72-3 and 72-2 and leave the broken part cold until it could be fixed the next working day by a crew. They needed only to throw some switches.

Noreen Wick was watching from the window when Flynn drove up. The rain dripped off his hard hat and glistened on his coat. She watched him don his climbing gear and ascend the pole. The van's spotlight shone at its top, where three small cylinders hung below the three wires. The cylinders housed switches that were, at this moment, turned off.

Flynn had noticed Noreen Wick and her children in the window. He anticipated their disappointment. After 11 years he's learned a lot about how people react to a blackout. Some have faith in you—like Noreen Wick, who went back to knitting by candlelight. Others get angry, but their attitudes usually mellow quickly: "If the power has been out for a whole day, they're mad at you," he says. "No matter what you do, they're mad at you. But if it's out two days, they're back to being glad to see you."

At night in heavy rain, people don't leave their houses much. But at the last set of switches, out came John Safian to meet the van. Safian writes poetry; he enjoyed the storm and the darkness. He was friendly but concerned. The house next to his was bright, but his was black. "Those guys have lights," he said, gesturing with a beer can as Flynn put on his climbing gear; "I can't imagine why I don't."

It was the most familiar complaint. Flynn smiled. He pointed to the pole that stood between the two houses. There were three switches in cylinders up there. They told the story: Safian and his neighbor were on different circuits. Once he threw the switches, Flynn told

Safian, he'd have his power back. Safian grinned and took a sip of beer. The rain poured, and Flynn went up the pole.

Return to Power

The last problem a power company faces during a blackout is that often you just can't turn the power back on. This isn't usually a problem when a small neighborhood is out; you aren't adding much load to the system when you light it up. So, even extensive outages—like those caused by Gloria's rampage—can be relatively easy to pick up, because they come on one by one. But plugging a million people in after a transmission blackout is like trying to switch on six ovens and a power saw out of one socket.

"If you try to pick up a city," says Robert Iveson of the Electric Power Research Institute, "that'll make a generator grunt." And when a generator has to work too hard, the frequency goes down and, bingo, the whole load-shedding process may begin again.

So returning power has to be orchestrated to load up the system gently. Switches are thrown by power dispatchers in control rooms like ECC, or manually in the field by people like Flynn. Sometimes, if the switches aren't available, says Ken Miyoshi, "you literally have to cut copper." Even when everything is fixed, some places light up before others.

But out in Sunland-Tujunga that rainy night, the load was not enormous. Flynn could carry it himself. This time he didn't touch the switches by hand. He reached up through the rain with a short orange fiberglass wand called a Hot Stick. With the end of the stick, he pushed the switches closed: one, two, three. As each closed, a crisp snap of electricity was heard. Softly, sweetly, all over the neighborhood, lights came on and the glow of civilization returned to Sunland-Tujunga.

It was 10:05: P.M. At the Electric Trouble Center, Barricklow wrote down: "2205 hrs, tie closed." The power had been out for 1 hour and 41 minutes. At 10:29 at ECC, Phil Peterson got a message on his screen that all was normal at Distributing Station 72. Out in the rainy streets, Al Garrison got into the van and drove to Ventura Boulevard, where circuits 83-4 and 83-6 had locked out. Michael Flynn headed for Woodman Avenue, where a car had run into a pole. And up on Plainview Avenue, Noreen Wick said good night to the girls, put away the knitting, climbed into bed, and reached over to turn out the light.

© Nina Barnett

GARBAGE IN, ENERGY OUT

by Jeffrey H. Hacker

In Columbus, Ohio, 2,000 tons (1,800 metric tons) of garbage a day are burned in a waste-incineration plant that generates 50,000 kilowatts of electricity per hour. The mayor boasts that every 30 pounds (13.6 kilograms) of garbage can light two streetlamps for 24 hours. In Baltimore, Maryland, a new waste-to-energy complex burns 2,250 tons (2,040 metric tons) of garbage a day, producing steam that helps heat 500 downtown buildings, and electricity that is sold to the Baltimore Gas & Electric Company. Detroit is building a plant that will burn 4,000 tons (3,600 metric tons) of garbage a day, generating enough steam for half of Detroit Edison's business-district customers and electricity for 40,000 homes.

Are waste-to-energy plants the solution to the nation's waste-disposal problem? Are they an important energy resource for the future?

In the United States today, more than 110 such waste-burning facilities already are in operation, with another 100 planned or under construction. Virtually every major city is considering building at least one. Although only about 6 percent of the nation's garbage currently is disposed of by incineration, the figure may reach 30 to 40 percent by the end of the century.

As a source of energy, however, waste-incineration plants account for only a minuscule fraction of total U.S. production and consumption. The sale of steam and electric power generated by a plant may offset the cost of disposal, but the amount of energy itself is negligible compared with that from other sources. The plant in Saugus, Massachusetts, for example, which opened in 1975 as the nation's first commerical facility for converting refuse into energy, produces only about one-twentieth as much power as a nuclear reactor. Even the most enthusiastic supporters of the technology see it primarily as a means of waste disposal.

While incinerators are gaining popularity among state and municipal officials, environmentalists voice strong opposition, and citizen groups throughout the country seek to bar construction in their communities. The burning of garbage, they contend, produces toxic ash and a range of pollutants that pose serious threats to human health. Many of these emissions, they point out, are not even subject to federal regulation. Finally, environmentalists also worry that the rush to burn garbage will do nothing to reduce the nation's enormous output and will gut efforts to expand recycling.

No Room at the Dump

The amount of garbage generated in the United States today is unparalleled. With disposable consumer goods ranging from pens and shaving razors to diapers, plastic dishes, and even cameras—plus kitchen scraps, other household trash, and industrial debris—the American "throwaway society" churns out more than 150 million tons (136 million metric tons) of solid waste every year. That comes to an average of about 410,000 tons (370,000 metric tons) a day, or enough to fill 41,000 garbage trucks. The average citizen throws out some 4 pounds (1.8 kilograms) of garbage per day, far more than in any other country in the world. Residents of Oslo, Norway, for example, generate an average of about 1.7 pounds (0.75 kilogram) of garbage daily, while the average West German, Japanese, Swedish, and Swiss citizen produces about 2.5 pounds (1.1 kilograms) a day.

At present, more than 90 percent of U.S. solid waste is simply loaded on trucks and dumped in landfills—basically holes in the ground covered with dirt. Often covering thousands of acres, these giant waste sites may produce dangerous amounts of hazardous chemical effluents. And with the garbage piling up so fast, many landfills are reaching capacity. Since 1979, more than 3,500 have been shut down, either because they reached capacity or began to pose a health threat. Some 16,400 still remain, but their days are numbered. The U.S. Environmental Protection Agency (EPA) has predicted

With over 400,000 tons of new garbage added daily, U.S. dumps (facing page) are rapidly reaching capacity. By burning trash to generate energy, plants like the one diagramed below offer a resourceful solution to the garbage crisis.

Wheelabrator Environmental Systems Inc.

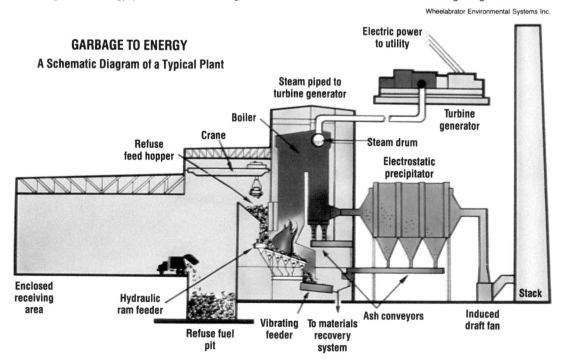

GARBAGE TO ENERGY
A Schematic Diagram of a Typical Plant

that 27 of the 50 states will run out of room to dump their garbage by 1990. Cities with little or no landfill space remaining, such as Philadelphia and Boston, have no choice but to ship their garbage elsewhere—at enormous cost.

The mounting waste-disposal crisis and the need for alternatives to dumping were dramatized in 1987 by the 6,000-mile (9,700-kilometer) odyssey of the garbage barge *Mobro*. Loaded with 3,186 tons (1,445 metric tons) of solid waste from Islip, New York, the scow was turned away in its search for a dump site by six states and three countries. The journey came to an end in July, when an agreement was reached to have the trash burned in a Brooklyn, New York, incinerator; the 400 tons (360 metric tons) of ash would be trucked back to Islip and dumped in the municipal landfill. But environmentalists argued in court that the ash would be too toxic to bury in the town dump, and for weeks the barge remained anchored off Coney Island. The garbage finally went up in smoke on September 1, but the problem of waste disposal did not.

"The whole thing of the barge epitomizes the problem," says Nancy New of the National Conference of State Legislators. "We've been very concerned about hazardous waste, and rightly so. But in fact now we are faced with the sleeping giant of solid waste."

A Power-ful Alternative

American cities and towns have begun to recognize that the "sleeping giant" of solid waste requires new and extraordinary measures. While recycling has had exemplary success in a number of communities, it still accounts for a small percentage of total U.S. waste disposal. The environmentalist Barry Commoner maintains that as much as 80 percent of U.S. municipal garbage can be recycled, but even the most ambitious local programs have reduced waste levels by no more than 25 to 30 percent. In Japan, which boasts the world's most successful recycling program, incineration still plays a major role in solid-waste disposal.

Following the lead of Japan and such other countries as West Germany, Norway, Sweden, and Switzerland, city officials throughout the United States in the 1970s began to favor waste-to-energy plants as the most far-reaching solution to dwindling landfill capacity—and a clever way to cut energy costs. Right or wrong, cities and counties in at least 40 states began building or planning such resource-recovery facilities. A municipality typically contracts with a manufacturer (of which there are about 20 today) to build the plant. The manufacturer or another outside company usually runs the facility as well, although some communities handle operations themselves.

Of the 210 municipal waste-combustion plants currently in operation, under construction, or on the drawing boards in the United States, about two-thirds employ what is called "mass-burn" technology. The defining feature of mass-burn incinerators is that they take garbage in its raw form without separating its components. The garbage is dumped into a deep fuel pit and hydraulically fed into a funnel-shaped furnace/boiler that can reach six stories high. The boiler, located within or above the furnace,

The 6,000-mile odyssey of the garbage barge Mobro drew world attention to the mounting waste-disposal crisis in the U.S.

AP/Wide World

At the Reuter resource recovery plant in Eden Prairie, Minnesota, workers sort metal and glass from garbage that passes by on a conveyor belt (right). The remaining paper and plastic trash is compressed into pellets (below) that are sold to industry as fuel.

Photos: © John Cross

produces steam from the hot combustion gases. The steam can be used directly—to heat buildings, for example—or drive a turbine to generate electricity. The output of electricity can range from 11 megawatts from a facility that burns 550 tons (500 metric tons) of garbage a day, to more than 100 megawatts from a plant that burns 4,500 tons (4,100 metric tons) a day. Meanwhile, the volume of trash is reduced by 60 to 90 percent.

The other type of incineration plant (which accounts for 23 percent of total U.S. capacity, according to the EPA) is known as refuse-derived-fuel (RDF). These plants differ from mass-burn incinerators in that they sort out and remove many toxic and recyclable materials from the garbage. The remaining material is processed into fuel, usually in the form of small pellets or bales. This fuel is then burned along with coal to produce energy.

Burning Issues

In addition to steam and electricity, waste-to-energy plants also are generating serious concern about the environmental threats posed by air emissions and ash residue. The situation in Baltimore typified the problem, especially with early combustion plants. The city spent $25 million on its original facility, which opened in 1976. Because of a variety of operational problems, however, the plant proved highly polluting and was closed down in 1981. The following year the city decided to try again, and began building its present facility on the same site.

One problem with the early U.S. waste-to-energy plants was that they were based on European technology. Operators discovered that American garbage was different from European garbage. U.S. trash contains more plastic and toxic metal, which produce higher combustion temperatures and health-threatening emissions. Plants based on the European model therefore proved inadequate to U.S. needs.

Environmentalists maintain that serious dangers still exist today. Even in new waste-to-energy plants, the burning of plastic, metal, and glass produces dioxin—a carcinogenic (cancer-causing) compound—and such toxic-acid gases as hydrogen chloride and sulfur dioxide. To control air emissions, the EPA in July 1987 mandated that all new incinerators be equipped with "scrubbers." These remove most dangerous particulates by spraying gases in the smokestack with acid-neutralizing solutions. Opponents of incineration insist that not all toxic compounds, such as dioxin, are captured by scrubbers, and that many existing plants are not even equipped with them.

Much of the debate over waste-to-energy plants has drifted to another environmental issue—that of ash residue and how to dispose of it. Samples of so-called "fly ash," which collects in the pollution-control equipment attached to the incinerator smokestack, show high concentrations of dioxin and furan (another carcinogenic compound), as well as such toxic metals as lead and cadmium. Many facilities simply combine fly ash with the less toxic "bottom ash" from incinerator grates to achieve established safety levels. Yet tests have shown that bottom ash itself sometimes contains dangerous levels of toxic substances. Thus, how to dispose of the potentially poisonous ash residue has become a central question for the future of waste-to-energy plants in the United States.

Some members of Congress have become convinced that municipal incinerators should be subject to stricter environmental controls than those established by EPA. With the support of a number of states and local governments, bills were introduced in 1987 to regulate air emissions and the disposal of incinerator ash.

Dollars and Sense

As the environmental debate continues, many communities find waste-to-energy plants attractive for purely economic reasons. The cost of construction can be enormous—ranging from $1.2 million for the plant in Batesville, Arkansas, to $570 million for the new facility in Broward County, Florida—but there is a major offsetting factor: the sale of energy. One investment banker estimates that the sale of electricity can finance up to half the initial outlay. According to federal law, utility companies must buy the electricity generated by waste-to-energy plants and pay the same rate as they would for electricity produced by their own most expensive plants. In addition, the town pays the plant owner a "tipping fee" for each ton of garbage deposited.

Local governments favor waste-to-energy plants because the tipping fees are significantly lower than the costs of conventional disposal. With landfill space diminishing and with an increasing number of cities having to transport their waste long distances, the cost of dumping has been increasing dramatically in recent years. For example, Philadelphia's average disposal costs have risen nearly fivefold during the 1980s, reaching about $100 per ton. That figure, and much higher, is expected to become commonplace in the near future. While tipping fees at waste-to-energy plants vary widely, they nonetheless represent a savings compared with fees charged for dumping.

Environmental issues aside, activists contend that recycling is much more economical than either dumping or burning. As opposed to paying tipping fees, towns that collect and separate their solid waste could be *paid* $5 to $20 per ton. More important, say environmentalists, wide-scale recycling would have the attractive benefit of reducing the excessive amount of waste produced in the country. Burning garbage should come as a last resort after recycling and waste-reduction programs have been implemented.

The Future

Whatever the pros and cons, environmental or economic, waste-to-energy plants are here to stay. Indeed, they represent a rapidly growing industry. By one estimate, the capacity of such facilities is expected to reach 40 percent of total U.S. solid-waste output by the end of the century—more than 200,000 tons (180,000 metric tons) per day. In New England, waste-to-energy plants coming on line by 1990 will have the capacity to dispose of two-thirds of the region's garbage. Incinerators will not eliminate the need for landfills, but they are rapidly becoming a key component in battling the U.S. waste-disposal problem. In addition, they are providing a new and growing source of energy.

By the same token, the spread of waste-to-energy plants underscores the need for environmental safety and for an integrated system of solid-waste disposal. Even the most enthusiastic supporters do not view garbage burning as a completely risk-free method of disposal nor as the single answer to the nation's garbage crisis. While there has been growing recognition that reducing dangerous emissions requires sophisticated (and often costly) technology, many state and local governments have also begun to recognize the importance of an integrated approach to waste disposal. Reducing the amount of garbage to be burned—and separating out the glass, plastic, and metal—can greatly increase the savings, both economic and environmental, of waste-to-energy combustion.

As with so many other modern technologies, the benefits and opportunities offered by waste-to-energy plants pose fundamental questions and raise major new challenges to technology itself, to policymakers at every level, and, most of all, to the public at large.

Windmills in California's Altamont Pass produce energy from strong, persistent winds blowing in from the Pacific.

Transforming the Sea Wind

by Robert J. Hutchinson

Last year, when all the other America's Cup contenders were in Australia preparing for the big race, skipper Dennis Conner tested his boat, *Stars and Stripes,* in Hawaii. Why? Because Hawaii's optimum spot within the trade-wind system gives it breezes that would make any sailor's heart sing a new song. The trades churn the deep steel-blue water of the Pacific into swirling chasms of airy foam; they can fill a spinnaker so it looks as if it will expand indefinitely, like a giant sheet of rubber. "I've sailed all over the world, up and down both coasts of the U.S. as well as in the Caribbean and the Mediterranean, and I've rarely seen such consistent, strong winds," says one Hawaii Yacht Club member. "Conner brought *Stars and Stripes* here because he knows this is the place to push it to the limit."

It is hardly surprising, then, given these northeasterly trades that blow firmly and dependably so much of the year, that Hawaii has invested heavily in commercial wind power. It is surprising, however, that until quite recently, the development of such energy systems on the windy coasts of the U.S. has been limited to a few experimental machines—even though in other sea-oriented places, such as Denmark and the Netherlands, among others, windmills have long proven to be a safe and sure source of renewable energy.

California and Hawaii Leading

California, also blessed with strong and relatively stable ocean winds, is the only mainland state to have made any substantial investment in this new technology. Based on an ideological

© Daniel Forster/duomo

America's Cup winner Dennis Conner exploited Hawaii's steady trade winds to test his boat Stars and Stripes.

commitment to alternative energy sources, and on the belief that it could be economically attractive, Hawaii and California have taken the initiative to pave the way for wind energy development. To lessen the state's dependence on oil, Hawaii's strong state legislature forced the Hawaiian Electric Company to buy wind power at a rate equivalent to the cost of oil. In California, attractive tax incentives, on top of federal energy exemptions, led to a flurry of development in the early 1980s, and even more substantial growth today. At least 90 percent of the wind-generated energy in the U.S., and up to 70 percent of the world's total, is produced in California.

Last April, Hawaiian Electric Renewable Systems, a subsidiary of Hawaiian Electric Industries, installed a state-of-the-art generator— known as the MOD-5B—at its "wind farm," as these sites are known, on Kahuku Point, the northernmost part of the island of Oahu. This generator, built by the Boeing Company,

funded by the National Aeronautics and Space Administration (NASA) and the U.S. Department of Energy (DOE), weighs nearly 160 tons (145 metric tons) and has a single blade 320 feet (97 meters) long (longer than a football field). At peak capacity the MOD-5B can generate 3,200 kilowatts of power. During one year, it will produce electricity equivalent to that generated by 58,400 barrels of oil—enough to provide energy for up to 1,300 homes.

And that's only one unit. Fourteen 600-kilowatt Westinghouse wind generators were erected last year as part of Oahu's $24 million, 9-megawatt Makani Moa'e wind farm that is synchronized so it can provide electricity to the Hawaiian Electric Company's main power grid. On the Big Island of Hawaii, Hawaii Electric Light Company was the first utility in the nation to contract for more wind-generated electricity than it can use under the existing practices of the industry. That is, power companies are now reluctant to commit to greater usage of wind power because of the relative instability of the source and because they do not have a way to store the power. Wind power now provides more than 3 percent of the electricity in the company's power grid, and proposals call for raising that level to as much as 7 to 10 percent.

The Big Island currently has 379 wind generators of various designs and capacities at Kahua Ranch, Lalamilo, and South Point. Thirty-seven Mitsubishi 250-kilowatt generators have been proposed for South Point by the Kamaoa Wind Energy Company. (Generators that produce less than 200 kilowatts are considered small; if they produce 200 to 500 kilowatts, they are considered of "medium" size; and if they produce more than that—like the MOD-5B— they are "large.") Also, California-based Zond Energy Systems and U.S. Windpower are considering construction of additional farms in Maui's Honolua Valley.

Meteorology and Topography

Hawaii's trade winds are caused by the heating of the ocean waters near the equator. The warm water heats the air, which then moves in a circular pattern, first up high into the atmosphere and north, then down and south.

Turbines in California are driven by strong sea winds that are caused by a kind of vacuum effect: during the day the sun heats the land in central California, causing the air to rise; cooler air over the Pacific Ocean is then sucked inland to replace it. At night the process is reversed:

the land loses heat quickly, and the ocean—
which takes longer both to heat up and to cool—
heats the air above it, and the now-colder inland
air is swept out to sea.

"Good coastal wind doesn't have to travel
very far inland to become only average as far as
wind energy is concerned," says Earl Davis,
director of meteorology at U.S. Windpower in
Livermore, California, the world's largest private wind-power developer. "Topography enhances the natural wind from the ocean when it
first comes ashore," he explains. "Typically
what happens is that as it goes perhaps a half-
mile or a mile inland, it loses a lot of that
enhancement because of surface friction."

Davis stresses that it is difficult to general-
ize about the probable advantages of placing
windmills on the coast. Each site would have to
be evaluated independently, according to the
overall wind-flow patterns, taking into consideration various land features, such as mountain
ranges, near where the wind first comes ashore.
"Hawaii is a good example of that," he adds.
"On the north shore of Oahu, at Kahuku, there
is enhanced wind, but at Diamond Head (on the
southern end of the island), it's not enhanced
because of the wind's angle of attack and the
topographic features it first encounters."

Most of California's commercial wind turbines are located at three mountain passes,
where the Pacific wind is enhanced by very different topography: the San Gorgonio Pass,
northwest of Palm Springs; the Tehachapi Pass,
a low mountain saddle between the Sierra Nevada and the Coast ranges; and Altamont Pass,
due east of San Francisco. In each of these
areas, oceanic winds are funneled into passes,
intensifying the velocity. The magnitude of
wind-farm development in these areas is difficult to imagine: by the end of 1986, Altamont
Pass alone had more than 6,900 units, mostly
small three-bladed turbines on steel towers. The
generators stretch up and down the rolling hills
just north of U.S. Windpower's headquarters.
In 1978 the National Energy Act granted a 15
percent tax credit for wind energy development,
and California added a 25 percent credit, which
in the early 1980s caused windmills to sprout
like the state's famous poppies. By 1982 California had 1,034 turbines; in 1986, 15,511.

Aesthetic Eyesores?

Critics charged that the machines were merely a
tax dodge, and worse, a potentially dangerous
eyesore. The concern that wind turbines could

Hawaiian Electric Industries

*In Hawaii, where wind energy provides more than three
percent of the state's electricity, the burgeoning windpower facilities include a 600-kilowatt turbine on the north
shore of Oahu (above). In California, vertical-axis "egg-
beaters" (below) operate independently of wind direction.*

© Roger Ressmeyer

In arid Arizona, multivaned windmills produce the energy needed to pump up underground water for crops and cattle.

be dangerous came from the tendency of some early developers to install machines without proper testing in order to take advantage of tax credits while they lasted. Some of these projects—irreverently called ''tax farms''—were seriously undercapitalized, without funds for adequate maintenance, and many developers had underestimated just how much air turbulence the machines would have to withstand. There are cases where wind turbines flew apart: in 1984 a machine in the hills north of Palm Springs threw a blade 400 feet. Fortunately, no one was injured.

Although with improved design, safety problems are not a major concern, the eyesore issue remains and is not as trifling as it may appear. Unlike the giant MOD-5B in Hawaii and the mammoth coastal wind turbines in Denmark and Sweden—which, like the Old Dutch windmills, have actually become tourist attractions—the thousands of small turbines spinning away in California's mountain passes look as unsightly as telephone poles to many people. And they make a lot of noise: on windy days the machines emit a loud, low-frequency thump that environmentalists fear may disturb wildlife, not to mention people who live nearby. They create a loud whoosh, whoosh—in a pulsing

beat that one photographer aptly compared to a heartbeat magnified through a powerful speaker system.

In March 1985, the city of Palm Springs sued wind-park developers and the U.S. Department of the Interior's Bureau of Land Management, which granted the right-of-way to the developers' use of land near the resort community. The litigation was intended to force the companies to dismantle, move, or camouflage some of the existing machines and to stop them from building any more until an agreement could be worked out. The city reached an out-of-court agreement that it be consulted before any future turbines are erected, but it was not successful in forcing the companies to remove or significantly camouflage the machines.

It is not only image-conscious communities like Palm Springs that have had second thoughts about wind turbines. In 1978 the residents of Block Island, Rhode Island—long accustomed to old-fashioned windmills used to pump water and mill corn—became hosts to DOE turbines. Although relatively small and quiet by today's standards, the 200-kilowatt machines were then ''giants'' and were indeed the first generation of what were then considered very large turbines. The islanders quickly tired of the noise and the sight of the generators, and after they proved to cost more to operate than they produced in energy, the windmills were ignominiously abandoned and left to rust after the developers ran out of money.

Supporters of wind power point out that windmills certainly are no uglier than the huge offshore oil platforms that desecrate the nation's coastlines. And, these people add, a little bit of noise pollution is certainly preferable to the kind of mass devastation that oil spills are likely to create.

Appropriate Sites

Besides aesthetics, when good locations for wind farms are being identified, there are other, equally important, considerations. P. Anders Daniels, a scientist on staff at the University of Hawaii's Department of Meteorology, who has completed a detailed survey of the wind fields in the Hawaiian Islands, has identified as key factors in site selection: (1) wind speed and reliability; (2) air turbulence; and, most important, (3) conditions that aggravate corrosion.

Up to now, scientists have seen that while coastal regions may provide good wind and air with little turbulence, the problem of severe corrosion from salty ocean air makes higher, inland placement of wind machines more advantageous. But Daniels' research has led to some startling conclusions: He has found that the amount of ocean-related corrosiveness is dramatically less at a certain height right on the seashore than at most other points immediately inland. The reason? The sun heats the earth, which warms the air just above it, forming what is known as a "boundary layer." The warm boundary air at the water's edge causes the salt-saturated sea air to be carried far inland, where it mixes with the wind. "The salt concentration in the boundary layer is parabolic," agrees U.S. Windpower's Davis. "It builds up as you go away from the beach." Although each coastal area varies, the least corrosive air is usually found about 100 feet (30 meters) above the seashore, according to Daniels. He also points out that about 300 feet (90 meters) inland, where the air is more corrosive, "you also get weaker winds, and there is far more turbulence."

Building on those findings, Daniels suggests that an ideal way of tapping wind power would be to erect high concrete towers right at the water's edge, to hold specially designed intermediate-to-large turbines. "If you could build a wind turbine out in the ocean, that would

Northern Power Systems

Modern windmill designs have been criticized both for their lack of aesthetic appeal and for their noise pollution. One solution has been to build offshore facilities (above). Although safety concerns are minimal, windmills are nonetheless frequently inspected (below).

© Cameramann Int'l

be very good, but the next best spot would be right on the shore,'' he says. Daniels believes that if just a few of the larger turbines were erected instead of hundreds of smaller ones, the aesthetic objections would be considerably lessened.

Coincidentally, the U.S. Navy has launched an independent program that parallels Daniels' suggestion: it has installed wind machines on the seashore, and out in the ocean. The Naval Civil Engineering Laboratory at Port Hueneme, California, currently supervises numerous wind energy projects around the world, most of them on or near the seashore. The laboratory operates two 20-kilowatt turbines right on the beach in Bermuda, and other small units on Scagg's Island, California, and on the Hawaiian island of Oahu at Kolekole Pass north of the Naval Air Station at Barber's Point, and at the Kaneohe Marine Corps base. Moreover, the Navy has plans in the works for up to twenty-five 20-kilowatt turbines at San Clemente Island, California, as well as tentative proposals

for machines on the island of Niihau, Hawaii, and Johnston Atoll.

The Navy's most successful use of wind machines on or near the sea is probably its recent installation of six very small 10-kilowatt turbines on platforms off the coast of South Carolina for its Tactical Air Crew Training System. ''These platforms are designed to carry computers and equipment that communicate with airplanes,'' says Dharam Pal, the principal investigator of the Navy's Wind Energy Program at Port Hueneme. ''We used to use diesel generators to power the computers and other equipment, but diesels don't work all that well—they're not reliable. So we came up with wind power combined with photovoltaic cells.

''The wind machines are on unmanned platforms that rest on the ocean floor in 100 to 250 feet (30 to 75 meters) of water,'' Pal adds. He says that any corrosion problems are all solvable by using designs that take corrosion into account, and by maintenance as simple as regular lubrication of the bearings.

One reason wind power is not as popular as enthusiasts would like it to be is the basic technological problem that was noted previously: there is no efficient method of storing and equalizing electricity. Higher voltage is produced during periods of stronger winds, but constant voltage is necessary for the electricity to be used in utility companies' power grids, so the utilities are reluctant to depend upon wind energy.

An equally important deterrent to the industry is the fact that wind power is still quite expensive. True, the wind is free, but the turbines, towers, and maintenance crews are not. In the late 1970s the cost of electricity from wind machines was estimated to be more than $1.50 per kilowatt-hour (in constant 1984 dollars). Design, maintenance, and performance improvements have reduced the cost more than tenfold, so today's generators produce electricity at about 10 to 15 cents per kilowatt-hour. However, oil-fired steam generators produce it for as little as 3 to 6½ cents. Wind farms are able to remain in the market only through governmental price-fixing. Wind-power developers are optimistic, however, that technological improvements soon will have a moderating effect on its cost.

An International Phenomenon

Despite these persistent problems, wind energy projects are being developed around the world. Most Western European nations, particularly

In sea-oriented countries such as Holland, windmills have long provided a sure source of renewable energy.

On British Columbia's Swindle Island, windmills and solar panels combine to power a telephone-company facility.

Denmark and Sweden, are designing or erecting major wind farms. Denmark is currently the world's number two producer of wind energy, with more than 500 turbines clustered along its coasts. Both Belgium and the Netherlands are refurbishing old windmills and designing new ones. A naval engineer at the University of Glasgow in Scotland and a scientist in Germany have both experimented with wind turbines to power ships. The German experiment involved outfitting a 100-foot (30-meter) vessel with a 250-kilowatt wind-powered generator. Algeria, India, Rumania, Australia, and the island countries of the Pacific and the Caribbean—where the high cost of importing oil makes renewable energy attractive—are all enthusiastic proponents of wind power.

Two experimental systems are operational in Japan's Ryukyu Islands: a 100-kilowatt turbine on Miyako Island, and a 300-kilowatt unit built by Mitsubishi on Okierabu Island. And more are on the way. In China, where a third of the population is still without electricity, and where windmills have been used for centuries to pump water, wind parks are being planned. A scientist in the Chinese Academy of Agriculture thinks that his country is a prime location—especially for the development of wind-driven pumps—since there is adequate wind speed available for 5,000 to 6,000 hours each year. China foresees using wind energy for such projects as the reclamation of sea marshes for cultivation, aquaculture development, and irrigating rice paddies.

As more and more countries discover the potential advantages of wind energy, the sight of large windmills may become as common on many coasts as lighthouses once were. Public resistance will undoubtedly keep the rows of smaller wind turbines off beaches and headlands, but, as Anders Daniels suggests, large machines, like Hawaii's new MOD-5B, may be tolerated.

It might be a fitting irony, a closing of the technological circle, if society returned to the wind and sea for power. The giant blades of windmills like the MOD-5B and its successors will catch the trades as they flow across the smooth ocean and into the coastal mountains, lighting up cities on the shore.

THE
ENVIRONMENT

F. Carter Smith/NYT Pictures

Tons of debris continue to wash up on U.S. shores, despite laws aimed at reducing ocean pollution.

REVIEW OF THE YEAR

THE ENVIRONMENT

In 1987 a series of events brought the international and global dimensions of environmental problems into striking prominence. Confronted with increasing evidence of potentially disastrous depletion of the earth's vital atmospheric ozone layer, the world's major nations finally reached agreement on an explicit program to curb the chemical emissions believed responsible. International concern was brought to bear on another climatic threat: the rapid destruction of the vast rain forests in South America. The long-deplored degradation of the oceans, the earth's climatic "engine," also evoked collective action. Even community trash became an international cause célèbre as a barge-load of New York refuse cruised for nearly six months, vainly seeking a dumping-ground. On the domestic front, noteworthy progress against such basic problems as air pollution, water pollution, and toxic substances remained scant.

THE OZONE LAYER

At a September 1987 conference in Montreal, Canada, sponsored by the United Nations Environmental Program, 36 nations signed an agreement to reduce the production and use of chlorofluorocarbons and halons, chemical compounds widely used in aerosol propellants, plastic foam, refrigerants, and fire extinguishers. When released into the atmosphere, these chemicals can destroy fragile ozone (O_3) molecules, which form a protective blanket in the atmosphere that moderates potentially lethal ultraviolet radiation from the sun. The Montreal Protocol calls for freezing the use of the compounds at 1986 levels, progressive reductions over the next decade, and a host of other measures.

RAIN FORESTS

The earth's climate and ecology are influenced substantially by the tropical forests that cover one-fifth of the world's land area. According to U.N. officials, these forests are being depleted at a rate of 27 million acres (11 million hectares) a year—50 acres (20 hectares) a minute—mainly by transitory agriculture and logging. At a 16-nation conference in Bellagio, Italy, a $1-billion-a-year program was endorsed to arrest this consumption, said to adversely affect some 1 billion of the world's people. Another significant step was achieved when the environmental organization Conservation International arranged for the reduction of Bolivia's international debt by $650,000 in exchange for preservation of 3.7 million acres (1.5 million hectares) of Amazon forest.

OCEANS AND WATERWAYS

The U.S. ratified a 29-nation treaty aimed at reducing ocean pollution. Congress banned the dumping of plastics by U.S.-registered ships anywhere in the world, and all such dumping within 200 miles (320 kilometers) of U.S. shores. Long-lived plastics, ingested or entangled, are blamed for high mortality among fish and marine mammals.

After protracted objections by environmental groups, a six-year effort in the United States to get federal approval for burning toxic wastes at sea aboard specially built ships was abandoned by a disposal firm as economically infeasible. European nations are planning to curb the practice as well.

In its annual assessment of water pollution abatement, the U.S. Environmental Protection Agency (EPA) reported that about 75 percent of the area of the nation's waterways was "clean enough to support the uses [that] states have set for them," such as fishing, swimming, and drinking. The agency, under a federal court order, promulgated new discharge limits on 66 previously unregulated industrial contaminants. The measure was calculated to remove 130 million pounds (60 million kilograms) a year of pollutants from U.S. waterways.

International attention focused on the barge *Mobro,* which, laden with 3,100 tons (2,800 metric tons) of trash from Islip, New York, made a 6,000-mile (9,600-kilometer), 162-day voyage down the Atlantic coast and around the Caribbean, in futile search for a disposal site. After being rejected in six states and three countries, the barge returned to New York City, which incinerated the refuse. The odyssey dramatized the plight of countless American communities that are rapidly running short of dumping space. The real shortage appeared to be in the funds needed to haul waste to the nation's still-vast uninhabited areas. The cost is indeed high: *The New York Times* reported that big-city trash-disposal expenses range from $13 a ton in Los Angeles to $70 in Boston.

HAZARDOUS CHEMICALS

Six years after the federal government launched a multibillion-dollar effort to clean up hazardous-chemical-disposal sites, the problem appeared to be growing rather than shrinking: 99 more disposal tracts were added by the EPA to its "high-priority" remedial list of 880: meanwhile, the six-year tally of neutralized sites reached only 13. The EPA, with 450 sites already under initial studies, and thousands more with which to deal, hoped to tackle 175 more sites by mid-1989.

After more than a decade of debate, Congress reached agreement on a tentative plan to bury the nation's radioactive waste at Yucca Mountain in the Nevada desert.

The National Council on Radiation Protection reported that the average American's exposure to radiation was 360 millirems per year, twice the long-standing previous estimate. The federal standard of acceptable occupational exposure is 5,000 millirems per year. The increase was attributed largely to new data on household radon exposure. The EPA reported that a 10-state survey showed that one in five homes had excessive levels of radon, a colorless, odorless, cancer-causing gas naturally released from radioactive rock. The agency issued a guidance pamphlet for builders on averting undue accumulations of the gas through proper sealing and ventilation.

Amid disagreement over details, congressional committees blocked enactment of bills setting a nine-year deadline on removal from the market of pesticides shown to cause cancer, birth defects, and other disorders. In the past 15 years, the EPA has banned 32 of 600 pesticide ingredients that might so classify. Forty-seven more were voluntarily taken off the market. The rest remain to be evaluated.

AIR POLLUTION

A fifth year of congressional debate over tightening the Clean Air Act produced only an impasse. Under the existing law, 1987 was the deadline for municipal compliance with federal air-quality standards before economic sanctions would be mandated. About 60 cities are considered to have substandard air quality. Congress extended the deadline to August 1988.

A major bone of contention in the congressional debate was acid-rain fallout from atmospheric pollutants believed to come mainly from power plants. While the U.S. Government insisted that the acid-rain problem needed more study before stiff controls on pollution sources are imposed, Canada complained of foot-dragging by the Americans.

GLADWIN HILL

Evacuated neighborhoods in New Jersey and elsewhere lack disposal sites for their radon-contaminated soil.

Keith Meyers/NYT Pictures

Ecology
of the
Canopy

by Erik Eckholm

Butterfly heaven,'' exults Donald Perry from his mobile perch above the jungle roof. The first sunny morning all week, and the butterflies are out; a dozen varieties, a dozen different color swatches, flit by within half an hour.

Perry, naturalist, dreamer, and impresario of the treetops, is becoming acquainted with his new habitat, a patch of rain forest in the hills of Costa Rica in Central America. We cruise with ease through the upper stories, a zone biologists call their last frontier. Our vehicle is a moving steel platform dangling from cables stretched between giant trees 700 feet (215 meters) apart. By remote control, with a small joystick, Perry directs distant winches that move us forward and backward, up and down. Bouncing gently, we might as well be in the basket of a hot-air balloon.

It is early December, only five days since the tramway was up and running above a curving gorge. Inching through the vines, aerial ferns, and orchids that give the forest its tropical air, the thick brown mud below seems more than a world away.

© Gary Braasch/Wheeler Pictures

From an aerial tramway, biologists take eye-level looks at life in the canopy of the Costa Rican rain forest.

As though seeing nature for the first time, Perry jumps and points to each new bird or bug that flutters into view, racing the platform to examine every flower. To his companion, a New Yorker without training in tropical biology, the unremitting greenery slowly seems less strange as the eyes pick out oversized but obvious relatives of common houseplants: stupendous climbing philodendrons; the droopy leaf clusters of the Shefflera; the shiny, ribbed leaves of a 100-foot (30-meter) tree.

Extraordinary Interrelationships

It takes reminding that we are making a rare foray into territory that scientists consider equivalent to an unexplored continent. The discovery of life in the rain forests has hardly begun, but the findings already made about the multitudes of plants and animals and their extraordinary interrelations leave many biologists almost breathless.

"If I were 30 years younger, I'd be hanging up there in the ropes myself," says Edward O. Wilson, a 58-year-old Harvard biologist.

Thanks mainly to the warnings of conservationists, by now nearly everyone has heard superlatives about the dwindling rain forests of tropical Africa, Asia, and Latin America. Why they abound with so many species is debated. Many scientists, though not all, Wilson says, attribute it to a combination of factors: the equable climate that allows year-round growth, and the relatively long history that some areas in the tropics, known as "refugia," have enjoyed without major climate change, allowing more time for species to evolve. Whatever the reasons, jungles comprise the richest ecosystems on Earth, and the least examined. They are home to millions of unnamed plants and animals and have untold lessons to teach about the history and workings of life.

The Arboreal Realm

This holds doubly true for the upper stories, from some 30 feet (9 meters) above ground to the 150-foot (45-meter)-plus crowns of forest behemoths. There, all-important sunlight drives a riotous dance of life.

"Biologically, that's the hot spot of the forest," says Alan P. Smith, an ecologist at the Smithsonian's Tropical Research Institute in

Today the incessant rains have stopped. Years of scraping and scheming, more than two weeks of grueling construction on steep, slippery hillsides, are finished, and Perry's audacious contraption is actually working.

"I'm exhilarated," says Perry, a lean, 6-foot-4-inch (1.9-meter) man of 40 who, lacking in formal academic backing, calls himself a "free-lance biologist."

If nothing else, the machine gives a ride that Disney would have envied. The view of two roaring waterfalls and lush jungle is sensational; the 150-foot (45-meter) drop below us hints at danger. More than a toy, though, this is an important step toward many a biologist's dream: to move through the forest canopy with the freedom of a bird. In coming years, Perry hopes, even bigger "automated webs" will open new realms for jungle researchers.

Panama. "That's where most of the photosynthesis is, and most of the plant-animal interactions. That's where the growing tips of the plants are."

Perhaps two-thirds of the rain-forest species live aloft; many plants and animals are born, reproduce, and live their entire lives without ever touching the ground. It is estimated that as many as half of all life-forms may live in the jungle canopy (most, without doubt, insects).

This arboreal realm remains largely out of scientists' reach. Simply climbing the trees is usually out of the question. They brim with stinging ants, scorpions, spiders, and wasps, not to mention the occasional deadly viper. Many have weak branches, already sagging with heavy vines and piggybacking plants.

In the past, Perry and others have adapted mountain-climbing techniques to haul themselves up tall trees on ropes, sometimes to camp in lofty observation platforms. A handful of researchers have built ladders and walkways through the branches. For scientists to see what they need to see, platforms and catwalks would carve up the forest so thoroughly that natural patterns would be destroyed. Then there is the question of safety; in 1984 a British researcher in Venezuela fell to his death from the trees.

At first, the jungle seems to offer little more than a hundred shades of green. Only sporadically is the verdure broken by the jolting flash of a flower's red or yellow or white. A preposterous procession of overburdened leaf-cutter ants, a hovering dragonfly, and, at a lucky moment, a passing troop of parrots may offer the only hints of wildlife.

But the forest rewards patience. Watch, and one among the brown leaves fluttering to earth jumps sideways, revealing itself to be a hefty morpho butterfly, camouflage-brown on the underside, but, you are startled to see, brilliant azure on the top.

More than patience, the forest rewards knowledge. Each high-wire trip through the canopy reveals more variety. "You get a glimpse of canopy life now and then from a fallen branch or tree," says Michael Grayum, a botanist who has spent the past three and a half years collecting the flora of Costa Rica for the Missouri Botanical Garden. "But I've never seen it like this."

A cruise with him is instructive not only for what plants he identifies, but also for those he, unapologetically, cannot. There might be 150 different plant species within view along the tramway's span, he guesses, some of them never described in the literature. "Here it's so diverse that nobody can know everything."

Overabundance of Orchids

We stop alongside trees laden with epiphytes, plants that grab nutrients and water from the air and transform many branches into exotic gardens. Epiphytes—the word comes from Greek for "upon plants"—use trees for physical support but do not, like parasites, sap nutrients from their hosts. They include not only the ferns, mosses, lichens, and liverworts seen in northern forests, but also arboreal cacti and bromeliads. The latter, relatives of the pineapple, often store rainwater at the base of their erect leaves, supporting microcommunities of insects and even frogs.

And, more than anything else, the epiphytes include orchids. Most of the world's 20,000 species of orchids live on the trunks or branches of tropical trees. In Costa Rica alone, more than 1,100 species of orchids have been identified. When we take time to look, several orchids are in flower. A white flower the size of a hand is easily spotted. Others, strings of yellow or purple blossoms hardly bigger than dewdrops, are easy to miss.

We direct the platform ahead and down to the branches of an enormous fig tree, its fruits clustered about the shiny leaves. The leaves in the middle of the crown had seemed a different color, and up close we see why: these are actually two stranglers entwined.

Grayum explains the fierce, silent struggle under way. The fig is one of the strangler figs known as "tree-killers" in Central American vernacular. These begin life as epiphytes, germinating in a humus-rich crotch of a big tree. They send roots down to dig into the ground and suck up the nutrients and water that power a relentless sunward push. As the leaves above spread, stealing ever more sunshine, the roots fuse around the host tree's trunk. Squeezed and increasingly bereft of light, the host dies, and there, innocent-looking, stands the usurper.

But here the second tree is another variety of strangler tree, and the two may fight until one triumphs. More likely, Grayum observes, they will coexist for years in an uneasy détente.

Butterflies Abound

On a sunny morning, prime time for butterflies, I traverse the treetops with Isidro Chacon, a butterfly expert with the National Museum of Costa

UPPER CANOPY

120 feet

90 feet

LOWER CANOPY

60 feet

30 feet

GROUND LEVEL

© Rafal Olbinski

Each level of the rain forest is home for a different mix of plants and animals. The most species live in the upper stories, where the sunlight is more plentiful and the humidity is less oppressive.

Rica. He has heard that this site is rich in butterflies, and is eager to see for himself.

As soon as we embark, he nets a blue, black, and yellow Heliconius. He holds the insect by the wings and examines the clusters of plant pollen attached to its front legs. This species mixes pollen and nectar "like a milkshake," Chacon says. After being poked and probed for several minutes, the released insect flies off, none the worse. Above us a green hummingbird stops for a quick rest on the steel cable, perhaps mistaking it for one of the lianas, woody vines that creep and dangle everywhere.

Next, Chacon nets a brilliant yellow-and-black funeral moth, a species whose body is poi-

sonous enough to make a bird vomit and remember not to make the same mistake again. Several butterfly species that lack such poison have evolved nearly identical coloration, he says, offering them a sort of borrowed security. The moth species is usually quite hard to collect; this specimen disappears into a paper packet and Chacon's pocket. Other butterflies are fluttering above a nearby tree, and we move on to watch, enjoying a box-seat view of behavior that researchers have usually had to study through telescopes.

In the late afternoon, just after we glide past a primeval tree fern, Perry halts next to a colorful vine. On stiff stalks are tiny closed flowers and rows of red, ladle-shaped nectaries

Some canopy animals, such as the military green parrot (left), the white bat, and the poisonous red frog (facing page), have evolved brilliant coloration. Even so, they readily blend into a background of flowering plants, which include over 1,000 species of orchid (lower left). By contrast, the venomous eyelash viper (lower right) is barely visible among the moss-covered trees.

Both photos: © Loren McIntyre

that attract a variety of hungry birds. A few years ago, watching at another site, Perry made a circumstantial case that this vine uses birds' feet to transport its pollen from one plant to another; the gummy pollen, he believes, sticks to the feet of nectar-sippers and is rubbed off later. If true, Perry says, this is a reproductive strategy scientists have rarely seen.

It is good luck that the same plant grows here, he says, so that observations can continue. Perry's critics in the scientific world charge that many of the observations he has made during more than a decade of research in Costa Rica have been reported as anecdotes in his 1986 book *Life Above the Jungle Floor,* and in popular magazines, rather than as carefully documented cases in journals. He has no intention of carrying out the tedious studies necessary to convince skeptical scientists of his birds'-feet theory. "I'm not going to spend five years proving something I think is obvious," he says.

Stirring Public Interest

"Don Perry," a friend of his says, "is the sort of person people talk about—whether they love him or hate him."

For about a dozen years now, Perry has been a promoter of canopy exploration, garnering no little publicity himself in the process. Other scientists say that he has not buckled down to painstaking research. Also factor in his penchant for the telegenic gesture—it is no coincidence that the new cable system, which has already been visited by a film crew, has a stunning backdrop—and it is no surprise that some colleagues see him more as showman than scientist.

Perry freely admits his lack of interest in producing meticulous articles for scientific journals. "I'm a naturalist," he says. Nor does he apologize for the publicity he wangles, asking: "Why shouldn't I pick a beautiful site that will make the jungle seem more accessible to laymen?" He figures he has done more than many academic specialists to stir public interest in rain-forest ecology and conservation.

A self-described Californian who says he "feels out of place" in upstate New York, where he now lives with his wife, Perry received a doctorate in biology in 1983 from the University of California at Los Angeles. His time has increasingly been divided, he says, between his popular writing and his quest for better tools that researchers can use to reach the jungle roof.

Perry remembers exactly when he became interested in treetops. In 1973, while a graduate student at California State University at Northridge, he went hang gliding with a friend, John Williams. In high winds, Williams had a mishap, and the glider ended up stuck atop some 30-foot (10-meter) trees. Climbing up to help disassemble it, Perry recalls, "I actually began enjoying myself. My perspective shifted, and I had a very distinct impression of being a monkey or an ape." (At times, Perry's rapture for the treetops borders on the mystical. He says, for instance, that when he first climbed tall trop-

ical trees in the mid-1970s, he felt "an amazing sense of déjà vu.")

Bored with lab work, Perry was then shopping for a thesis topic. A professor told him of the dearth of knowledge about the canopy of tropical forests. With his own money, augmented by some modest grants, he set out for Costa Rica, a country where many scientists pursue tropical studies because large forest areas are protected and the government is hospitable to research.

Adapting Technology

To reach the heights, Perry modified a mountain-climbing method that other researchers had already been experimenting with. Devices called Jumars, or ascenders, which slide freely up and down a rope when loose, but lock firmly when weight is applied, were the key. Hanging in a body harness attached to one ascender, feet in stirrups attached to a second one, a person can creep up a rope like an inchworm by moving the devices up one at a time while putting weight on the other.

The challenge was to get a strong rope over the right branch. First, you need to know the trees well enough to pick a strong one (perhaps half of jungle species are too weak). Then you need a way to get a line over and down from the target branch, which may be more than 100 feet (30 meters) above and covered with entangling vegetation. Perry's innovation was to use a crossbow to shoot an arrow carrying a nylon fishing line over the branch. That first line was used to pull up a bigger rope, and that one, provided it did not become caught in bark or branches, to pull up an even sturdier rope. Several researchers now use similar techniques to study arboreal ecology.

In search of greater mobility, Perry enlisted his friend Williams, an engineer, to help design a web of rope hung from three giant trees. An ingenious system of pulleys allowed Perry to swoop in every direction. While Perry himself used the system in 1979, it proved too difficult and dangerous for most researchers' tastes.

Next, Perry embarked on what he calls the automated web for canopy exploration. The current system, also engineered by Williams, uses three steel cables, strung between two strong trees along the side of a twisting ravine. On signals radioed with the joystick, hydraulic winches run by a 10-horsepower gasoline engine move the platform along the cables or up and down. Two people can ride with ease.

The tramway is located in a private forest reserve, Rara Avis, 40 miles (65 kilometers) north of San José, established by Amos Bien, an American biologist who is creating a center for nature-loving tourists and for research. The land borders a national park, and its stream waters are safe to drink, good evidence that the clearing of forests to make cattle pastures, which have replaced so much of Costa Rica's unprotected jungles, has been held at bay here.

Before flying their equipment to Costa

© Gary Braasch/Wheeler Pictures

Makeshift roads provide the only means to comfortably cross the mud that forms when forest land is cleared.

Rica last November, Perry and Williams had assembled the system in Topanga Canyon, California, to make sure it worked. But then, getting the equipment to the jungle site and getting the cables strung was an adventure in itself.

The rains were heavy, and even four-wheel-drive vehicles often stalled in the soupy channel that was the last 8 miles (13 kilometers) to the building site. Once the equipment was there, five people took a week in the rugged, overgrown terrain, knee-deep in mud, to hang the cables.

To raise the heavy cables, smaller lines were first pulled through the branches. Positioning the pulleys to achieve the right "hang" and smooth movement took days more. Finally, after two and a half soggy weeks of construction, Perry took his first invigorating ride.

The Reproductive Imperative

Much of the action in the canopy revolves around the sex lives of plants, the foundation of the ecosystem. For many species, this means the transfer of pollen, male sex cells from flowers on one plant, to flowers on another.

Just the mention of pollen nearly provokes a runny nose in this hay-fever victim. Strangely,

as I ride on Perry's platform amid opulent greenery, my sinuses are clear. This is an unintended benefit of the great diversity of plants in the rain forest. In the more repetitious ecosystems of the temperate zone, many plants can rely on the random action of the wind to carry their pollen. Releasing the powder to the breezes wastes prodigious amounts, including the particles that torment passing humans; but when many of the plant's relatives are about, some of the pollen will reliably reach its destination.

Not so in the rain forest, where a plant is apt to be surrounded by a multitude of other species. Instead, the delivery of pollen by specialized bees, beetles, bats, butterflies, moths, or birds is common. The plant must entice a creature not only to pick up some pollen, but also to deliver it to a member of its own species. For this, a bird that flies randomly from flower to flower won't do. Instead, astonishingly specific physical features and interdependencies between plants and animals have evolved.

The sexual strategies of orchids alone include some improbably exquisite arrangements. Some orchids offer sweet nectar as a bribe for go-between services. Others offer, instead of food, packets of perfume to "orchid bees." The cruising male bees store the perfumes in pockets on their hind legs and use them indirectly to find mates. A male cannot entice a female by himself, but with the fragrance he can attract other males; the buzzing mass of males draws in receptive females.

Still other orchids lure insects with pure deceit, mimicking nectar-bearing flowers without bothering to produce any of the fluid. Perhaps most outlandish are the orchids that mimic female insects, achieving pollination when the duped males attempt to copulate with them.

Researchers have also discovered that several different varieties of orchid can harness the same insect, avoiding wastage by attaching their pollen to different locations on its body. Because the flowers have unique, precise anatomical structures, each bit of genetic material picked up by a feeding bee has a good chance of being rubbed off in another flower of the same species. One scientist found 13 specific locations for pollen on the body of a single bee.

Tantalizing the Scientist

Knowledge of such rain-forest marvels leaves scientists feeling merely tantalized, which is why so many are keeping a close eye on Perry's efforts to gain access to the jungle roof. Recent work by a ground-based student of canopy ecology, Terry L. Erwin of the Smithsonian Institution in Washington, suggests how much more awaits discovery.

Erwin fogged tropical trees with biodegradable insecticides, catching everything that fell in a tray. His findings astounded biologists. From 19 specimens of a single type of tree in Panama, for example, he collected more than 1,200 different species of beetles. They included some that fed on the tree, some that fed on fungi, some that fed on fellow beetles, and some that were scavengers. One in seven, he estimated, lived on that tree species and no other.

Extrapolating from this and from similar studies he made in Peru and Brazil, Erwin estimated that the world's rain-forest canopies house anywhere from 10 million to 30 million species of insects.

While Erwin's extrapolation remains controversial, many scientists say it is plausible.

Ground-based personnel maintain radio contact with researchers aloft in the tramway.

Even if he is only half-right, the findings transform the understanding of the scope of the earth's life. Only about a million and a half species have ever been described, half of them insects. Scientists have described only about 222,000 species of flowering plants, and expect to find only tens of thousands more. Only about 43,000 vertebrate animals are known.

The insect discoveries have thrilled Edward Wilson, the Harvard biologist. Erwin sent him the ants collected from a single tree in Peru. Wilson found 43 species, including several new ones. "That's equal to the entire number of ant species in Canada or the British Isles," Wilson marveled. "How on earth can 43 species of ants coexist on the same tree?" he wonders. "Ants are so fierce and territorial."

At Home in the Treetops

As Perry knows, the true success of his canopy vehicles will be determined by how much scientists are actually able to use them for research. In part because of concerns over liability in case of an accident, and perhaps in part because of uneasy relations, none of the established centers for tropical research asked Perry to build the prototype in their territories.

That, he predicts, will change as soon as more researchers see what new worlds the system can reveal. "This is a very, very powerful tool for field biology," he says with confidence. "As well as a fun toy."

Perry's cheeky statements have cost him. Without the support of federal science agencies or major foundations, he had to piece together $30,000 to build the current cable system from unconventional sources: a Rolex Award for Enterprise, a fellowship from the Institute of Current World Affairs in New Hampshire, a small grant from the H. John Heinz 3d Fund, and money from private individuals.

For their next project, Perry and Williams envisage an expanded version, incorporating cables from a third tree in a way that would permit sideways sweeps as well, giving researchers ready access to all the life over 4 acres (1.6 hectares). Perry is already imagining still another step: a fully automated system of video cameras and sensors, broadcasting information via satellite to distant researchers.

All that will have to wait a bit, though, until Perry finishes his book on human evolution. The thesis? That, far more recently than assumed, our ancestors remained arboreal creatures, at home in the treetops.

A Dead Chief's REVENGE?

by Haraldur Sigurdsson

T hursday is market day in Nyos, a time when people of the region flock to the village to sell their produce and often to spend the night with friends. The valleys around Lake Nyos, which is about 2 miles (3 kilometers) from the village, are renowned for their fertile soil and abundant crops of beans, plantain, rice, corn, yams, cassava, and potatoes.

Suddenly, at about 9:00 in the evening on the market day of August 21, 1986, an explosive convulsion took place in Lake Nyos and propelled a huge fountain of carbon dioxide into the air. Denser than air, the gas cloud flowed into Nyos and other settlements in the surround-

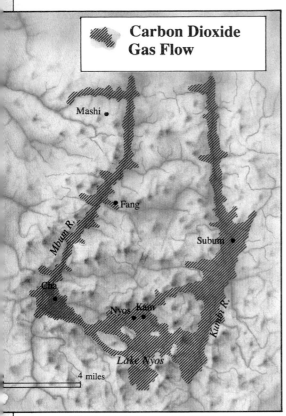

Carbon Dioxide Gas Flow

Mashi

Fang

Subum

Mbuan R.

Cha

Nyos Kam

Kumbi R.

Lake Nyos

4 miles

Left. © T. Orban/SYGMA, maps. Joe LeMonnier, with permission from Natural History © American Museum of Natural History 1987

ing valleys, up to 14 miles (22.5 kilometers) from the source, killing 1,746 people and more than 8,300 animals. Some survivors of the disaster attribute it to the wrath of their dead tribal chief, who on his deathbed in 1983 ordered that his best cattle be driven off the sheer cliffs above Lake Nyos as a sacrifice to the spirit of the lake, MamiWater. But the chief's family failed to honor his last wish, and many today believe that the 1986 calamity was an expression of the chief's posthumous displea sure. The disaster attracted worldwide attention, and scientists from many countries traveled to Cameroon to study the lake in order to determine a more realistic cause of the eruption.

Disaster Scenario

Lake Nyos is in the hilly grasslands of western Cameroon, within the so-called Cameroon volcanic line: a string of volcanoes that extends 900 miles (1,450 kilometers) from the South Atlantic Ocean to the northeast, along the border of

Carbon dioxide from Lake Nyos flowed through two river valleys (see maps above), killing scores of people. The lake was still discolored days after its eruption (left).

Cameroon and Nigeria. The lake occupies a volcanic crater about 4,000 feet (1,200 meters) in diameter and 680 feet (200 meters) deep, which was last active about 1,000 years ago.

Four days before the lethal event, local cattle herders noticed unusual bubbling on the lake's surface, which prompted 25 of them to move to a distant village. There were also unconfirmed reports claiming there was an emission of foaming water and vapor from the lake two to three weeks earlier. At about 4:00 P.M. on August 21, remaining herdsmen heard strange bubbling sounds and saw the slight emission of vapor from the lake. At about 8:00 P.M., villagers in Cha, 4 miles (6.5 kilometers) northwest of the lake, heard two loud noises, followed by three rumbles at about 9:00 P.M., when activity built up to the climactic disaster.

The 1986 lethal gas burst from Lake Nyos was, in fact, the second time in recorded history that a gas burst from a crater lake had occurred in an extinct volcano. The first such event took place on August 15, 1984, when a cloud of gas burst out of Lake Monoun, also in Cameroon, killing 37 people. At the request of the Office of Foreign Disaster Assistance in the U.S. Department of State, I traveled to Cameroon early in 1985 to investigate that event with Joseph Devine, then a graduate student in oceanography. We were joined by Cameroonian geologist Felix Tchoua in our study of the lake and its surroundings, and we collaborated later with William C. Evans and others from the U.S. Geological Survey (USGS) in the chemical analysis of water and gas samples.

The eastern part of Lake Monoun contains a submerged crater, which is about 1,200 feet (365 meters) wide and 300 feet (90 meters) deep. Our study of the lake showed that its deep waters contained very high levels of dissolved carbon dioxide (abbreviated hereafter as CO_2), held in solution by the high pressure at that depth. The gas had chemical characteristics indicating that it could have come only from the earth's mantle (the layer of the earth that underlies the 40-mile (65-kilometer)-thick crustal rocks). We were convinced that the gas was gradually seeping into the bottom of the crater lake from fractures and faults in the neck of the old volcano, and that the gas had accumulated in the lake over a long period of time. A fresh scar on the eastern rim of the crater showed where a landslide had rushed into the bottom of the submerged crater the night of the 1984 lethal event. We proposed that the landslide had upset the density stratification of the lake (the amount of CO_2 in different water layers) and stirred up the CO_2-rich bottom water. When the CO_2-rich water reached shallower water levels and therefore lower pressure, the CO_2 was suddenly released with explosive force. This started a chain reaction, as the accompanying frothing reduced the density of the water, further decreasing the solubility of the gas remaining in solution in the lake. The resultant gas burst produced a cloud of CO_2 that flowed away from the lake and over a nearby road. Before sunrise the next morning, 37 villagers on their way to work or market unknowingly walked into the invisible and odorless cloud of CO_2 and quickly died of asphyxiation.

We first suspected that the disaster was connected with an underwater volcanic explosion on the crater floor, but neither the chemistry of the water nor of the gas was consistent with any volcanic input other than the gradual seepage of CO_2 into the lake. The Lake Monoun event was thus a new natural phenomenon that defied classification, since it was neither a purely volcanic nor a lake phenomenon.

Killer Cloud

When we had completed our research on Lake Monoun, we had a fairly complete picture of this process and submitted our results for publication, but we had no inkling that this unique process would be repeated so soon and with such disastrous consequences in Lake Nyos. The fountain that rose out of Lake Nyos in 1986 consisted of a foam of water and expanding carbon dioxide. The plume of water rose 260 feet (80 meters) into the air and, as it cascaded down, washed soil and vegetation from the lake's shores. The gas separated from the water in the fountain and must have reached well over 300 feet (90 meters) above the lake, because dead cattle were found on the slopes at that height. Since CO_2 is about one and a half times denser than air, the gas flowed down the valley from the lake into the village of Nyos. On its way, it knocked down cornstalks, banana plants, and small fig trees. People in Nyos were apparently killed almost instantly while resting or sleeping in their mud-brick huts and thatched houses.

The earth's atmosphere normally contains

Animals also fell victim to the deadly gases from Lake Nyos. Herds of cattle were killed, apparently while standing around their owners' huts.

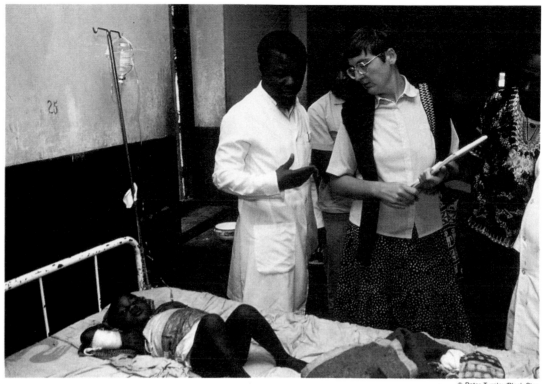

Doctors do not understand why many children only suffered temporary unconsciousness, while their parents died.

0.03 percent CO_2. Inhalation of air mixed with only 10 percent carbon dioxide leads to coma and death in about 10 to 15 minutes, and inhalation of air with 40 percent CO_2 causes nearly immediate death. Only 4 of 1,200 inhabitants survived in Nyos, so the gas flow must have been very concentrated.

Part of the gas flowed to the west from Nyos into the nearby village of Cha, causing more fatalities. The gas continued to flow north along the Mbum River valley, past the villages of Fungom, Bu, Kwoshing, and Fang, causing fatalities at Mashi, 14 miles (22.5 kilometers) from Lake Nyos. Gas also traveled northeast from Nyos, to Kam and the village of Subum, where about 300 died; it then continued along the course of the Kumbi River, up to 15 miles (24 kilometers) from the lake. About 5,000 people and all animal life in an area covering 24 square miles (62 square kilometers) were rendered unconscious by the gas cloud that spread along the two valleys.

Some 3,460 were hospitalized but regained consciousness a few hours later; others remained unconscious for up to three days. Many were disoriented, had difficulty walking, and experienced a drunken sensation at first. The lethal cloud lingered for a day after the gas burst, killing a number of children who wandered into gas pockets, which, being heavier than air, clung to low river valleys. A motorcyclist from Wum, 40 miles (64 kilometers) to the west, traveling to Cha, saw dead animals and a human corpse just outside the village. He then lost consciousness. Waking up about three hours later, he returned to Wum to report his strange experience to the world.

The Human Toll

The largest numbers of dead were males and elderly people. More than half the survivors were children younger than 14; many children regained consciousness the next day and found themselves in bed with their dead parents. Sixty percent of all survivors were females. (Doctors do not know why males were more vulnerable than females.) The distribution of survivors was completely random: outside the village of Nyos, survival was not always directly correlated with distance from the lake.

Above, below, and facing page: © Anthony Suau/Black Star

The residents of Cameroon were shocked by the magnitude of the tragedy. Many survivors attended Christian memorial services (left). Others of a more superstitious nature sacrificed animals to placate the angry spirits of the lakes (below).

Skin damage on about 5 percent of the victims and survivors was similarly random. Some had very large blisters on their extremities and torsos, whether the affected areas were exposed or clothed, whereas others in the same hut had no skin damage at all. A number of people suffered severe burns, most likely the result of losing consciousness while squatting near a cooking fire. At first, it was suggested that the skin blisters were due to acids or toxic chemicals in the gas cloud. This hypothesis was discarded, however, since clothing and vegetation were unaffected. The only other explanation that has come forward is that the blisters were a possible consequence of the coma or very deep sleep into which the victims and survivors alike fell. Similar skin damage has been observed in hospital patients with coma induced by drug overdose or CO_2 poisoning.

There were obvious similarities between the Lake Monoun and the Lake Nyos gas bursts, and I was quickly convinced that all the deadly gas in both events had come from within the bodies of the lakes. Several scientists felt, however, that the scale of the Lake Nyos calamity and such observations as skin damage, which they speculated could have been caused by sulfuric acid derived from volcanic gases, indicated that a volcanic explosion on the lake floor had occurred at Nyos and that the lethal CO_2 was of direct volcanic origin. This controversy was hotly debated by 200 scientists from 20 nations at the International Conference on the Lake Nyos Disaster, held in Yaoundé, the capital of Cameroon, in March 1987. The result was that virtually all the chemical, medical, and physical phenomena could be accounted for by the hypothesis of a gas burst from the deep waters of both lakes. While the unlikely process of a volcanic eruption on the lakes' floors could not be directly disproved, the conference of scientists applied the time-proven principle of Occam's razor: "Do not use a complex explanation when a simple one will suffice."

Studying Lake Samples

Thanks to an international research effort and the finely tuned instruments of science, we now understand almost all aspects of the Lake Monoun and Lake Nyos disasters. Some of this knowledge comes from very simple but critical observations of the lakes' levels, while other evidence is derived from sophisticated measurements of the chemistry of the gas and water of the lakes.

In our first studies of the lakes, we recovered samples of deep water in bottles that were closed by remote control, but when those samples were brought toward the surface and lower pressure, the gases that normally dissolved at higher pressures effervesced and formed expanding gas bubbles that invariably popped our sampling bottles open. On our expedition to Lake Nyos early in 1987, Evans, of the USGS, and I were able to collect samples of bottom waters in steel cylinders that we closed by remote control from our inflatable dinghy. When brought to the surface, the steel cylinders contained a sample of the lake under a pressure about 20 times that of normal atmospheric pressure, the water pressure at the lake bottom, and a representative amount of the gas dissolved in water at that depth. Those samples showed that the lake was about 25 percent saturated with CO_2 after the explosion.

No studies of Lake Nyos had been made before the lethal gas burst, so we had no idea what the lake's original gas content might have been, but we suspected that on the evening of August 21, 1986, it had to be close to saturation, and that CO_2 had foamed out like champagne from a just-opened bottle. Fortunately, the Cameroonian geologist Emmanuel Gamjehad had observed that the lake level dropped by

Scientists have been analyzing the waters of nearby lakes to determine the likelihood of a similar eruption.

Immediately after the disaster, the United States and other countries sent food and medical supplies.

about 3 feet (1 meter) during the gas burst. This was not due to water loss, as no water flood was noted during the event. We therefore deduced that the drop in the lake's level was due entirely to the loss of CO_2 from the water, and that the missing volume corresponded to a loss of about 2 million tons (1.8 million metric tons) of CO_2. Since that amount represents about 80 percent of all the CO_2 that the lake could theoretically hold in solution, we believe that the lake was saturated with carbon dioxide before the gas burst. These values indicate that the volume of released gas was about 35 billion cubic feet (98 million cubic meters) at atmospheric pressure, which is sufficient to form a 50-foot (15-meter)-thick pure CO_2 layer over the 24-square-mile (62-square-kilometer) area affected. There was obviously a good deal of mixing of air and CO_2 during the burst and subsequent gas flow, and consequently, the volume of the active lethal gas cloud was much larger.

Carbon dioxide is the main gas that escapes from the earth's mantle, which is also the source of magma, or molten rock, which erupts from volcanoes. Studies by the French scientists Michel Javoy and François Pineua have shown that CO_2 from the mantle is released primarily from the underwater chain of volcanoes making up the global system of midocean ridges, and that this carbon output amounts to about 240 million tons (217 million metric tons) per year. In that context, the Nyos burst constituted less than 1 percent of the annual output of carbon from the earth's mantle and had no effect on the proportion of CO_2 in the earth's atmosphere (currently about 380 parts per million of this gas.)

Possible Triggering Mechanisms

In the case of Lake Monoun, we feel confident that the gas escape was caused by a landslide that brought gas-rich bottom waters to shallower levels, but what could have triggered the gas burst at Lake Nyos? Any triggering mechanism would have had to cause the upward motion of CO_2-saturated deep water, leading to release of the gas. At present we do not have the evidence to help us choose the most likely of several possible answers. Rockfalls from the vertical 650-foot (200-meter)-high granite cliffs on the west side of Nyos are common, and a large rockfall could have upset the stratification of the lake waters. Another possibility is that if the deep waters were saturated with CO_2, a small additional input of the gas from springs on the lake bottom would have led to supersaturation, possibly causing the sudden outburst. Once bubbles had formed, a chain reaction would have been set in motion. When oxygen-poor deep waters rose to the surface, they would have contained some unoxidized iron in solution. As these waters became oxidized at the surface, the iron would have formed a ferric hydroxide precipitate that would have stained the surface layer of the lake reddish brown for days or weeks after the event. Such a phenomenon was, in fact, reported at Nyos. The iron particles have now settled out, and Lake Nyos is currently clear and calm, populated by hundreds of white cattle egrets that feed on the abundant tadpoles that appeared after the gas burst.

The Plight of the Cameroonians

Cameroonians distinguish two types of lakes in their land. "Good lakes" are a source of fish, easy to get to, and good for bathing and water supply. "Bad lakes" are difficult to reach, yield no fish or other products, change color at times, and are inhabited by bad spirits such as Mami-Water. The local people today put Lake Nyos in the second category. The 3,460 evacuees have not been permitted to return to their villages. In the meantime, their fields have become overgrown with weeds, and their huts need repair after the torrential storms of the rainy season from June to September. The evacuees have lived more than eight months in tent villages 30 to 60 miles (50 to 100 kilometers) away from their homes, unable to carry on their agriculture, restless and unhappy. Government officials and experts have decreed that the area

cannot be reoccupied until scientific studies have been carried out to estimate the risk. This is a predictable position for the authorities to take, since no one wants to assume the responsibility for returning the population to a potentially dangerous area. However, in view of the enormous population pressures in Africa today, any vacant, fertile land creates a vacuum that soon fills with industrious people willing to face any risks. The immediate problem of inadequate food is a disaster that families face every day.

Lake Nyos still contains 25 percent CO_2. If relatively simple measures were taken, however, the lake could be made safe and the region could be repopulated. These include the removal of a 130-foot (40-meter)-high natural dam at the north end of the lake that would reduce the lake's volume by about 35 percent and also reduce its gas-storage capacity. The removal of the dam would be a field experiment that would induce a small gas burst that could be monitored and studied by scientists and thus provide a better understanding of such bursts. A large-diameter pipe should then be installed from the bottom of the lake to its surface, to continuously drain the gases from deep water. The pipe would contain the sole outflow from the lake and would drain gas-rich bottom water when fresh surface and rainwater flow into the lake in the rainy season. This system would ensure that high gas levels could never again build up in the deep waters of Lake Nyos. The same measures applied in Lake Monoun would similarly make that lake safe.

Despite the danger of an eruption similar to that of Lake Nyos, local residents continue to live near and enjoy the small lakes throughout western Cameroon.

© Bruce Mathews

Chemicals used to keep golf courses green may pose a danger to golfers and wildlife alike.

HAZARDS of the GAME

by Jolee Edmondson

Feast your weary, smog-sore eyes on them: flawless, ultragreen havens surrounded by suburbs and country and even wilderness. So pristine, so halcyon, so pastoral, so in tune with nature, such a tonic to look at. Who would ever imagine that golf courses could be hazardous to the environment?

In the past 20 years, since the dawn of ecological awareness, a case has been building against those seemingly innocuous places where polite people in pastel outfits chase little white balls. Some environmentalists go so far as to label golf courses dangerous toxic-waste sites,

while others conservatively suggest that they are a potential problem. Either way, it is clear that fairways are no longer just playgrounds but hot issues as well. Golf courses are encountering the same hard scrutiny as freeways and factory yards.

"Today, when a developer builds a golf course, he has to go through at least two years of bureaucratic delays—one environmental hearing after another—before he gets approval to start," says Roger Rulewich, senior associate at Robert Trent Jones Inc. of Montclair, New Jersey, arguably the world's most prominent golf course architectural firm. "Sometimes it gets to the point where they throw up their hands and give up on the idea. And it's going to get even tougher."

Yesterday's Greenbelts

What a breeze it was a couple of decades ago to carpet the land with fairways. No environmental impact statements to file. No public inquests. It was merely a matter of finding the right spot and bulldozing. Everybody perceived golf courses as pleasant recreational facilities or even greenbelts. Or they didn't think about them at all. Veteran golf course architect Lawrence Packard recalls that in 1970, when he designed the Island Course in Innisbrook—a resort in south Florida—the first six and a half holes were made from a marsh his crew filled in with sand. An abominable act by modern precepts. "I know that we wouldn't be allowed to do that today," concedes Packard. "But back then there were no laws."

There are more than 12,000 golf courses in the United States. An average of 110 courses are built annually, each consuming approximately 150 acres (60 hectares). This steady gobbling up of land is bound to have an effect on the environment, the most obvious being the further depletion of rapidly shrinking wildlife habitats. As with any kind of development in rural or semirural regions, the construction of a golf course means a major upheaval for native creatures. But not total destruction of habitat. Fairways are not made of chrome and glass but of grass, which can cause confusion among wildlife species. Here are these enticing, meadowlike expanses fringed by myriad types of vegetation. Instead of fleeing the area, some animals are drawn back to what appears to be lush grazing grounds, only to be met with flying balls, electric carts, and a relentless parade of human beings.

Destructive Wildlife

Most golfers relish the sight of wildlife—to a point. When huge gaggles of geese defecate on their fairways and root up their turf, and deer gouge their greens, enchantment turns to exasperation. At a number of golf courses, the conflict between man and beast has become intense. In California the superintendents at two Palo Alto courses have permits from the state Department of Fish and Game allowing them to shoot at flocks of coots that swarm in like air squadrons every winter. In a highly publicized 1983 incident, a member of Congressional Country Club in Bethesda, Maryland, became so angry with a Canada goose that was interfering with his game that he killed the bird with a pitching wedge—a deed that aroused both furor and amusement in golfing circles. There is also hearsay to the effect that some golf course managers set traps and lay poison.

The damage done by wildlife to golf courses can be extensive. Witness Kananaskis Golf Club near Banff, Alberta, Canada. It lies in the middle of an elk migration route. After each spring thaw, the superintendent invariably finds the fairways and greens covered with immense brown splotches resulting from the seepage of urine through the snow. An attempt at a solution to the problem involved encompassing the course with an 8-foot (2.5-meter) fence. But with the help of snowdrifts, the elk effortlessly cross onto the fairways.

The majority of golf course superintendents try every conceivable humane means to keep their domains relatively free of "destructive" wildlife. Several courses in the Northeast filled their ponds with plastic swans on the premise that the ever-troublesome Canada goose is afraid of swans. It worked for a while—until the geese became accustomed to the sight of the bogus birds and started swimming alongside them. A golf course in Poughkeepsie, New York, has laid thin stainless steel wires across its water hazards to prevent the lighting of geese. In Bellingham, Washington, a superintendent takes his dog out every morning to run the Canada geese off the course—an effective deterrent so far. Some greenskeepers even advocate the use of explosive devices as a scare tactic.

Chemical Contamination

It is in the sphere of pesticides and fertilizers that golf courses come under the heaviest fire from environmentalists. Fairways and greens are doused regularly with volumes of chemical turf-care products. Hence the burning question: how polluting is a golf course to the community or woodlands in which it nestles? One side claims that there is no potential for runoff of contaminated water from golf courses, while the other side insists that runoff is a frequent occurrence. And the battle goes on. Two things are certain: (1) There is little documentation to support either argument. (2) Golf course developers and superintendents are facing mounting restrictions in terms of water management.

Golf-course construction in Arizona. The heavy irrigation needed to create the lush fairways demanded by golfers has the adverse effect of making the land inhospitable to native desert species.

In the lawless past, the builders of golf courses paid no heed to erosion, letting soil and water flow where they might while their layouts were under construction. Nowadays, stringent preventive measures are mandatory. Fences, hay bales, and gravel dams are common on evolving fairways. At a newly opened country club in Orlando, Florida, the developer was forced by local environmental agencies to contain every drop of water on his course by building retention basins throughout the property, a tedious and costly procedure.

It is the contention of experts in the golf field that, once a course is completed, the chances of chemicals being leached through the soil are nil.

"Any kind of movement is highly unlikely," asserts Roger Rulewich, "because the grasses and roots are so dense that they imprison the compounds, not to mention the fact that many of these pesticides, herbicides, and so forth are degradable."

Nonsense, says Sheila Daar, executive director of Bio Integral Resource Center, an organization in Berkeley, California, that has spent 17 years developing less-toxic pest-control pro-grams. "There is always going to be some kind of runoff," she says. "In this state alone there are data showing that there has been massive groundwater pollution as a result of pesticide application to soil—and that includes lawns, farms, and golf courses. When it rains, where else is the water going to go? A percentage of it will soak into the soil, but soil only absorbs so much per hour. So the rest of it is going to remain on top of the grass, and it's going to go somewhere—into the local creek or the storm sewer, which then feeds into the lake or another body of water, all of this depending on how the golf course is graded."

Sheila Daar continued: "Also, while some percentage of the pesticides is absorbed in the soil and biodegraded by microorganisms, a large percentage of those pesticides moves down into the lower depths of the soil into the water table, and then there's no way to get rid of it. A major crisis in our country now is the pollution of our groundwater. The technology to detect groundwater contamination is still very primitive, so the details are still far from fully known. But 23 pesticides have been identified in California's groundwater."

Cape Cod Study

The federal government wants to get specific regarding fairways and groundwater. To determine the impact of golf courses, and only golf courses, on the aquifer, the Environmental Protection Agency (EPA) has funded a two-year study on Cape Cod—an ideal test site because of its self-contained environment. Monitoring wells have been installed around all the golf clubs in the area.

Meanwhile, Thomas Watschke, professor of turf grass science at Pennsylvania State University, is in the midst of a definitive probe financed by a joint grant of $290,000 from Penn State and the U.S. Geological Survey (USGS). His objective is to find out precisely how much, if any, runoff is produced by golf courses, lawns, and sod farms. Although the verdict hasn't been reached yet, early evidence is pointing toward acquittal.

"My judgment at this stage," says Watschke, "is that there is in essence no problem, because the grass per unit area of a very well managed [obviously a key phrase] turf is so dense that the overland velocity of water that would be running off of it would be reduced to the point where nothing runs off, or most of what could be contaminated water goes into the grass thatch/soil complex and just doesn't go anywhere. In more sandy soils, of course, the potential for runoff is greater. In our experiments, we're really going the distance. We've been simulating storms that are equivalent to 6 inches [15 centimeters] of rainfall per hour. So far, there are no signs of runoff."

Not to be ignored is the threat posed by surface contamination. There are countless bird mortalities on golf courses every year, many of which are traced directly to turf that has been saturated with chemicals. A dramatic case in point: on the afternoon of May 7, 1984, a prevalently used pesticide named Diazinon was applied to three fairways at Seawane Country Club in Hewlett Harbor, New York. A flock of brant came to feed on one of the treated fairways. By nine in the morning, several hundred of the fowl were reported dead on the course and in the adjacent harbor. Over the next three days, the fatality count climbed to an estimated 700. A large number of the dead birds were submitted (along with sod samples) to the pathology unit of the New York State Department of Environmental Conservation. Diagnosis: death caused by ingestion of poison, i.e., Diazinon.

To zero in on insecticides as they pertain to wildlife, Ward Stone, chief pathologist of the New York State Department of Environmental Conservation, has launched an in-depth investi-

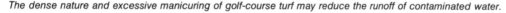

The dense nature and excessive manicuring of golf-course turf may reduce the runoff of contaminated water.

© Bruce Mathews

Both photos: © Terrence Moore

Heavy watering of desert fairways (left) has rotted dozens of saguaro cacti (right) adapted to arid environments.

gation funded by Return a Gift to Wildlife, the state's tax-checkoff program. Golf courses may provide a refuge for fowl and mammals, as many enthusiasts have suggested, but how safe is that refuge?

Hazardous-Waste Sites?

"I'm very concerned about golf courses," says Stone. "I think some of them should be studied as if they were hazardous-waste sites. What's more important—nice green grass or the welfare of Canada geese, mallards, brant, and wigeon? We're starting to find that little birds such as robins are dying on golf courses as well, not just the big waterfowl."

Environmentalists attribute toxic golf courses to poor maintenance practices. "The label is the law," says Karen Murphy, regional coordinator of the Western Washington Toxics Coalition. "The only rule greenskeepers have to abide by is the instructions on the label of these pesticides. That's pretty insubstantial information. Golf courses use not one but many fungicides and pesticides, and they're all mixed together. Nobody really knows what happens when you mix these chemicals. They're playing with dynamite, as far as I'm concerned. Granted, golf course superintendents have to be licensed pesticide applicators, but the amount of

work they have to go through to obtain their license varies from state to state. And there's always the possibility of a licensed greenskeeper delegating the application of pesticides to an unlicensed person."

Norma Grier, director of the Northwest Coalition for Alternatives to Pesticides in Eugene, Oregon, charges that in many cases of avian mortality on golf courses, "pesticides have not been watered-in properly."

Concerned Superintendents, Spoiled Golfers

Regardless of all the accusations and negative implications, it would be a gross distortion to portray golf course superintendents as the Bad Guys, scoundrels who run around fiendishly poisoning fairways. Far from it. Most of these men, particularly the 7,000 who are members of the Golf Course Superintendents Association of America (GCSAA), are conscientious, very human beings intent on learning more about the interchange between golf courses and the environment.

"We've gotten a lot of disturbing publicity," says Don Hearn, president of GCSAA. "I think there are a lot of misconceptions about us. None of us are antienvironmentalists. We all live on Planet Earth, too, so we want to do what's right. Besides, we have to walk on that turf, therefore we certainly don't want to use anything that would harm our own health. I think we're moving away from the blanket-type applications that may have been carried out in the past. I think we're all becoming more aware of the potential problems with many of the products we use. Education is the answer. We hold regular conferences and seminars and invite speakers who are experts on the toxicity of pesticides. We welcome information. And we have no intention of fighting for the continued use of products that do damage to the environment."

Perhaps the real culprit in all this is the American golfer. He is spoiled rotten. He wants his fairways verdant and velvety, his greens looking like emerald oases. The slightest blemish, and he gets ornery. Golf courses in this country are traditionally overmanicured. Thus, the ritual use of pesticides, fertilizers, fungicides, herbicides, and other chemicals.

Bent Grass

"A golf course has to be perfect—it's been set up as a utopistic lawn," says Sandra Marquardt of the Environment Policy Institute. Marquardt, who previously was information coordinator for the National Coalition Against the Misuse of Pesticides, says, "It is a completely controlled, artificial environment. Most of the greens are composed entirely of bent, a very fine-bladed grass that can be cut very short. So these greens are a monoculture; and whenever you have a monoculture, you have problems. Bent is a weak grass with short roots that can't stand up to weeds, therefore it has to be sprayed and fussed over constantly. Also, it's a grass that's native to colder climes but grown on greens everywhere—one more reason why so many chemical agents have to be used on it."

Golf courses are not, however, forever and hopelessly lost in a noxious fog. Alternatives to chemical turf-care products are beginning to trickle into the marketplace. One such product, marketed under the name Dipel, is a naturally occurring bacterium that attacks only caterpillars; some other agents wipe out everything, including beneficial insects. Also, kelp fertilizers are being viewed as a viable option to chemical fertilizers.

Course developer Michael Hurdzan sees a bright, relatively chemical-free future for golf courses. "Genetic engineering is the big trend with turf grass," he says. "Scientists are starting tissue cultures and bombarding them with radiation. They're developing grasses that have more natural resistance. When you have grasses that are well adapted, less water, less fertilizer, and fewer pesticides are required."

As for the predominance of bent grass on greens, the golf industry is digging in its collective feet. "It isn't because superintendents want to grow nothing but bent grass," explains Don Hearn, "but because of the pressure that's applied to us by club members. They have got to have their courses perfect. Bent grasses are the finest grasses there are. They're made to be used at extremely low heights of cut. If we turned putting greens into bluegrasses, fescues, and buffalo grasses, I don't know what we'd call them—they wouldn't be putting greens anymore, at least not by U.S. standards."

The Scottish Example

American golfers would do the environment a favor by imitating the Scots, who originated the sport. Their links were designed by Mother Nature. They just sort of happened five centuries ago. The grasses were fertilized by the

Bent, a fine-bladed grass used for greens throughout the U.S., requires chemicals to grow in warm climates.

droppings of indigenous birds and were kept cut by rabbits. Bunkers were formed by sheep and other animals that burrowed into the turf as protection against the elements. Years and years of receding oceanic tides rendered the sandy soil on which they're laid out. The enduring result: shaggy, wide-open playing fields with random clumps of gorse and craterlike "pot bunkers." The greens consist mainly of native fescues. Maintenance on these links is minimal. Indeed, golf in Scotland is a different game from that which flourishes in this country. And the environment is the benefactor.

"The weather in Britain, which basically has only one climate, is conducive to fescues," says Hearn. "Fescues do so well over there that they can be mowed short. Here there are too many variables and contrasting conditions to have strictly links courses. But the real obstacle lies in the fact that the golfers' demands in Britain aren't nearly what they are in the United States. Unfortunately, I don't foresee American golfers going in the direction of genuine links. To the contrary, they're becoming more spoiled."

Exchanging Ecosystems

The construction of a golf course, wherever it may be, means certain death for the existing ecosystem. It is this basic reality that deeply concerns environmentalists. With the demise of more and more ecosystems, extinction of various and sundry creatures is inevitable. The golf industry's attitude regarding this subject tends to be cavalier. A white paper on "Golf Courses and the Environment" issued by the American Society of Golf Course Architects makes reference to the "arbitrary or frivolous" protection of "insignificant" plants and animals such as the furbish lousewort and Stephens kangaroo rat. The report concludes that there is "no evidence showing that these species are essential for the maintenance or improvement of the quality of life."

In essence, golf course developers are saying, What's the big deal? One ecosystem goes out and a new and different one comes in. So?

"There's no such thing as an insignificant species," responds Dr. Ron Kendall, director of the Institute of Toxicology at the Huxley College of Environmental Studies in Bellingham, Washington. "We just don't know where the threshold is. We don't know at what point we kill off one of these species and the whole system caves in. We don't really know what is significant and what isn't."

A classic example of ecosystems replacing ecosystems is seen in the Palm Springs area of California. Sixty-five golf courses are spread out over this resort mecca, causing the disappearance of legions of lizards, snakes, and desert rodents. Emerging as substitute inhabitants—a wide variety of fowl.

"Any golf course in the desert has a tremendous impact on the ecology because it turns that part of the desert into a tropical environment, eliminating typical desert growth and wildlife," says Ted Robinson, seasoned architect of golf courses in the Southwest. "On the other hand, we're providing homes for certain birds that never visited this region before. They've been coming in by the droves—I don't know where from. All I know is that we've got lakes on golf courses here that are now the permanent homes of egrets, which we never saw in the desert before. So while we're detrimental for one form of life, we're creating a habitat for others."

Land development in Palm Springs and proximity has been so overwhelming that local environmental groups have retrenched.

"I guess they feel the tide is too strong," muses Robinson.

Clearly, the most pressing problem confronting golf courses in arid regions is water. Millions of gallons are required daily in Palm Springs to keep the fairways there looking like strips of green felt. The toll on the public water supply is enormous. Protests have been fierce. But there looms a solution. Robinson predicts that nearly all desert golf courses will be irrigated by municipal sewage effluent by the year 2007. Ecologically, this seems sound, since it aids in detaining waste that might otherwise flow into streams and rivers. Some golf course superintendents, however, aren't too happy about this inevitability, citing, among other things, the high cost of installing effluent irrigation systems and the possibility that the salt content of treated sewage water may adversely affect the turf. Regardless, the shift is in full gear throughout the country, not just in desert areas. Already, many Florida golf courses are irrigated with effluent.

Environmental Pluses

Needless to say, some environmental groups are contemptuous of golf courses. But they might be surprised to learn that there are a few ways in

In Australia, golf courses are built to accommodate native wildlife without detracting from the game (above). Rather than ecology, however, golfers perhaps worry more about the incidental hazards of their sport—such as finding a diamondback in the rough (right).

Both photos: © Brian Morgan/Golf Photography

which fairways actually benefit the environment. For one thing, they provide a firebreak in densely wooded regions. Also, golf courses have been responsible for keeping hundreds of thousands of acres in open land.

Because of increasingly rigid regulations imposed on developers, golf courses sometimes end up actually improving the environment. It took the builder of Spanish Bay Golf Club in Monterey, California, almost eight years to hurdle environmental roadblocks and start construction. What sealed his ultimate triumph was his agreement to a trade-off: he would be allowed to build his golf course only if he was willing to reconstruct some 50 acres (20 hectares) of dunes.

"Back in the '20s and '30s," says Don Knott of Robert Trent Jones II of Palo Alto, California (the firm that designed Spanish Bay), "this site consisted of huge silicon sand dunes. The silicon was mined during the '40s, and eventually nothing was left but bare bedrock. The idea was to integrate the dunes with the golf holes. Over 500,000 cubic yards [380,000 cubic meters] of sand was brought in and shaped to look like the dunes of yesteryear. We seeded

them with native grasses and plants. We also restored a riparian area that had been destroyed by mining operations, and planted it with willows and riparian vegetation."

Golf courses and the environment. So close, yet so separate. Are they destined to become intimate friends, or doomed to eternal rivalry? The answer hangs in the balance, for all the facts are not in. As Roger Rulewich says, "We won't know the whole story until another decade from now."

A dense forest lies hidden behind the sand dunes of New York's Fire Island. Abundant wildlife, including Virginia white-tailed deer (left), thrives among the salt-resistant plants. Elevated walkways (above) protect the delicate ecosystem from tourist damage.

ℱorest in the 𝔇unes

by Michael J. Mooney

From the lookout some 25 feet (7.6 meters) above the hot, exposed swale, the view is eastward along low-lying Fire Island, New York. To the left are the boat-dappled waters of Great South Bay, where multicolored sails of beached boats rise above the trees near a marina. To the right, between rises in the primary dunes, great Atlantic rollers sweep in slowly to crash heavily on the broad, fine-grained sand. From water to water in a glance of the eye: that is how narrow Fire Island is at the National Seashore.

A Closer Look

Taking an imaginary cross section through Fire Island from ocean to bay, one passes from the ocean beach to the primary dune paralleling the beach. Beyond the primary dune is the intermediary swale zone, an open, desertlike, exposed valley that provides convenient movement along the length of the island. On the far side of the swale, the secondary dune system rises up to 40 feet (12.2 meters) above sea level.

From the ridge of the secondary dunes over to the bay and along the axis of the island for

Left: © Pat Toops; above: Fire Island National Seashore

Just an Illusion

One of the striking visual aspects of the Sunken Forest is that it is not really sunken. It just looks that way. Actually, it is tucked protectively into the leeward side of the secondary dune system with its upper story, or canopy, effectively pruned or shaved by the salt wind at about the height of the secondary dunes. As a result, the topmost branches grow almost horizontally away from the sea, and so protect the vulnerable ecosystem beneath.

Even the salt-resistant red cedar and related evergreens that extend above the pruned canopy have been so affected. Hardy shrubs and salt-resistant trees on the swale side of the secondary dunes also exhibit this pronounced lean.

Planing and leaning result from the combined effects of the sea wind and osmosis. When wind-deposited salt particles on exposed tree and plant life absorb natural moisture, the resulting desiccation kills the exposed branches and leaves. Meanwhile, the prevailing sea wind exerts an almost continuous pressure on the tree's physical structure, inducing it to lean as it grows away from the sea wind.

Here and there is a break in the canopy where a tree succumbed to age or elements and gave lower vegetation a chance to flourish.

The salt spray rose thrives in the ocean air of Fire Island, where its roots add stability to the sand dunes.

© Paul Stoutenburgh

more than a mile (1.6 kilometers) is a carpet of dense green foliage, which looks as if it were trimmed with a giant pair of pruning shears. At first glance, this carpet appears to be only hedge-high. The raised boardwalk curves down, however, to a shadowy portal leading into the strange and unexpected world of the Sunken Forest.

Leaving the bright, breezy world of dune, swale, and sea, one enters a dim, cool, sun-dappled silence, punctuated by birdsong and the hint of furtive animal life. Here the booming surf is barely an intermittent whisper, though it is just a couple of hundred yards away. A light-plane drones overhead, and sometimes a motor-boat hums in the distance.

Nearly everywhere, fully grown trees stand festooned with catbrier vines. Many of these trees are contorted, having grown in response to the changing availability of light. There is little undergrowth, since so little light filters through the dense canopy. Instead there is mostly the detritus of past growing seasons: leaves, twigs, berries, vines, and the occasional dead tree. Seen from below, the overhead canopy that had appeared to be only hedge-high is actually 30 feet (9.1 meters) from the ground!

Hidden Source

One of the unusual features of the Sunken Forest is that it has its own supply of fresh groundwater. Though entirely surrounded by saltwater, the Sunken Forest has a 200- to 230-foot (60- to 70-meter) lens of fresh water beneath it, which is fed and sustained solely by precipitation filtering down through the porous topsoil. There are even low-lying places in the forest where fresh water wells to the surface to form bogs.

The Sunken Forest has been called a "primeval maritime forest," a term that defines an unusual ecosystem of trees, vines, and associated undergrowth that evolved through the process of natural succession, took root, and reached climax. It now thrives in a largely sheltered, sand-based maritime environment on this offshore barrier island 3 miles (4.8 kilometers) out into the Atlantic!

Wildlife here is surprisingly abundant, and, unexpectedly, land-based species predominate. About 11 species of mammals are native to the area, and include the red fox, cottontail rabbit, long-tailed weasel, and even a herd of Virginia white-tailed deer. More than 20 species of bird life breed here, and include the catbird, yellow-bellied sapsucker, black-capped chickadee, eastern wood pewee, red-winged blackbird, and the brown thrasher, along with the common species of sparrows, jays, and thrushes. During the massive spring and fall migrations, dozens of other species are drawn to the profusion of berry shrubs and trees.

Grandfathers of the Forest

Trees are far and away the ecological "first citizens" of the Sunken Forest. Here are many aged specimens of American holly with their alternately smooth and warty trunks, scarred where old limbs have fallen away. Some specimens date to the early 19th century. In fact, this domain has been called a true holly forest in its own right. Nowhere else can this tree be found so extensively this far north, thanks to the effects of the offshore Gulf Stream.

Then there is the one-of-a-kind sassafras, that distinctively eastern North American tree where simple, mitten-shaped, and triple-lobed leaves share the same twig. Lesser stands of red cedar, sour gum, black oak, and red maple complete the arboreal scene.

The island and its Sunken Forest took a long time to form. During Pleistocene times, some 10,000 years ago, the North American eastern seaboard extended well south of today's Fire Island. As the glacial ice cap retreated, the sea rose and inundated the land to the extent where only a long ridge of dry land remained—the future Long Island.

Over the centuries, longshore currents sweeping westward from Montauk Point carried sand along the south shore and deposited it as an elongated sandspit just offshore. In time this spit grew to become the forerunner of today's Fire Island. Wind and wave have since expanded and sculpted it into dunes, swales, and beaches that are still evolving.

Just 200 to 300 years ago, what is now the Sunken Forest was an expanse of arid, wind-blown sand. But soon the seeds of pioneering dune plants blew in, settled, and took root in this hostile, salt-dominated environment. American beach grass, followed by other dune plants, began to stabilize the still-growing dunes by trapping blown sand and holding it in place. The plants added nutrients to the sand and provided the basis for larger, more diversified plant life, such as bearberry, bayberry, and beach plum.

As the secondary dune grew in size and stability, woody plants in the form of shrubs, vines, and small trees gradually took hold and set the stage for the black cherry, oak, and high-bush blueberry community. These species have been succeeded by today's fully grown forest community.

Fire Island is still growing westward at a steady rate. Predictably, this growth has engendered an illusion of permanence, where the unknowing visitor imagines it was always this way and could not be destroyed. But the Fire Island barrier beach is an exceedingly fragile ecosystem, and cautionary signs everywhere admonish visitors to: "KEEP OFF THE DUNES."

Resident national park rangers warn against blowouts, where seemingly local, small-scale dune damage accelerates quickly through wind erosion and can cause major environmental damage. For example, the loss of one clump of beach grass can lead to the progressive demise of an entire dune. When enough dunes go, so goes Fire Island itself.

The Sunken Forest nearly did not survive the mid-1960s as a natural entity. Prior to 1964, commercial exploitation threatened, but residents of nearby Point o' Woods fought the effort and bought up the land to preserve it in its natural state. Soon it was absorbed into the newly formed Fire Island National Seashore as a natural treasure for future generations.

Out of the wind: on the protected northern side of the island, the forest grows even more luxuriantly (above). Many birds nest on Fire Island, including the endangered least tern (left); many more species use the island as a stopover during migrations.

Both photos: © Paul Stoutenburgh

Continuance or Catastrophe

How long the Sunken Forest will last depends on two factors: humans and nature. As long as the National Park Service controls and protects the environment, no ill should come from humans unless a stray match ignites the underbrush during an unusual dry spell.

Nature, on the other hand, is less controllable. A single superstorm, such as a hurricane of unusual proportions, could wreak irrevocable damage if the storm surge struck a vulnerable point along the beach at a time of abnormally high tide. This unwelcome combination could tear asunder the primary and secondary dunes and lay open the maritime forest to erosive forces that might destroy much of it.

Taking a longer view, nature will have the last word by phasing out not only the Sunken Forest, but Fire Island itself. The same winds and waves that created the island are gradually nudging it closer to "mainland" Long Island; that is, Fire Island is growing along its lee shore and ebbing along its windward ocean shore.

Sometime in the geological future, this barrier island ecosystem may just fade away and become the new south shore of Long Island. Then, perhaps, the barrier island cycle will begin again.

HEALTH
AND
DISEASE

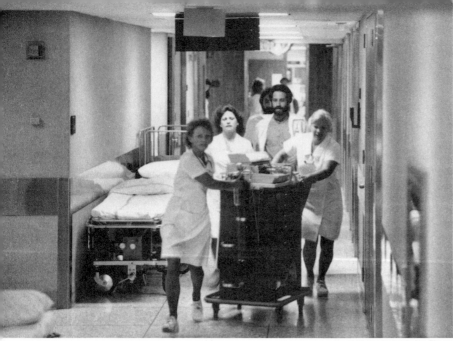

A special trauma team reacts to a medical emergency. Such highly trained nurses are becoming increasingly scarce: the long hours, high pressure, and relatively low pay have led many potential nurses to choose more financially rewarding professions. Hospitals, medical schools, and colleges are studying ways of encouraging students to choose nursing as a career.

© Charles Harbutt/Archive Pictures

REVIEW OF THE YEAR

HEALTH AND DISEASE

Important advances were made in 1987 in understanding the genetic basis of many diseases and in using advanced technologies to treat illness. But while scientific research has given physicians new tools, it has also created complex ethical, legal, and economic dilemmas.

Controversy surrounded many of the year's major medical stories, as people tried to deal with difficult questions raised by such issues as AIDS, surrogate motherhood, and death. As modern machines have enabled physicians to maintain heart and lung activity in patients who have lost all brain function, there have been increasing calls for expanded definitions of death to include total and irreversible cessation of brain function. Many states adopted such standards and also expanded the right of patients to refuse life-sustaining medical treatment.

Governments were less successful in trying to come to grips with catastrophic medical costs. Serious shortages of registered nurses plagued medical facilities—a problem that may worsen during the coming years. The cost of medical malpractice insurance continued to escalate wildly. In Florida some physicians were faced with paying as much as $160,000 a year for $250,000 worth of coverage. Some canceled their policies; others protested by curtailing services.

AIDS

The specter of AIDS (acquired immune deficiency syndrome) continued to garner numerous headlines as the number of known AIDS cases increased throughout the world, and cures and preventative vaccines remained elusive. In the United States, more than 48,000 cases and 27,000 deaths were recorded by the end of 1987. The nation's Centers for Disease Control estimated that 1.5 million Americans were infected with the virus, and it projected 270,000 cases of disease and 179,000 deaths by the end of 1991. This increase will be matched by an enormous increase in the cost of caring for the AIDS patients. Many experts anticipate that it will cost up to $16 billion to provide medical care for AIDS victims in the United States in 1991, as compared with the $1.1 billion spent in 1986.

While the great majority of people were sympathetic to the plight of AIDS victims, fear of contracting the disease sometimes led to prejudicial behavior toward AIDS victims, including boycotts of schools that admitted AIDS-infected children, and cases in which physicians and other health care workers refused to treat AIDS patients. An earlier-held belief that the virus can be transmitted only through infected blood, semen, and other body fluids was disproven with the disclosure that a laboratory worker became infected simply by working with the virus.

Throughout the world, numerous programs designed to combat the AIDS epidemic were proposed or instituted during 1987. Foremost were comprehensive education programs and mandated blood screening of certain groups, such as foreigners, military personnel, prison inmates, prostitutes, and applicants for marriage licenses.

In March 1987, azidothymidine (AZT) became the first drug approved by the U.S. Food and Drug Administration (FDA) for the treatment of AIDS. AZT does not cure AIDS. Rather, it inhibits reproduction of the AIDS virus, thereby helping to prolong the lives of some patients. However, AZT is extremely toxic, causing serious side effects that preclude its use by many AIDS victims.

Later in the year, the FDA approved two experimental AIDS vaccines for human testing. Other vaccines are being tested in Africa by scientists from France and Zaïre. And still others are being tested in chimpanzees as a prelude to possible human studies. Experts warned, however, that an effective vaccine for widespread use probably would not be available until "well into the 1990s."

GENETIC BASIS OF DISEASE

The list of diseases that have a genetic basis grew significantly during 1987. Two different aberrant genes—one on the X chromosome, the other on chromosome 11—were linked to manic-depressive illness in families that have a history of suffering from the disorder. The gene that causes neurofibromatosis, the disfiguring condition commonly known as Elephant Man's disease, was located on chromosome 17 by two research teams. Another group of scientists found the gene that causes a rare form of neurofibromatosis, on chromosome 22.

Evidence was found that at least some types of Alzheimer's disease, the degenerative brain disorder, are inherited. One research team found a "marker" on chromosome 21 linked to the illness. (Markers are genes that lie close to the gene or genes that actually cause a disease and are inherited along with them.) Working independently, four groups of researchers isolated—also on chromosome 21—the gene responsible for manufacturing amyloid. This protein is the principle component of clumps of dead and dying nerve fibers, called plaques, that form in the brains of Alzheimer victims.

Genes involved in protecting against the development of certain cancers also were found. In recent years, scientists have discovered more than three dozen oncogenes—genes that transform a normal cell into a rapidly dividing cancer cell. Now another type of gene is being found. Called anti-oncogenes, they appear to suppress cell division, ensuring that such growth occurs at the proper pace. When the anti-oncogenes are missing or inactivated, cell growth is unregulated and cancers form.

A defect in an anti-oncogene on chromosome 5 was linked to the development of up to 40 percent of all colon cancers. A defective anti-oncogene on chromosome 3 was found to contribute to the development of at least 20 percent of all lung cancers. And in December 1987, scientists reported evidence of still another defective anti-oncogene that appears in all major types of lung cancer.

While these genetic discoveries have no immediate application, they may eventually lead to early diagnosis, improved treatments, and perhaps even prevention of the diseases.

SURGICAL TECHNIQUES

In a dramatic 22-hour operation, a 70-member medical team at Johns Hopkins Hospital in Baltimore, Maryland, separated Benjamin and Patrick Binder. The seven-month-old twin boys

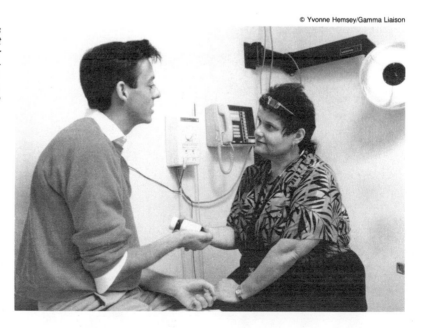

An AIDS patient (left) is administered AZT, the first FDA-approved drug for treating the disease. Thousands of Americans already have died from the disease, and perhaps 1.5 million more are infected with the virus.

were born joined at the back of their heads; they shared a broad area of skull plus a major vein that drains much of the brain. To prevent neurological damage and the possibility that they would bleed to death, the twins were placed in a state of suspended animation for one hour during the course of the surgery. Their body temperature was lowered to 68° F (20° C), their blood was drained from their bodies, and their hearts were stopped. These steps reduced brain function to near zero. This allowed surgeons to cut the shared vein and construct a new vein in each baby. When the procedure was completed, circulation was restarted, and body temperatures were returned to normal.

Most Siamese twins die at or soon after birth. Few attempts have been made to separate twins joined at the head, and in all previously known cases, the babies either died or experienced severe neurological damage. The Binder twins' recovery was complicated but promising, although there were indications that they had suffered some brain damage and might have vision problems.

New milestones in transplant surgery were reached during 1987. At Johns Hopkins the first known three-way transplant operation was performed. A healthy heart was removed from a 28-year-old man suffering from cystic fibrosis, a disease that destroys the lungs. The heart was implanted in a second man, who suffered from heart disease. And the healthy heart and lungs of an accident victim were implanted in the cystic fibrosis patient. The surgeons who performed the operation contend that heart-lung transplants are more likely to be successful than lung transplants alone, a view that is not shared by all transplant surgeons.

Surgeons at the Hospital of the University of Pennsylvania performed the first successful transplant of an entire knee, the largest and most complex of human joints.

Surgeons in Mexico pioneered a promising treatment for Parkinson's disease, a disorder of the nervous system that develops when the brain doesn't produce enough dopamine, a chemical that carries messages between nerve cells. The surgeons transplanted adrenal tissue into the brains of Parkinson patients. The tissue, taken from the patients' own adrenal glands, produces norepinephrine, a hormone that is chemically similar to dopamine. At least some of the patients showed significant improvement. For example, one man who had been confined to a wheelchair by the disease was once again able to walk and even play soccer with his son.

Anencephalic babies are born with most of the brain missing and die within a few days of birth. Even though they exhibit no brain function, is it ethical to keep such babies alive by respirator so that they can be used as organ donors? The issue arose when a couple who gave birth to an anencephalic baby girl took her to Loma Linda University Medical Center in California and, after she was declared brain-dead, allowed her healthy heart and lungs to be transplanted into a baby boy. The boy, the youngest person ever to undergo a heart transplant, was born with a heart defect that is fatal within weeks of birth.

SURROGATE MOTHERHOOD

Millions of couples of childbearing age suffer from infertility, which is commonly defined as the inability to conceive after a year or more of trying. Many of these couples turn to adoption or in vitro fertilization. Another alternative is surrogate motherhood, which enables a man to have a genetically related child if his wife is unable to

Doctors at Massachusetts General Hospital scan DNA patterns for genetic markers associated with a defective gene thought to be the hereditary basis for Alzheimer's disease.

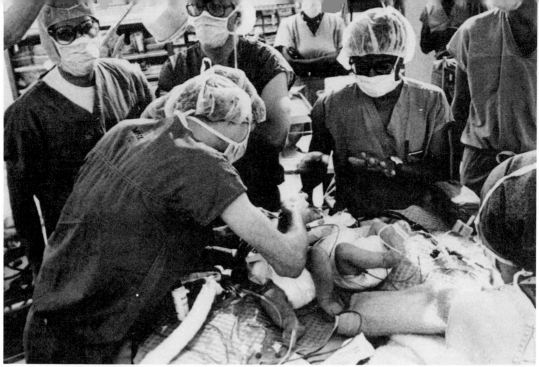

In September 1987 a 70-member medical team successfully separated 7-month-old Siamese twins joined at the head.

bear children. The man's sperm is used to impregnate a "surrogate mother," who bears the child and then turns it over to the couple at birth. The procedure is generally arranged through a lawyer or a specializing agency; all costs are paid by the couple, who also pay the surrogate mother a fee of $10,000.

More than 500 babies have been born to surrogate mothers since the first such agreement was made in 1976. The great majority went as planned. But in 1986 Mary Beth Whitehead, a young mother of two who had signed a surrogate agreement with William and Elizabeth Stern, refused to relinquish the baby she had borne for them. The case was heard by New Jersey Family Court Judge Harvey R. Sorkow, who in March 1987 awarded the baby to the Sterns, stating that the contract was legal and that it was in the child's best interests to be with the Sterns. He noted, however, that "there can be no solution satisfactory to all in this kind of case."

Some groups, including Roman Catholics and Orthodox Jews, condemned the practice. Others supported it but agreed that there was a need for legal guidelines. In the ensuing months, legislators in a number of states introduced bills to regulate surrogacy.

HEART AND CIRCULATORY PROBLEMS

High cholesterol levels put millions of people at risk of developing atherosclerosis. This disease is characterized by the formation of fatty deposits that clog arteries, and it is the cause of heart attacks that annually kill hundreds of thousands of Americans. Scientists at the University of Southern California School of Medicine reported that a regimen of drugs combined with a low-cholesterol diet can slow and even reverse the buildup of fatty deposits, thereby reducing the risk of heart disease.

In September the FDA approved lovastatin, a drug that reduces blood levels of certain forms of cholesterol by up to 39 percent. In November the FDA approved a genetically engineered drug, TPA (tissue plasminogen activator). TPA is a protein that breaks down clots. It is produced by the body in minute amounts. However, tests have shown that administering a concentrated dose of TPA to a person shortly after he or she has suffered a heart attack helps unblock the flow of blood to the heart. This reduces and may even prevent irreversible heart damage.

A procedure called LDL-plasmapheresis, developed in Japan, is being tested in the United States and elsewhere, particularly on children who suffer from familial hypercholesterolemia, an inherited condition in which blood cholesterol builds up to dangerous levels. The procedure "washes" low-density lipoproteins (LDLs), the most dangerous form of cholesterol, from the blood. The patient's blood is shunted to a device that contains a chemical that attracts and holds the LDL so it can be removed. The cleansed blood is then sent back into the patient's body.

JENNY ELIZABETH TESAR

© Howard Sochurek

New medical vision: physicians view one patient through six images, each created by a different scanning device.

Medicine's New Supersleuths

by Bernie Ward

What color is thought? What shape a heartbeat? How loud is blood? Imponderables. Unanswerables. The kind of rhetorical questions that for centuries have danced with angels on the head of a pin. Until now. Until the present marshaling of medicine, radiology, computer graphics, biomedical engineering, and neuroscience that are literally turning the body inside out, dissecting without cutting, and blazing unexplored pathways into the deepest recesses of the human psyche.

The answers to those unanswerables are being revealed by diagnostic imaging, an umbrella team covering an alphabet soup of procedures and techniques—CT, MRI, SONO, DSA, PET, SPECT, and MEG. Individually and collectively, they are equipping the physician with a powerful new vision—the ability to

see inside the body without surgery and with a precision that portends, in the words of one advocate, ". . . a scientific revolution unlike any other in man's history."

Critics may find only the slightest trace of hyperbole in that statement, considering the enormous range of information about the human condition that this mélange of exotic electronica can provide.

They may, for example, help guide the surgeon's hand and eye in approaching brain tumors once thought inoperable. Borrowing a technique from other branches of science, a digital Doppler effect may detect a blocked artery signaling a risk of stroke. With a three-dimensional computer graphic as a blueprint, the orthopedic specialist may perform a "rehearsal" surgery to determine the precise size and placement of bone grafts before the actual operation is undertaken. Equally dramatic, a new device just approved by the Food and Drug Administration (FDA) may soon pinpoint the exact function of the brain producing such neurological disorders as epilepsy, Alzheimer's disease, perhaps even substance dependencies, and do so painlessly and without invading the body.

Diagnostic imaging began with the invention of the X ray in 1895, one of modern medicine's revolutionary crossroads. Some of the imaging procedures now in use are major evolutionary steps in that technology; others, however, may represent new revolutions of their own, diverting the course of medicine toward alternate futures.

Among the more significant developments as defined by the American College of Radiology (ACR) are: computerized tomography (CT); sonography (SONO); digital subtraction angiography (DSA); positron emission tomography (PET); single photon emission computed tomography (SPECT); magnetic resonance imaging (MRI); and the latest, magnetoencephalography (MEG).

CT Scans

CT (also known as the CAT scan) is based on the X-ray principle, but produces cross-sectional images of parts of the body or organs that are particularly useful in depicting bone structure in fine detail, or tiny differences between normal and abnormal tissues. A conventional X ray produces an image from only one angle. The revolving X ray of the CT creates multiple-angled views, which a computer then analyzes and processes into a single, vivid video image.

Developed in 1972, the CT technology continues to advance at a startling pace. The patient is placed inside the doughnut-shaped CT machine, where thousands of sensors mounted on the interior pick up the radiation emitted from X-ray tubes that revolve around the patient. The computer graphics employed in converting the CT's X-ray information are similar to those that re-create digital images from data beamed back from deep-space probes. In this case, however, radiologists are probing the depths of the human body for clues to tumors, blood clots, or other problems that otherwise might be uncovered only through surgery.

The full potential of the CT as a diagnostic tool is still being explored. For example, a new and improved cine CT now takes stop-action photos of a beating heart. While only a handful are in operation, one use is to calculate the blood flow through grafted coronary arteries—measurements once possible only via surgery. The cine CT may also help pinpoint with greater precision the holes in the hearts of children with congenital defects before corrective surgery. Similarly, using CT images as "dress rehearsals" may aid neurosurgeons in risky operations involving brain tumors.

Three-dimensional Images

Those preoperative blueprints have become even more valuable with the recent addition of three-dimensional images created by the computer working in tandem with CT (and MRI). The 3-D capability has proved especially useful in preplanning reconstructive surgery or in detecting osteoporosis—even before a bone is broken.

Much of the pioneering work in 3-D imaging was done at CEMAX, Inc., a Santa Clara, California, manufacturer that offered this scenario of the technology at work:

"A surgeon pushes a button, and a three-dimensional image of his patient's skull appears on the computer screen. A portion of the skull is missing as the result of an auto accident. The surgeon manipulates the image, viewing it from a variety of angles, peering inside and comparing the left profile to the right. He adds muscle and skin tissue. He then directs the computer to design an implant with the exact shape, contour, and size of the missing bone. Finally he uses a milling device driven by the computer to carve the precise implant that he will put in place during reconstructive surgery."

Head trauma, birth defects, joint replacements, and implants are just a few of the areas in which 3-D imaging is providing new insights for the surgeon and benefits for the patient. Less critical, perhaps, but just as meaningful to the individual involved is the use of 3-D imaging in cosmetic surgery. Here a computerized image of the patient's face is projected in full color on a screen, and the plastic surgeon, utilizing a stylus, erases or reshapes certain features being projected—thus "painting" a picture of the patient after surgery, but before the investment of time, money, and pain in an operation.

Specialists at the University of Kansas Medical Center, one of the country's leading research centers in 3-D imaging technology, are currently looking at a number of different ways it may be applied in the future.

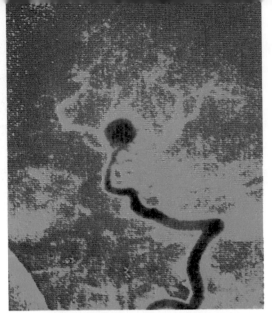

Digital Subtraction Angiography

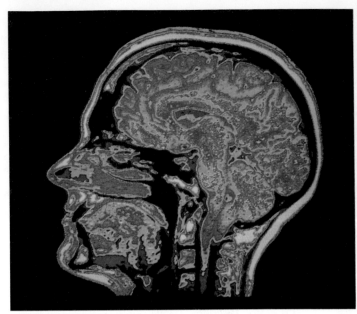

Magnetic Resonance Imaging

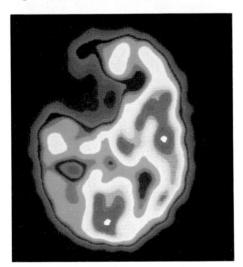

Radioisotope Imaging

Various color-enhanced images of the head illustrate the diagnostic power of computerized scanning techniques. At top left, an X-ray image enhanced by digital subtraction angiography (DSA) reveals a life-threatening aneurysm (blood clot) in an artery at the base of the brain. Using positron emission tomography (PET), a form of radioisotope imaging (bottom left), evidence of stroke damage appears as a darkened region on the left side of the brain. The bright colors elsewhere in the brain indicate a normal flow of blood. From magnetic resonance imaging (MRI; above), doctors found brain tissue slumping into the base of the skull. MRI machines find particular application in viewing the brain and other soft tissue, since the technique's combination of radio waves and magnetic fields avoids the damage possible from X rays. The three-dimensional profile on the facing page was created from dozens of computerized tomography (CT) scans (also known as CAT scans). The white cross marks the location of a tumor. The three pictures along the left display different angles from which the tumor can be targeted. Along the right the various configurations of the scanner are displayed. Lungs, spinal cord, and eyes—organs sensitive to radiation—are specially color-coded to minimize unnecessary exposure.

"We're trying to find ways 3-D can be most appropriate in radiology," reports Dr. Samuel J. Dwyer III, professor of radiology at the center. "We've applied it with CT to the head and body for soft-tissue lesions. We've used it in some spine work, in breast imaging, and in radiation oncology, where we've compared it with dose imagery to see how well the lesions are being healed."

One advantage is that the computer graphics act like a high-tech mixing bowl, allowing radiologists to combine different procedures (dose imager, CT, and MRI, for example) to produce a single image that reveals highly detailed information.

"A second thing 3-D provides is that it really helps the patient and the family," Dr. Dwyer continues. "It helps them understand a little better what's happening to the body. Projected images are very hard to read unless you're a trained clinician.

"In a sense, computer graphics allow the surgeon to look into the future. He can move things around, put them back together, and orient them into new perceptions before surgery."

PET and SPECT

While CT reveals the anatomy of the brain, for example, PET and SPECT techniques show the brain at work, if not fully explaining how it per-

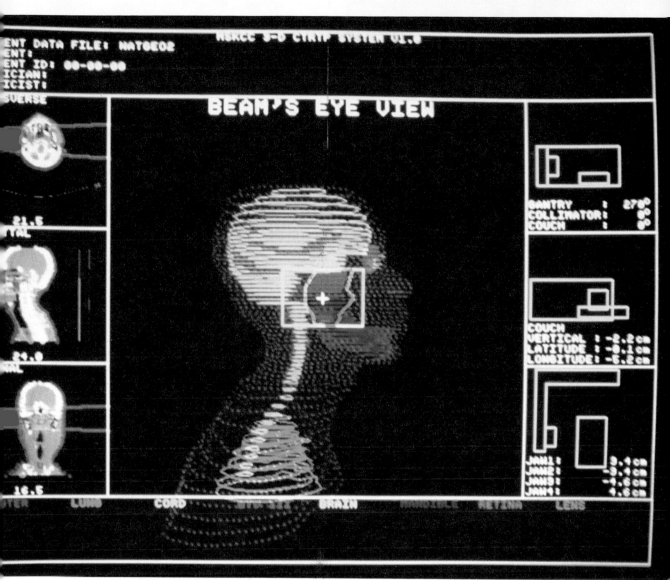

Computerized Tomography

forms its marvelous deeds. A researcher at the National Institutes of Health (NIH) likened CT to a road map and added that PET and SPECT show the traffic moving on those roads. And a broader understanding of the traffic flow, its detours and gridlocks, could help in solving mysteries such as aging and intelligence.

PET and SPECT track substances tagged with radioisotopes on their journeys through the circulatory system and focus in as they collect on the organ to be studied. When the positrons in the carrying solution collide with electrons in the body, they explode in a burst of gamma rays that are picked up by external sensors. A computer scan translates that data into patterns whose bright, psychedelic colors provide an inside look at life routinely going about its business. From the activity on display, the physician might learn of chemical or metabolic changes that could be precursors of disease.

For instance, changes in blood flow to the muscles of a heart under stress might indicate some hidden defect that, if left untreated, could produce a heart attack.

Elsewhere in the body, PET and SPECT are probing some of the brain's deepest secrets. Radioisotopes carried in a glucose solution (the brain's favorite food) light up the computer screen with an awesome display of action within, and with an accuracy never before pos-

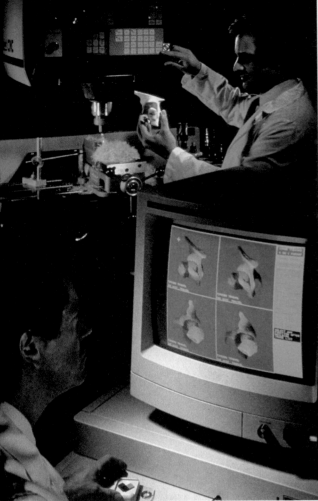

Cemax, Inc., Santa Clara, CA

Using three-dimensional tomographic data, implants can be custom-made to precisely fit a patient's anatomy.

sible. Sight, sound, movement—all stimulate different parts of the brain that show up in different colors and patterns on the screen. Thus, by spotlighting normal as well as abnormal activities, the imagings may add to our knowledge of emerging brain tumors, schizophrenia, manic-depressive illnesses, Alzheimer's, Parkinson's disease, Down's syndrome, Huntington's chorea, and the interaction of the brain with certain drugs.

Ultrasound

One of the most widely used imaging procedures is often the most thrilling. Where other techniques search for the life-threatening, sonography (or ultrasound) depicts new life. Through sonography, millions of anxious mothers have had their first peek at baby months before birth.

Prenatal exams may be the most common use of the sonogram today, but it is also employed in the study of internal organs such as the heart, liver, or gallbladder. An extension of World War II technology, a sonogram is produced when a small transducer (transmitter-receiver) gently caresses the body in the area to be examined. High-frequency sound waves strike the internal organ or fetus, bounce back to the transducer, are converted into electrical impulses, and then reconstructed into a video image by the computer.

For the watching mother, the pulsating signals emerge as the first look at her unborn child actually stretching, yawning, or sucking its thumb. Since there is no radiation, sonography has become the imaging of choice during pregnancy, for not only does it capture baby's first snapshot, it may also spot defects or problems the obstetrician can prepare for prior to birth.

More recently, the Doppler effect has become part of the sonography repertoire. The Doppler effect is the shift in light, sound, or radio waves produced when an object moves away from or toward a given point. The transducer, the computerized image, and the accompanying sound and rhythm of the blood flow may provide the cardiologist with the data needed to diagnose a blocked artery or a possible fault in the heart itself.

Digital Subtraction Angiography

Visualizing the heart and circulatory system without surgical risk is also the function of digital subtraction angiography (DSA), which does just what the name implies—subtracts by computer one picture from another to reveal hidden defects.

A digital X-ray scanner takes one image of the heart and arteries and repeats the process seconds later after a contrast-carrying liquid is injected. The computer subtracts the first image from the second, eliminating all nonvascular tissue that might impede a clear view. The arteries, now graphically highlighted by the contrast agent, become clearly visible, as does any blockage that might spell trouble for the patient.

Magnetic Resonance Imaging

But of all the imaging procedures now in use, nothing quite matches MRI for its phenomenal, almost overnight growth, or for the excitement it generates among radiologists. So enthusiastic are they, in fact, that the importance of mag-

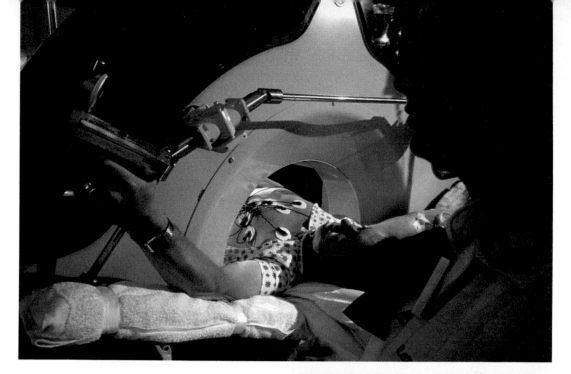

With a PET scanner arched over his chest (above), a patient stimulates his heart by squeezing a hand grip. PET determines the level of blood flow to heart muscle by detecting trace amounts of radioisotopes in the ventricle walls, and imaging them in white, orange, and yellow. In a PET scan of a heart under stress (right), the predominantly yellow upper half indicates a partially blocked artery.

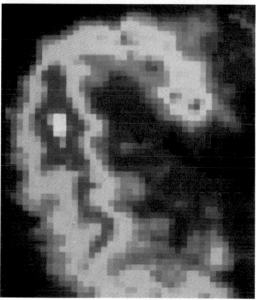

netic resonance imaging has at times been compared to the invention of the X ray.

"I'm not sure if it's quite the same as going from no X ray to X ray, but MRI certainly is a giant step," says Dr. Raymond Del FaVa, a radiologist at St. Francis Hospital in Evanston, Illinois, and chairman of the ACR's public relations committee. "It's just beginning, but already MRI is the modality of choice for almost all central nervous system imaging, and it does so more exquisitely than any other modality we now have.

"MR could be a complete revolution in medicine. CT certainly was. That changed everything, and now MR shows promise of doing the same thing. One of the wonderful things about it is that it is noninvasive and uses no ionizing radiation."

One of the most publicized contributions of MRI, Dr. Del FaVa notes, it its visualization of the early lesions or plaques in the brain caused by multiple sclerosis, a diagnosis previously made only by ruling out everything else. Here, as elsewhere throughout the central nervous system, MRI is giving medical detectives an unprecedented edge in the early detection of a variety of problems. It has as yet not proven as effective in other parts of the body, but Dr. Del FaVa and others believe that continuing research may fulfill that potential soon.

The MRI principle is based on the simple biological fact that the body's tissues and components are composed of different atoms, each displaying individual characteristics and behavior patterns. MRI is an outside agitator stirring up those atoms.

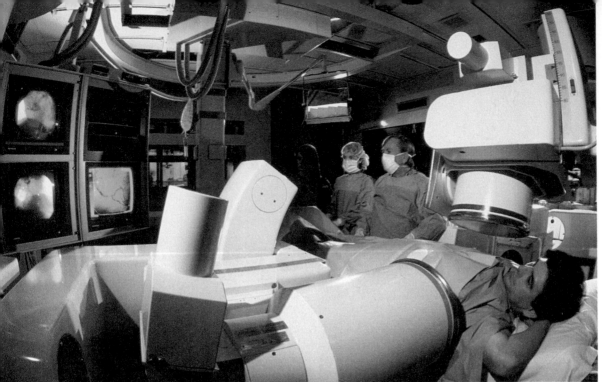

The digital biplane angioscope above views the heart from two angles. The screens present the two heart images, plus a digital recorded picture and (on the darkened screen) physiological data. In a DSA image of a middle-aged man (left), a constriction of the coronary artery (appearing as a break, center-top) has drastically diminished the blood supply to the lower heart.

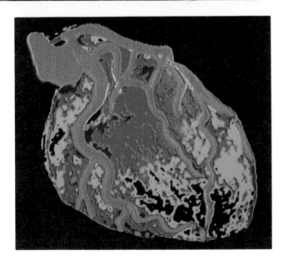

Focus on Water

A patient is placed inside the MRI unit, which consists of coils of supercooled electromagnets capable of creating a magnetic field 60,000 times more powerful than that generated by the earth. Since the most common element in the body is water, MRI was developed to focus on the hydrogen atoms in that water. During the scanning process, the magnetic field is switched on and off, rapidly agitating and upsetting the nuclei of those atoms. As they realign themselves (their ''resonance''), they give off tiny electrical pulses that are picked up by a computer and transformed into a picture of the inside of the body unlike any seen before.

Different water densities in different organs and parts of organs allow MRI to distinguish between those differences with startling clarity and precision. Since bones and teeth contain little or no hydrogen atoms, they are literally erased by MR imaging—leaving an unobstructed view of soft tissues. Brain tumors or those affecting the spinal cord, for example, become clearly visible under the relentless eye of MRI, and, quite often for the first time, the surgeon learns where his enemy is hiding before they meet in the operating arena.

Research is focusing on elements other than hydrogen—phosphorus or sodium, for instance—whose atoms react differently under the magnetic stimuli and would thus provide similar information on other parts of the body.

A measure of the importance the medical community places on MRI is the number of machines now on the market. The first of the $2 million MRI units did not become available commercially until about 1980. In mid-1986 the number had increased to 325. In May 1987 the ACR said that figure is now over 600; if MRI proves as effective in all areas of the body as radiologists hope it will, Dr. Del FaVa predicts that already-rapid growth will "explode." Indeed, the major manufacturers of the MRI units are now projecting a growth of 30 percent annually over the next few years.

"We've just gone in with five other hospitals on the purchase of one MRI," Dr. Del FaVa continues. "I think there will be a lot more of that going on because of the cost and as it becomes more useful for all areas of the body. We're going in as a consortium now, but we made sure we could be out of it in three years to have our own machine, because in that time I think MRI will be standard operating procedure."

In the meantime, private enterprise, with an eye on the astounding potential of MRI and its present average cost of $750 per scan, is rushing to fill the increasing demands for its services. Private imaging centers specializing in MRI have opened for business, many located near major medical centers. In some cases, MRI units mounted in custom tractor-trailers go door-to-door delivering the service to hospitals and radiologists. In both cases the services solve one of the problems created by MRI, since the intense magnetism it generates requires highly insulated rooms or entirely separate buildings.

MEG Techniques

Even as MRI occupies center stage in medical imaging, yet another revolutionary procedure waits in the wings to make its debut.

Its name is MEG.

The anatomy of the brain has been well mapped out, pinpointing which part does what. Of the form, we know much; of the function, much less. And so science is focusing a great deal of attention on exactly how the brain performs some of its marvelous tasks. And what happens when it goes haywire. The latest imaging technology just emerging from the laboratory may help explain some of those magnificent mysteries.

MEG (or magnetoencephalography) is the process of gathering information produced by a neuromagnetometer, a device that received FDA approval only in late 1986. It is now being used for various research projects at New York University Medical Center, UCLA Medical Center, NIH, and the Scripps Clinic and Research Foundation, among others.

"MEG is more revolutionary than evolutionary," says Stephen James, president of Bio-magnetic Technologies, Inc., which builds the device in San Diego.

"The technologies developed so far look at the structure of the brain and tell doctors what the problem is in the anatomy," James continues. "There has been no instrument that looks at function in the brain, and disorders like epilepsy, Alzheimer's, or Parkinson's are invisible to CT, MRI, and some others. What we're doing for the first time is pinpointing functional activity in the brain down to a resolution of 0.07 to 0.11 inch (2 to 3 millimeters), and doing so without radiation and noninvasively.

"I think MEG's role in the medicine of the future will be to diagnose the disorder definitively and to monitor the treatment of that disorder."

Basically, the neuromagnetometer measures the extremely weak magnetic field signals given off by the brain in its electrical activity, and also filters out the immense amount of background magnetic "noise" emanating from other sources. "It's like hearing a whisper in a whirlwind," James says. To sort out that information, the MEG sensors are simply placed against the head and measure the activity in "real time"; i.e., the researcher is able to observe the neural functions as they occur.

Future Potentialities

The many diagnostic imaging tools now available are indeed opening new windows on the internal workings of the mind and body. In the hands of skilled physicians, they are helping extend life spans and improving life qualities with their capability of spotting developing problems at early stages.

But even as wondrous as are their present applications, the present is not the future. What then? What next? Some scientists believe that if diagnostic imaging can identify an emerging tumor in its earliest stage, why not the chemical changes that may be under way long before the tumor manifests itself? Might they eventually screen for potential disease or the susceptibility of alcoholism?

And if the technologies are useful in detection, prevention, and treatment, why not enhancement? As we come to understand more about how the brain functions, why not imaging scanners to aid in focusing attention, comprehension, memory, and problem-solving abilities? Why not exercise machines for the mind?

Why not?

ANATOMY OF A HEADACHE

by Edwin Kiester, Jr.

It was a headache to make history. On April 8, 1865, Ulysses S. Grant's Union Army was chasing Robert E. Lee's Confederates across Virginia. Grant invited Lee to surrender, but the Southerner demurred. The two armies settled down near Appomattox Court House for the night.

It was not an easy night for Grant. "I was suffering very severely with a sick headache," he recorded in his journal, "and stopped at a farm house on the road some distance to the rear of the main body of the army. I spent the night in bathing my feet in hot water and mustard, and putting mustard plasters on my wrists and the back part of my neck, hoping to be cured by morning."

At dawn the next day, Palm Sunday, Grant felt no better—until a message arrived from Lee. The Confederate general had changed his mind overnight. "When the officer reached me, I was still suffering from the sick headache," Grant wrote, "but the instant I saw the contents of the note I was cured." Pain and nausea gone, the Union general rode off to accept Lee's surrender and end the Civil War.

Most headaches are not so momentous—or so swiftly and miraculously cured. Take the case of Ann Grimes, a patient at the headache clinic at the University of California, San Francisco (UCSF), who has been fighting blinding headaches for 30 years. The siege began when she was in second grade, and by age 20 the bouts of searing pain and vomiting were coming six or seven times a month. At 40, the headaches had decreased in frequency but not in intensity. Sometimes they flattened her for 36 hours at a time.

Of all human ills, headache may be the most ancient and universal, as well as the best documented. Five thousand years ago, an anonymous Sumerian poet described his "sick and blinding" headache in terms Grant or Ann Grimes would have recognized. Aristotle wrote about headaches; John Calvin, Madame Pompadour, and Leo Tolstoi are only three of the famous who have suffered from them.

Just about everyone has nursed an aching head at some time or other. However bothersome, the pain usually disappears with a couple of aspirin and a good night's rest. For an unfortunate 10 to 20 percent of the population,

Portrait of pain: a headache sufferer used zigzag lines to depict the visual aura that may precede a migraine.

however, chronic, recurrent, and intractable headaches are an incapacitating fact of life. Headaches account for 11.5 million doctor visits a year, 5 million lost workdays, and a cool $1 billion for aspirin and other painkillers. That impact may be understated. Only half of chronic-headache victims ever see a doctor, and most go to work in spite of the pain.

Bad Chemistry?

What causes headaches? And what can be done to stop them? For centuries, humans have been tussling with these questions, concocting a long and colorful history cluttered with supernatural explanations and witch doctors' remedies. Today, thanks to an international research effort, science is beginning to close in on the old enemy. New technology allows doctors to actually peer inside the skull and watch a headache develop, leading to a more basic understanding, which in turn could lead to surer cures.

Many prominent researchers are now convinced that some headaches, especially the notorious migraines, arise from an upset in the brain's delicate chemistry and could be distant cousins to the "nerve storms" of epilepsy. There is a suspicion that fluctuations in the levels of a neurotransmitter known as serotonin enhance the brain's ability to sense pain. That shift to a focus on the central nervous system has brought into question the long-held view that the head hurts only because swollen blood vessels stretch trigeminal nerve endings in the face and scalp.

Fanciful Cures

Still, enough mystery remains to keep scientists fascinated—and debating among themselves. "We still can't always cure a headache," says Dr. Neil H. Raskin, vice-chairman and professor at UCSF and part of an elite 30-member international research group on migraine and headache. "But we're making progress. We've moved from the dark ages to the bright ages."

The early Christians simply relied on faith. Saint Gregory, Bishop of Tours in the 6th century, cured a severe headache merely by pressing his painful brow against the rail of Saint Martin's tomb. Other faithful were cured by touching the carpet above the resting place of Saint Julian.

Applying the "cure" directly to the pain-racked head has been a favorite and age-old remedy, foreshadowing today's soothing ice bag. Mexicans in the Sierra Madres stroked the head with a live toad. A priest-physician of Mesopotamia suggested tying on a curative headband woven of the hair of a virgin kid. The Romans and Europeans into the early 20th century tied on a hangman's noose.

As for antiheadache medicines and potions, prescriptions have included herbs, tobacco, marijuana, moss scraped from the head of a statue, roses and candied sugar, dill blossoms boiled in oil. Finally, in 1899, came the synthesis of aspirin, which, if it didn't cure the problem, could temporarily quell the pain. Aspirin and its relatives are still the mainstay for occasional pain relief, but some unfortunates require as many as 16 extra-strength pain relievers a day and may become hooked.

Categorization of Headaches

To the victim, one headache often feels like another. But scientists have broken down chronic headaches into categories, as a first step toward understanding and treating them. Perhaps 1 percent are "disease-related" headaches, caused by some underlying ailment or medical problem such as inflamed sinus, pain "referred" from toothache or earache, injury, or, more ominously though far more rarely, a brain tumor or stroke. These headaches are treated by removing the underlying cause, if possible. Tension headaches, which may result from stress and produce bands of pain around the forehead, account for about 90 percent of all chronic head pain. Remedies include pain medication, relaxation techniques, and sometimes a change of jobs.

The remaining 10 percent or so are the true nightmares, and it is here that research is concentrated and that most recent progress has been made. There are the "vascular" headaches and include the infamous migraines. The name comes from the traditional view linking the pain to distended blood vessels; although doctors now challenge the explanation, the classification stands.

Vascular headaches can be nonmigrainous, caused by severe high blood pressure, hunger, fever, or sometimes sexual orgasm. The type known as cluster headache, a recurrent, excruciating pain that centers behind one eye and principally affects men, is today considered only a distant cousin of migraine. Of the true migraines, two are dramatic but relatively rare: hemiplegic, which involves paralysis of one side of the body, and ophthalmoplegic, in which there is paralysis of one eye.

Migraines

Thanks to an impressive roster of big-name victims, it is classic and common migraine that has attracted the most attention. The Greek physician Galen coined the name in the 2d century A.D. He called it *hemikrania,* or "half a skull," because many attacks localize on one side. The name was later corrupted into the Old English *megrim* and eventually into *migraine.*

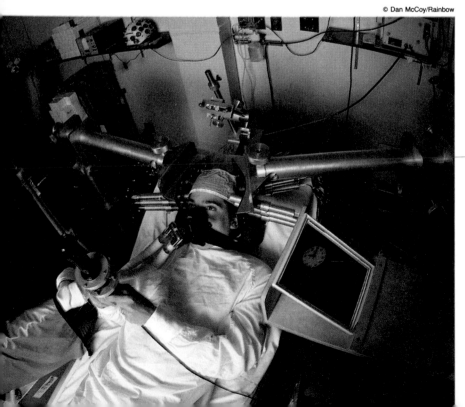

© Dan McCoy/Rainbow

At the University of Pennsylvania, a migraine sufferer wears a special helmet that monitors blood flow to the brain. Migraine and cluster headaches may occur when blood vessels in the scalp undergo a constricting spasm followed by a sudden dilation in reaction to the spasm. Many researchers, however, believe that reduced electrical activity in the brain is responsible for headaches.

Of all human ailments, headaches are perhaps the most ancient and best documented—but also the least understood. A 19th-century etching by George Cruikshank (below) offered one fanciful explanation for headache pain. In their perennial search for relief, headache sufferers have readily fallen prey to vendors of bogus remedies (right).

Classic migraine is both spectacular and unmistakable. It announces itself about a half hour before the headache with a dazzling warning called an aura. The victim ''sees'' sparkles or stars or luminous wavy lines as though a photographer's flashbulb had just exploded; or, most common, a ''fortification spectrum,'' a zigzag pattern like the parapets of a medieval walled city.

Although many people equate ''migraine'' with ''severe,'' the pain actually comes in degrees from mild to savage. In its most extreme form, it strikes like a sledgehammer on one side of the head, causing a throbbing, pounding, pulsating pain. An artery may actually be seen thumping in the temple. The victim becomes pale, clammy, nauseous, and may vomit, hence General Grant's ''sick headache.'' Bright light intensifies the pain and drives many migraineurs to a dark room until the attack ends. A lucky few recover within hours, but others are laid low for days.

Common migraine, which accounts for four-fifths of migraines, produces fewer fireworks but can be even more painful. It lacks the warning aura and more often involves both sides of the head. Like the classic form, it strikes at intervals—several times a week to several times a year.

Migraine runs in families. About 70 percent of migraineurs have migrainous relatives. It can also begin early in life, even in two- and three-year-olds. Among adults, 70 percent of victims are women, mostly those in their childbearing years.

Although migraines often strike out of the blue, they may be touched off in the susceptible by normally harmless stimuli. The list of migraine triggers includes food—cheese, chocolate, figs, red wine; bright lights (television, too); birth-control pills; abrupt changes of posture; shifts in weather; hunger; and the hot, dry winds of the desert.

A headache patient depicted the premigraine aura as an abstract crescent interrupting the normal field of vision.

Distinguishing Headaches

Individual headaches, however, very seldom fit the scientific pigeonholes. Migraine not only varies from person to person, but from episode to episode. One person may have attacks rarely and irregularly; Ann Grimes could almost set her watch by hers. Commonly, a migraineur will have a one-sided headache with an aura during one attack, whole-head pain without an aura the next, and sometimes aura with no headache. Some victims, bewilderingly, have all the secondary symptoms of migraine—nausea, light sensitivity, clammy skin—but no head pain. And an unlucky few have both migraine and tension headaches, sometimes one after the other.

At this time there is no surefire way to diagnose the most common forms of headache except from the patient's own description. A migraine cannot be distinguished from a tension headache by any scientific measurement. Hence, some doctors think the current classification system ought to be redefined. Others feel it ought to be dropped and headaches treated on a case basis. Neil Raskin, for one, suggests that all except "disease-related" headaches be lumped together as "benign recurring headache." "Headache represents a common pain syndrome," he says. "The symptoms we see are grouped on a continuum of severity from the mildest to the most severe, but the same pain process is occurring."

Arguments about the nature of headache are nothing new. In 1873 the distinguished British physician Edward Liveing published a treatise comparing the migraine aura to the nerve storm, or sudden electrical discharge, of an epileptic seizure. He was promptly contradicted by another prominent British doctor, P. W. Latham of Cambridge. Latham attributed migraine to a disturbance of the cranial blood vessels, and offered an explanation: "The sufferers possess what is called the nervous temperament; their brains are very excitable, their senses acute, and their imaginations free. The attacks are induced by prolonged mental work, protracted mental excitement, or any intense strain on the feelings." Migraine headaches, he confided, were quite common among Cambridge students during examination time.

Moreover, a horrified Latham chided Liveing, migraineurs and epileptics differed by "class." Epileptics, with their frightening "fits" and loss of consciousness, were shunned by society, whereas many migraineurs were prominent and wellborn.

Fellow neurologists sided with Liveing, but two developments caused Latham's views to carry the day. One was the dawning of the age of psychiatry; the other was the discovery of ergotamine: then known to act only on blood vessels, it was found useful in treating migraine.

The idea that migraine singled out only the best and the brightest was reinforced in the 1930s by Dr. Harold Wolff of the Cornell Medical School, known as the father of modern headache research. Noting the throbbing temporal artery in some migraine attacks, he explained that migraine began when the arteries to the brain constricted, reducing the blood supply. Then came a compensating "overshoot" that distended the arteries until they stretched the nerve endings in their walls and produced pain. His research had shown, Wolff said, that brain tissue itself could not feel pain.

Wolff could find no physical explanation for these supposed ups and downs in blood flow, so, like Latham, he suggested a psychological one. Nine-tenths of his own migraine patients, he said, were perfectionistic, obsessive, driven go-getters.

The Headache "Wave"

For 30 years, Wolff's idea that the precipitating factors in migraine were "all in the head" was scientific gospel. But in the mid-1960s, revisionism set in. Dr. James Lance of the University of New South Wales, Australia, today one of the world's renowned headache experts, demonstrated that 25 percent of migraineurs were indeed obsessive, just as Wolff had said. But so was 25 percent of the general population. The U.S. National Health Survey uncovered no link between chronic headache sufferers and either intelligence or career success. Quite the contrary, another study showed: headache increased as you went down the socioeconomic scale. Researchers reached the obvious conclusion: the movers and shakers didn't have more migraines; they were just better able to afford treatment.

Meanwhile, the long-eclipsed hypothesis of Dr. Liveing began to stir again. In the early 1940s, Harvard neurophysiologist and migraineur K. S. Lashley postulated that there was a wave, a phenomenon unknown at that time,

which moved slowly across the cortex during an attack, and which had a deadening effect on nerve-cell activity in the part of the brain controlling vision. In 1944 a Brazilian scientist, Manolo Leao, actually produced the event in the laboratory. He showed that a similar reduction in brain activity, including lowered blood flow, could be induced in laboratory cats. Starting from the rear, the nervous-system depression would slowly advance across the brain surface at 2 to 3 millimeters a minute, just as Lashley had said.

The "spreading depression of Leao," however, remained largely ignored for 40 years by a research community that considered headaches psychosomatic and the accompanying pain a circulatory problem. Then, in the early 1980s, Danish scientists accidentally discovered alterations in brain blood flow during classic migraine attacks that resembled Leao's phenomenon. Neurologist Jes Olesen and research fellow Martin Lauritzen of the University of Copenhagen found that when patients susceptible to classic migraine underwent angiography, a process of injecting dye into the arteries, a migraine attack ensued. Addition of a radioactive tracer enabled them to record blood flow at 10-minute intervals at 254 points within one hemisphere of the brain. The full-color pictures produced showed unmistakably that the aura coincided with at least a one-fourth drop in blood flow at the back of the brain, and that this "depression" moved forward in a manner similar to the depression of Leao. Moreover, the back-to-front depression spread like a relentlessly advancing wave, rather than following the spiderweb pattern of arterial blood circulation. The phenomenon appeared to originate in the nervous system.

These scientists also made another startling finding. The spreading depression of cerebral blood flow occurred only in classic migraine. Victims of common migraine showed no such disturbance.

Olesen and Lauritzen's discovery of a nerve storm moving across the brain was the dramatic piece of evidence that convinced many researchers that Liveing was correct a hundred years ago.

The Role of Serotonin

While researchers differ on details, today's most widely accepted hypothesis for the problems of General Grant and Ann Grimes centers on the neurotransmitter serotonin, one of the not fully understood brain chemicals whose minute secretions signal nerve cells when to fire and when to cease firing. Serotonin is usually an "inhibitory" transmitter, meaning that it switches off nerve impulses. Researchers have known for 20 years that serotonin levels in the blood decrease during a reported migraine attack. There is speculation that the sequence of aura and pain may indicate that certain brain circuits are suddenly and inexplicably starved for serotonin, with consequent disorder in their normal function.

But what makes the head hurt? "One thing seems sure to me, that Wolff's old idea of scalp arteries pressing on nerves is clearly wrong," Neil Raskin says. "If that were the case, we would have a headache after every hot bath or every run around the block." Arteries often do swell during a migraine, Raskin says, but that may be an effect rather than a cause. And Olesen's brain scans were unable to show an overshoot in blood flow after the aura, as the swollen-blood-vessel theory required.

More likely, the pain centers in disturbed, serotonin-controlled circuits deep in the midbrain. Support for this idea comes from unexpected results of medical treatment for pain elsewhere in the body. Dr. Raskin found that using electrical stimulation of the midbrain to relieve pain in the lower back caused headaches similar to migraine in some patients.

An alternative explanation is offered by Dr. Michael Moskowitz of Harvard. He suggests that neurotransmitters in the trigeminal nerves cause the blood vessels to become pain-sensitive and inflamed. These highly sensitive nerves are also the villains in toothache, earache, and sinus infection.

What sets off the process in the first place? Probably chronic-headache sufferers are born with a deficiency in neurotransmitter production, Raskin suggests. Just as some persons are prone to motion sickness, sufferers inherit a lowered tolerance for specific migraine triggers in amounts that the less vulnerable would shrug off. Susceptibility is a matter of degree. "I'm fairly well convinced that anyone can develop a vascular headache if the challenge is great enough," Raskin says.

Current Treatments

While the research goes on, doctors have to treat headache sufferers now. The first line of treatment continues to be drugs. From the early 1930s until very recent years, the drug of choice has been ergotamine, which is a derivative of

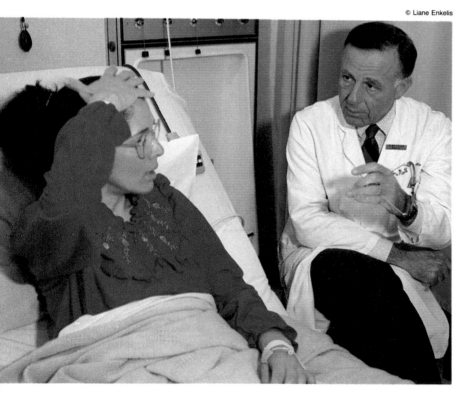

A migraine sufferer discusses her reaction to ergotamine—a fungus derivative that constricts the blood vessels. Physicians are still unsure of ergotamine's exact course of action. Nevertheless, more than half the patients receiving the drug report relief.

In biofeedback therapy, patients are trained to deflect blood flow away from the pain-producing cranial arteries.

© Dan McCoy/Rainbow

ergot, a substance whose history goes back almost as far as headache itself. Ergot, a fungus, was known in the Middle Ages; peasants who ate ergot-contaminated grain developed Saint Anthony's fire, a tingling and burning in the extremities that could lead to dry gangrene. About one in five victims died, and many lost their limbs. Ergot did its dirty work by constricting the blood vessels and reducing circulation to the feet and legs. The modern form similarly constricts the blood vessels, but doctors do not yet know exactly how ergotamine works, though it liberates the headache victim in more than half of all cases.

In recent years there has been a shift from ergotamine to nonsteroidal, antiinflammatory drugs, which can be equally, if not more, effective, and which have fewer side effects. Several other drugs have been found to help prevent migraine headaches, including the beta-blocking drugs used to treat coronary artery disease and hypertension, and the calcium-channel blockers, also used in cardiac ailments. Methysergide, a relative of LSD, is sometimes used in acute cases, but only as a last resort because of its serious side effects.

Drugs are no longer the only treatment for headache, however. Since the late 1960s, the Menninger Foundation in Topeka, Kansas, has been experimenting with nondrug treatments. The basic method has been biofeedback. Patients are taught to increase blood flow to their hands to deflect it from the cranial arteries and reduce pain. There is considerable debate, however, about the effectiveness of such techniques.

Psychotherapy for headaches has been tried ever since the days of Harold Wolff's migraine personality. But even a confirmed Wolff disciple, Dr. Arnold P. Friedman, founder of the Headache Unit at Montefiore Medical Center in New York City, has called the results disappointing.

Yet clinicians remain ahead of researchers. "It is astonishing how successful we have been in treating headache without really knowing what pain is or being able to define accurately how drugs can relieve it," Friedman once wrote. Ulysses S. Grant knew that and so does Neil Raskin. Good news helped the general eliminate a headache, and, according to the doctor's research, so will falling in love.

LYME DISEASE

by Jenny Elizabeth Tesar

Eleanor Bolton had always been a healthy, active woman who loved the outdoors. An avid hiker and camper, she and her family spent many a weekend tramping through New England forests and parks. Late last summer, shortly after returning home from a weekend in eastern Massachusetts, Eleanor (not her real name) noticed a large rash on her thigh. It didn't hurt, and after about a week, it disappeared. She assumed it was a harmless insect bite, and thought no more about it. Nor was she concerned when she became feverish, tired, and achy. Thinking she had a mild case of flu, she rested for several days. These symptoms also disappeared rather quickly.

Then, more than a month later, Eleanor began suffering from headaches and dizziness. Her knee joints began to ache. Soon ankle and elbow joints also became painful. Eleanor visited her doctor and described her symptoms. Many a physician might have misdiagnosed the problem. But Eleanor was fortunate, in part because she lives in New England, where such a mixture of symptoms has become familiar.

"Did you have an unusual rash within the past few months?" asked her physician.

"Yes, but it didn't hurt," she replied.

A researcher (top) sweeps for the tiny ticks that spread Lyme disease—a bacterial infection often characterized by arthritislike symptoms. Ixodes dammini (inset), the primary carrier of Lyme disease, more than triples its size when engorged with blood.

Top: Joe McNally/Wheeler Pictures; inset: Courtesy M. Fergione, Pfizer Central Research

"Did it look like a bull's-eye, with a pale spot in the center?" he asked.

"Why, yes," she replied.

"How about fever? Did you have what seemed to be the flu?" he asked.

"Yes, but later, several weeks after I noticed the rash," she said.

That response was enough for the physician to suspect that Eleanor might be suffering from a little-known—but increasingly common—illness called Lyme disease. A blood test soon confirmed the diagnosis. Treatment began at once, and Eleanor's symptoms started to subside. Occasionally, however, she still suffers from aching joints, and must receive intravenous injections of a powerful antibiotic.

Solving a Mystery

The ailment that came to be known as Lyme disease was first reported in late 1975, when two mothers in the seaside community of Lyme, Connecticut, contacted their state health department. They were concerned because their children had just been diagnosed as having juvenile rheumatoid arthritis, a relatively uncommon disease characterized by painful inflammation of the joints. When the health officials heard that the two children were not the only ones in Lyme who had recently fallen prey to rheumatoid arthritis, they, too, became alarmed. They contacted Allen C. Steere, a rheumatologist at the Yale University School of Medicine in New Haven, Connecticut, and asked him to determine what was causing this unusual outbreak of arthritis.

Steere interviewed many of the people diagnosed as having rheumatoid arthritis, and before long he made three important discoveries: (1) most of the victims lived in wooded areas rather than in the central, built-up part of town; (2) most showed their first symptoms of illness during the warm summer months; and (3) approximately 25 percent of the victims remembered that before the onset of the arthritic pain, they had had a skin rash shaped like a bull's-eye, with a pale central area surrounded by expanding redness.

On the basis of this information, Steere theorized that the people were suffering from a previously unknown disease caused by a virus and spread by an arthropod such as an insect, spider, or tick. He named the disease Lyme arthritis, a name eventually changed to Lyme disease as the disorder became better understood by the medical community.

Steere's theory received an unexpected boost when he came across a report published early in the century by Swedish physician Arvid Afzelius. Afzelius described a skin rash in patients who had been bitten by the tick *Ixodes ricinus*. Afzelius named the rash erythema chronicum migrams (ECM), which means "chronic migrating red rash."

ECM sounded very similar to the rash experienced by the Lyme-disease victims, leading Steere to conclude that the people in Lyme might be suffering from a closely related illness. Steere also learned that European physicians had successfully treated victims of the *Ixodes* rash with penicillin, which implied that the cause was a bacterium rather than a virus.

The next advance occurred in 1977. Nine of the people who came down with the bull's-eye rash that year told Steere and his associates that they remembered having been bitten by a tick. One of these people had carefully removed

A bull's-eye-shaped rash centered around the site of a tick bite is often an early sign of Lyme disease. At this stage, antibiotics readily cure the infection.

CDC

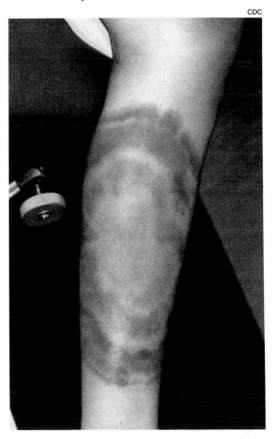

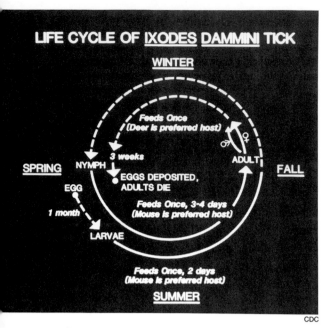

Although Ixodes dammini *prefers feeding on deer and mice, the tick also has been reported to feed on humans at all stages of its life cycle.*

and saved the tick. He gave it to Steere, who gave it to Andrew Spielman, a medical entomologist at the Harvard University School of Public Health. Spielman identified the tick as a previously unknown species of the genus *Ixodes*. He named it *Ixodes dammini,* after a former colleague, Dr. Gustave Dammin.

It wasn't until the fall of 1981, however, that the actual agent of infection was found. The discovery was made by Willy Burgdorfer, an authority on tick-borne diseases who was working at Rocky Mountain Laboratories in Hamilton, Montana. In the digestive tract of adult *Ixodes dammini,* he found numerous slender, spiral-shaped bacteria known as spirochetes. To determine if these were the cause of Lyme disease, Burgdorfer performed an antibody test. He cultured the spirochetes, then mixed some with serum from people infected with Lyme disease. The results were positive, indicating that the patients had been infected by that type of spirochete and had developed antibodies—special protein compounds—in response to the invaders.

Subsequent studies have revealed that the spirochetes belong to a previously unknown species in the genus *Borrelia*. In honor of the discoverer, the species was named *Borrelia burgdorferi*.

A Diet of Warm Blood

More than 6,000 cases of Lyme disease have been recorded in the United States since 1980, but health officials believe the actual number of cases is far higher. "If it weren't for AIDS," contends Russell Johnson, a microbiologist at the University of Minnesota, "it would be the number one new disease facing us today."

Within the United States, the greatest incidence of Lyme disease is in three areas: the Northeast, from Massachusetts to Maryland; the Midwest, especially Wisconsin and Minnesota; and the Pacific Coast, particularly California and Oregon. This correlates closely with the known distribution of *Ixodes dammini* in the Northeast and Midwest, and *Ixodes pacificus*— the western black-legged tick—in the West.

Cases of Lyme disease have also occurred in many other states. The disease has probably been carried to some of these places by ticks hitchhiking on migrating birds. It is also possible that additional vectors (disease-carrying organisms) may be identified in the future.

Like all ticks, an *Ixodes* tick passes through three stages during its life cycle: larva, nymph, and adult. All stages are very tiny, making them difficult to spot. The larvae are almost invisible to the unaided eye. Nymphs are about the size of the period at the end of this sentence. Adults are about half the size of the common dog tick, *Dermacentor variabilis*—some five-hundredths of an inch (15 millimeters) across if they haven't eaten recently, but triple that size when engorged with blood.

An *Ixodes* tick has a life span of two years. Eggs are laid in the spring and hatch into larvae a month later. The larvae feed once during the summer—a meal that lasts two days. By the time cold weather arrives, the larvae have entered a resting stage. The next spring they molt, metamorphosing into nymphs. The nymphs feed once—a meal lasting three or four days— and by summer's end they metamorphose into adults. The adults feed, mate, and, soon thereafter, the males die. The females live through the winter, until they deposit their eggs.

During all stages, *Ixodes* feeds solely on the blood of warm-blooded animals. Immature *Ixodes* feed primarily on mice and other small rodents. Adults usually feed on larger mammals, especially deer. But the tick has been found on many other wild and domestic animals, including birds, raccoons, rabbits, skunks, dogs, and horses. And all stages have been reported to feed on humans.

If the animal bitten by the tick is infected with *Borrelia* spirochetes, some of the spirochetes will enter the tick while it feeds. Then, when the tick attaches itself to another host and feeds again, some of the spirochetes will be passed on to the new host. Exactly how this occurs is not yet certain. The spirochetes may migrate from the tick's midgut to its salivary-gland ducts and hence to its mouthparts, to be injected into the skin or bloodstream. Or the spirochetes may be in fecal material that the tick leaves behind on its victim's skin.

Changing Symptoms

Like other spirochetal infections, Lyme disease generally occurs in stages. These stages may overlap or occur alone. They may manifest different symptoms in different people. And there may be remissions—that is, periods when the symptoms partially or completely disappear.

Usually, however, Lyme disease has three stages. The first stage, which develops within three to 32 days after the person has been bitten, is usually characterized by the bull's-eye rash that develops around the site of the bite. The spot where the bite occurred is generally hard or enlarged, like a small pimple.

Over a period of several days, the rash expands until it may be 1 foot (30 centimeters) or more in diameter. The rash doesn't itch, which means it may go unnoticed, particularly if it is on a seldom-viewed area, such as the person's back. About half of all Lyme disease victims develop additional lesions elsewhere on the body. These so-called secondary lesions are not associated with tick bites. They resemble the initial rash, though they tend to be smaller and they lack the central hard spot.

Without treatment, the rash usually lasts several weeks, though it may persist for as long as a year. Sometimes the rash is accompanied by flu-like symptoms, including fever, aching joints, headaches, and fatigue. During this stage the disease can usually be treated successfully with broad-spectrum antibiotics such as penicillin, tetracycline, and erythromycin.

Unfortunately, about 30 percent of the victims do not develop the rash. And many are not afflicted with flu-like symptoms. Thus, the disease is left untreated, and it progresses to the second stage. This stage, too, may be symptomless, although typically it is marked by inflammation of the heart muscle or the nervous system. For instance, in some patients the disease affects the impulse centers in the heart tissue that send out electrical signals that regulate

In many suburban areas, an abundance of tick-infested deer has hampered efforts to control Lyme disease.

heartbeat. The patients develop arrhythmia, or irregular heartbeat. The problem may be severe enough to require temporary pacemakers (electronic devices attached on the surface of the skin to substitute an artificial stimulation for the natural electrical currents).

Neurological complications during the second stage may include meningitis—an inflammation of the meninges, the membranes that enclose and protect the brain and spinal cord. Another symptom may be Bell's palsy, a type of facial paralysis that typically distorts the features on only one side of the face.

The third stage of Lyme disease may develop weeks, months, or as long as two years after the person was infected. This stage is characterized primarily by inflammation of the joints and the onset of arthritis. The pain tends to affect the knees and other large joints, and each attack may last anywhere from several hours to a few weeks.

The further the disease has progressed, the more difficult it is to treat. Some drugs that effectively fight the disease in its early stages, such as tetracycline, are not effective in later stages. About 50 percent of late-stage patients respond well to high doses of penicillin administered intravenously. Recent research indicates that cephalosporin antibiotics—drugs structurally related to penicillin—can be effective in treating many of the other cases of advanced Lyme disease. In any case, even if the disease is halted, any damage that already occurred to nerves, heart, or joints cannot be reversed.

So the key is early diagnosis. If a victim develops the characteristic rash and immediately sees a physician, diagnosis is relatively straightforward. If no rash occurs, however, or if the disease has progressed to advanced stages, diagnosis may be more difficult.

Two blood-serum tests are available to detect antibodies produced in response to the *Borrelia* spirochetes: immunofluorescence assay (IFA) and enzyme-linked immunosorbent assay (ELISA). In the IFA test, for example, a sample of the patient's blood serum is placed on a microscope slide. A laboratory specimen of the *Borrelia* and a fluorescent reagent are added to the serum. The slide is examined with a fluorescent microscope. If the person's serum contains antibodies, the spirochetes fluoresce, or glow.

Unfortunately, neither IFA nor ELISA have a high degree of accuracy. Many patients do not have an antibody response during the early stages of Lyme disease. Even in later stages, the test may give a false result. Research is under way on a urine test and other tests that may provide earlier and more accurate diagnoses.

Long Pants and Skin Checks

People who work and play outdoors in areas where Lyme disease is prevalent should use a tick repellent and wear protective clothing, including hats, long-sleeved shirts, and long pants carefully tucked into socks or boots. Upon returning indoors, they should carefully inspect their bodies for the tiny dark ticks. Pets that roam outdoors should also be checked.

If a person discovers a tick on his or her body, it should be carefully removed with a pair of fine-tipped tweezers. The tick should be grasped as close to the skin as possible, then gently pulled straight out. If a rash develops at the site, the person should immediately consult a physician.

States with a high incidence of Lyme disease have instituted a variety of programs designed to build awareness of the disease. Brochures and public meetings teach people the best protection against being bitten, how to recognize the tick, and the disease's symptoms. Posted warning signs discourage people from walking through tick-infested woods and fields, particularly during the summer months, when the ticks are most active.

At present there are no effective programs to control or eliminate the ticks or the spirochetes. Chemical controls have been of limited value, though this situation should improve as researchers determine when ticks are most susceptible to pesticides.

Another possible means of fighting Lyme disease is to limit deer populations in infested areas. Deer are abundant in most places where Lyme disease is common. Prohibitions against hunting, coupled with insufficient food supplies, have made the deer comparatively unafraid of people. As a result, they often graze close to homes, further increasing the likelihood that people will be attacked by disease-laden ticks. However, suggestions to ease restrictions against deer hunting have met resistance in most communities.

In the meantime, *Ixodes* ticks continue to proliferate and to invade new locations, exposing additional human populations to the debilitating disease first brought to the attention of the medical community by two mothers concerned over their children's health.

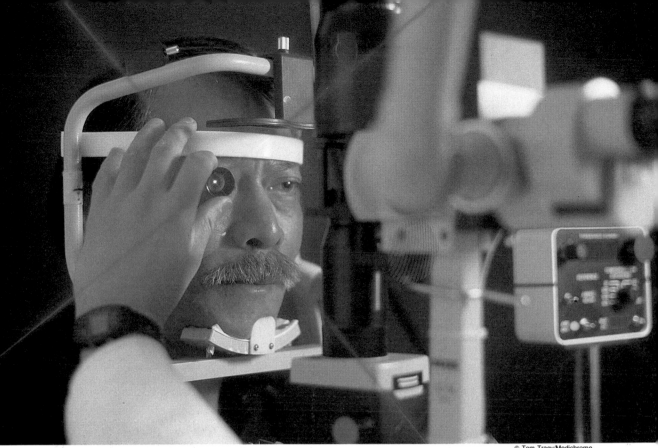

A thorough eye examination by an ophthalmologist can determine whether a patient's vision can be improved by radial keratotomy—a controversial operation that could improve nearsightedness.

A CURE FOR MYOPIA?

by Jana Pace

Each year, thousands of nearsighted Americans sit still, fortified only with a local anesthetic, while a doctor in a white lab coat plunges an exquisitely sharp knife into the outermost membrane of their eyes. There is no guarantee that the operation—called radial keratotomy—will result in perfect vision, but they go through with it anyway, emboldened by the possibility that when it's over, they will no longer be dependent on eyeglasses or contact lenses to see well.

Since 1978, well over 100,000 Americans with imperfect sight have undergone radial keratotomy at an average cost of $1,500 per eye. Hundreds of ophthalmologists (physicians whose specialty is the eye) now offer the procedure, typically learning the technique at two-day workshops held in the United States and abroad. The quick and relatively painless procedure can be accomplished in less than 30 minutes in the ophthalmologist's office. Vision improves overnight. But it may take months or even years after surgery for the cornea to heal completely and the full effect of the surgery to be felt or, more aptly, seen.

What Is Radial Keratotomy?

Ophthalmologists have known for over a century that by changing the shape of the cornea, they could change the eye's refractive, or light-

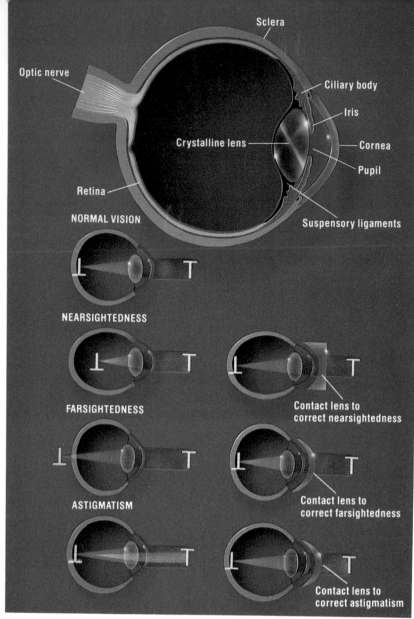

Sclera

Optic nerve

Ciliary body

Iris

Crystalline lens

Cornea

Pupil

Retina

Suspensory ligaments

NORMAL VISION

NEARSIGHTEDNESS

Contact lens to
correct nearsightedness

FARSIGHTEDNESS

Contact lens to
correct farsightedness

ASTIGMATISM

Contact lens to
correct astigmatism

© Edmond Alexander

The shape of vision. In the 10 percent of the population with normal vision, light rays are bent by the cornea and the lens of the eye so that images focus precisely on the retina. In nearsighted, or myopic, people, the eye is too long, and light rays fail to focus on the retina. Much debate in the medical community revolves around whether to correct myopia—a relatively benign condition—using contact lenses (which push back the point at which the eye focuses so that sharp images reach the retina) or by performing a radial keratotomy, with all its attendant risks. One complication of radial keratotomy is overcorrection, in which the operation renders the patient farsighted, with a focal point behind the eye. Contact lenses usually correct this condition. Radial keratotomy may also result in a misshapen cornea—a condition known as astigmatism, which is more difficult, if not impossible, to correct with contact lenses.

bending, characteristics. Radial keratotomy, or R.K., was first suggested by a German ophthalmologist in 1869, and first used in Japan in 1939. In the late 1960s, Soviet ophthalmologist F. S. Yenaliev brought radial keratotomy to the Soviet Union, where he refined it. It was imported from the Soviet Union by Dr. Leonard Bores, who performed the first operation in Detroit in 1978.

Keratotomy means literally ''to cut the cornea,'' the thin, tough, transparent membrane covering the eye's lens. With radial keratotomy, nearsightedness is corrected by weakening the cornea so that it can gradually reshape itself into a sort of natural contact lens. In a nearsighted

eye, the overly rounded cornea bends light rays too sharply, causing them to converge at a point somewhere in front of the retina, the light-sensitive tissue at the back of the eye. The image projected on the retina looks like a snapshot that is out-of-focus. A flatter, post-keratotomy cornea focuses light rays closer to, or preferably right on, the retina to produce a clearer, sharper image.

The operation itself is fairly simple and straightforward. First, a topical anesthetic in the form of eye drops is administered. The surgeon makes some measurements, including a measurement of the thickness of the cornea in several spots, with the aid of ultrasound.

Holding the knife at a 90-degree angle to the surface of the cornea, the surgeon then (in the words of one study prospectus outlining the procedure) "plunges the knife into the [cornea] with enough force to produce a slight indentation" of the horny membranes, and proceeds to make from four to sixteen evenly spaced incisions around the cornea, leaving a central clear zone. The exact number of cuts depends on the extent of the patient's nearsightedness, his or her age, and the surgeon's preference.

The diamond-bladed knife is finely calibrated so that the length of the blade can be adjusted before each operation to within a hundredth of a millimeter of the thinnest spot on the patient's cornea. (The cornea is about 0.2 inch—some 0.5 millimeters—deep). To get the greatest flattening effect, the surgeon must make each incision deep enough to penetrate at least 75 percent of the cornea, but not so deep that it or the eyeball beneath is perforated.

Each delicate wound is gently irrigated and checked for irregularities. Incisions that are too short or uneven are recut. Placed over the eye is an eye patch, which the patient can take off at home the next day. Any pain or discomfort often disappears once the pressure of the patch is removed. Most ophthalmologists prefer to postpone operating on the second eye for six months to one year. In the interim the "bad" eye is fitted with a contact lens.

Safety Debated

Is R.K. really the safe, effective answer to nearsightedness some have claimed? Or is it instead a radical and ill-conceived solution to a benign problem? Such questions have been hotly debated by eye doctors and researchers since the first euphoric reports about R.K. sounded here nearly 10 years ago.

The American Academy of Ophthalmology, a professional organization representing

With the myopic eye magnified by a special stereoscopic microscope, a surgeon prepares to cut multiple incisions in the patient's cornea using a diamond-bladed knife.

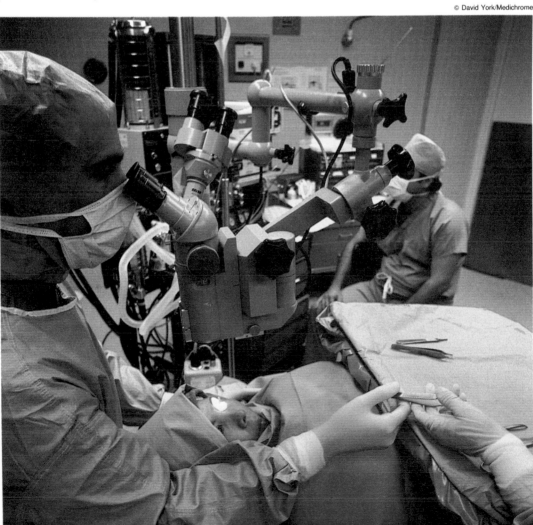

most of the nation's eye doctors, has adopted a wait-and-see attitude, saying that, at this stage, R.K. should be considered an "investigational procedure," a tag that practicing keratotomists claim has kept many insurance companies from providing coverage. Likewise, the National Eye Institute, the ocular branch of the National Institutes of Health, has called the procedure "experimental" and urges restraint in its use pending the results of ongoing studies.

Criticism of R.K. has had two recurrent themes.

The cost/benefit ratio of R.K. is lopsided. Nearsightedness is a relatively benign condition that can almost always be corrected with glasses or contact lenses. Are the risks of scarring, infecting, or even blinding an otherwise normal, healthy eye equal to the benefits that, critics say, are largely cosmetic?

Reliable data on the long-term risks of radial keratotomy are not yet in. The longest doctors have closely followed keratotomy patients in the United States is about five years.

Keratotomy candidate? Many myopic athletes have looked into the procedure as a means of ridding themselves of eyeglasses or contact lenses.

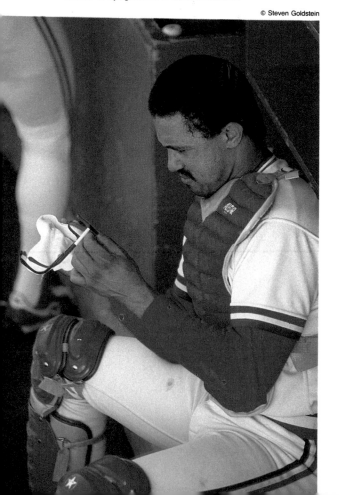

Will the results of the surgery prove stable? Will operated-on corneas prove more vulnerable to infection or injury 10 or 20 years after surgery? As keratotomy patients get older, will they have a higher risk of developing cataracts, glaucoma, or other eye conditions associated with old age?

Valuable information about R.K. is now coming in from several long-term studies of the procedure. One such study is the Progressive Evaluation of Radial Keratotomy (PERK), which got under way in March 1982. Researchers at nine clinical centers across the country performed the surgery on 435 volunteers with mild to severe nearsightedness, following a single, standardized procedure. The last eye was operated on in the fall of 1983. Results of the third-year follow-up visits of 410 participants were reported last November.

The first three years of the PERK study and several smaller clinical studies now in progress have produced a picture of R.K. that reveals it to be neither as risky as critics had feared nor quite as effective as its champions had hoped. Following is a summary of some of the findings.

Over and Under

While researchers agree that R.K. has successfully reduced nearsightedness in virtually every case, it is not true that every patient (or even most) who has had the operation obtains perfect vision. Changing the shape of the cornea lacks the precision and predictability of grinding a lens for a pair of glasses or contacts. After surgery, many patients are "undercorrected," meaning they are left with residual nearsightedness. Others have their nearsightedness (myopia) inadvertently replaced with the opposite problem of farsightedness (hyperopia). This is especially true of older patients and those with relatively mild or moderate nearsightedness at the outset.

Three years after surgery, for example, PERK researchers found that 16 percent of the participants in the study were overcorrected or farsighted to the extent that they now needed reading glasses sooner than they might have otherwise. More than one-fourth of the participants remained undercorrected to the extent that they still could not see well without glasses or contacts.

In a study by Arrowsmith and Marks of 142 keratotomies performed on 93 patients at the Arrowsmith Eye Institute in Nashville, Ten-

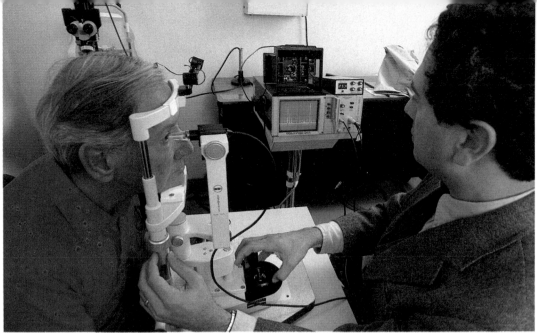

Using ultrasound, doctors can determine whether a patient's cornea is suitable for radial keratotomy.

nessee, 40 percent of the participants said they still wore corrective lenses at least part-time two years after surgery. Of these, about 11 percent reported wearing glasses or contacts all the time, 14 percent "usually" wore corrective lenses, 8 percent "sometimes" wore them, and 5 percent "rarely" did. (Eighty-five percent of the people in the same survey said they were satisfied with the results of the surgery.)

A study of 79 keratotomy patients by Deitz and Sanders, ophthalmologists in Kansas and Illinois, respectively, found 37 percent of the 109 eyes operated on were overcorrected four years after surgery. Sixteen percent were undercorrected.

People who achieve only a partial flattening effect from the surgery (most frequently those with very poor eyesight to begin with) can elect to have a second operation done on the same eye. Rather than deepen the initial incisions, surgeons usually prefer to make a new set of cuts between the old ones. Unfortunately, repeated keratotomies have proven even less effective and more unpredictable than first-time operations. One in four PERK study participants who underwent a second keratotomy experienced no improvement in vision.

Instability

When radial keratotomy was first introduced in the United States, doctors expected operated-on corneas to stabilize within three to six months.

Studies show, however, that this is rarely the case. It is now apparent that the cornea—a membrane without blood vessels—heals remarkably slowly. And in the process of healing, the cornea continues to change shape, generally becoming flatter. If the patient is initially undercorrected following surgery, his vision may move slowly toward "emmetropia," or "perfect" vision.

However, if the patient had perfect or slightly overcorrected vision after surgery, a continued flattening of the cornea will move him further away from emmetropia. Thirty-one percent of the eyes operated on in the Deitz and Sanders study were in this stage of "progressive hyperopia" three to four years after surgery.

Some patients also experience daily fluctuations in vision, with most becoming slightly more nearsighted from morning to night and then slightly less so as they sleep.

Doctors are not able to predict how soon a patient's vision will stabilize or how good it will be when it does. Half of all PERK study participants experienced fluctuations in vision between six months and one year after surgery. Thirty-three percent showed a continuing effect of the surgery in the second year, after which time most participants' vision became stable. Twelve percent still complained of large fluctuation in vision at the end of three years. In another study, some R.K. patients experienced fluctuation five years after surgery.

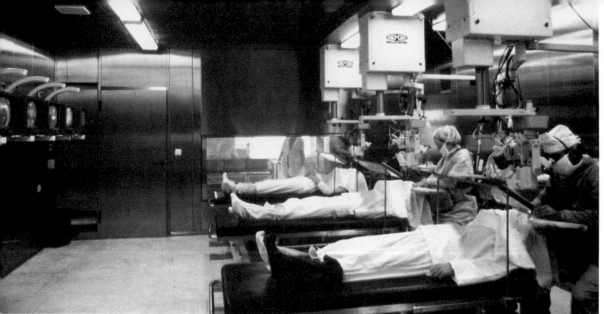

© Anna Clopet/US News & World Report

Assembly-line radial keratotomies in the Soviet Union have come under much criticism by Western eye specialists.

Complications

The best news coming out of clinical studies on R.K. is that severe complications appear to be rare. PERK researchers report that less than 1 percent of the participants in the study have experienced major problems. Other researchers and private practitioners report a very low rate of serious complications as well.

The worst complication reported was a patient who suffered a permanent loss of vision from an infection inside the eye that developed after the ophthalmologist accidently cut through the cornea during surgery. In other cases, cataracts have developed after radial keratotomy that have later been removed.

Infections of the cornea—rare in normal circumstances among non–contact lens wearers—have affected a few R.K. patients. A small number of keratotomy patients have also proven susceptible to incisional cysts, which keep the cornea from healing and may explain some cases of fluctuating vision; vascularization, the growth of blood vessels into cuts; and epithelial erosion, the sloughing off of the outer layer of cells on the cornea, causing recurrent pain. According to one keratotomist, these complications are similar to those experienced by contact lens wearers and probably no more common.

Perhaps the most disconcerting finding concerns the loss of ''best correct visual acuity'' by a few participants in virtually every study reviewed. These patients can no longer see as well wearing properly prescribed glasses or con-

tact lenses as they once could. In the PERK study, one year after the operation, 13 percent of the patients had lost one line of vision on the Snellen chart (the familiar big E in the doctor's office), and 3 percent had lost two lines, with corrective lenses.

In a study by Sawelson and Marks of 126 keratotomy patients at the Cedars Medical Center in Miami, Florida, 90 percent of the 198 eyes operated on could be further corrected with glasses or contacts to 20/20 one year after surgery, but the percentage dropped to 82 percent at three years and to 55 percent at five years after the operation.

For other patients, their best corrected vision has improved after radial keratotomy. Twenty-five percent of the PERK study participants found they had gained one Snellen line, and 2 percent had gained two lines when tested a year after surgery.

One possible explanation for the changes in the best corrected visual acuity of R.K. is that the shape of the cornea is often more irregular after the operation. This surgically induced astigmatism cannot easily be corrected with glasses or contacts. About 12 percent of the participants in the PERK study had acquired significant additional astigmatism when tested at the three-year visit, while 13 percent had had a noticeable but less significant decrease in astigmatism. In the Sawelson and Marks study, 54 percent of the eyes operated on showed a decrease in astigmatism at three years, while 19 percent showed no change, and 30 percent had additional astigmatism that was not present before surgery.

Complaints

Complaints of persistent glare, tearing, discomfort in strong light, and double vision have also been voiced by a small number of R.K. patients. These symptoms appear to be temporary. Eighteen months after surgery, 3 percent of Dr. Sawelson's patients reported a problem with "photophobia," or light-sensitivity, but in every case the problem had disappeared before the three-year visit.

Between the 18-month and 3-year visits, complaints of glare (which had caused three PERK patients to reduce their nighttime driving in the year after surgery) fell from 9 percent to 1 percent. Complaints of tearing fell from 1 percent to zero. Nine percent of the participants in the Arrowsmith study reported persistent glare two years after surgery, down from 11 percent at one year, and 4 percent reported ghosting, down from 9 percent.

Effectiveness

Unfortunately, radial keratotomy has proved most beneficial for people with relatively mild or moderate nearsightedness. Before surgery, none of the 435 participants selected for the PERK study could see better than 20/40, and over half had 20/200 eyesight or worse. (At 20/200, a person can read only the big E at the top of the Snellen eye chart from 20 feet away.)

After surgery, 78 percent of all participants could see 20/40 or better without corrective lenses, the visual acuity required in most states to drive without glasses. But of the 149 participants with the worst preoperative vision, only 63 percent had achieved the 20/40 benchmark one year after surgery, while 5 percent could still see no better than 20/200.

Meanwhile, all but 8 percent of those with the best vision going into the operation had qualified for restriction-free driver's licenses by the end of the first year. In a study done at UCLA by K. J. Hoffer, et al., 69 percent or better of the eyes with mild to moderate nearsightedness could see 20/40 or better two years after surgery, while only 20 percent of the participants with very poor eyesight could see that well.

The percentage of all participants achieving 20/40 vision or better in other studies was: Arrowsmith and Marks, 76 percent at two years (73 percent at six months); Deitz and Sanders, 83 percent at one year; and Sawelson and Marks, 73 percent at three years (70 percent at two years and 67 percent at one year). In addition, Arrowsmith and Marks reported that 39 percent of all participants had attained at least 20/20 vision two years after surgery (49 percent at one year), and Deitz and Sanders reported 20/20 vision or better in 40 percent of all participants at one year.

What's on the Horizon

The above figures represent operations done four, five, and more years ago, when radial keratotomy was relatively new to U.S. eye surgeons. Improvements have been made already in the surgeon's equipment and in techniques. A decade of experience with R.K. (with the human as guinea pig) has indeed yielded information on ways to make the procedure safer and more predictable. For instance, many surgeons are using fewer incisions (4 or 8 instead of 16) that are not quite as deep, and they are leaving a larger central "clear zone."

Ophthalmologists are also limiting their keratotomy practices to those patients likely to benefit most from the operation, and refusing the cases of extreme nearsightedness that were attempted early on. Thus, it is likely that success rates will improve in the future.

Further refinement of the techniques and tools could also benefit patients of R.K. Surgeons now use an ultrasonic pachymeter to gauge the thickness of the cornea accurately, and a diamond-tipped micrometer knife that is capable of cleaner, more uniform cuts.

The most promising new technology on the horizon involves the excimer laser developed a decade ago as a research tool. Unlike other lasers, the excimer uses the atoms of two different elements to produce a beam of ultraviolet light that does not burn tissue away, but causes it to decompose chemically. Experiments on butterfly wings have shown the laser is capable of making incredibly clean cuts, only a few millionths of an inch deep, without damaging the surrounding tissue.

The laser is now being tested to determine the viability of using it in refractive corneal surgery, though tests on sighted volunteers are still at least a couple of years away. If the experiments are successful, eye surgeons will have a tool to "sculpt" the cornea in a matter of seconds with more precision and less scarring than has ever been possible before.

PAST, PRESENT, AND FUTURE

Naval experts built a replica of a trireme—a three-tiered ancient Greek warship—and successfully tested it in the Aegean.

REVIEW OF THE YEAR

PAST, PRESENT, AND FUTURE

FOOD AND POPULATION

In 1987 the world population passed the 5 billion mark, and the U.N. World Food Council, at its annual meeting in Beijing, China, said that more than 10 percent of these people are malnourished and facing starvation, despite steadily increasing surpluses of food in the world.

The world produces nearly 2.2 billion tons (2 billion metric tons) of grain (mainly wheat, corn, and rice) every year—more than enough to provide the daily caloric requirements for every person in the world. Regrettably, it does not do so; people in the relatively rich countries of Europe and North America (and Australia and Japan) eat about four times as much grain, per person, as people in the Third World. Moreover, they eat better, because most of that grain is converted into meat, milk, and eggs, which constitute a better diet than grain itself.

Although famines like those in Africa and Kampuchea, which brought shocking pictures to our TV screens in years past, seem to have faded in urgency, the chronic hunger that affects half a billion people every day, as they struggle for survival, has not receded. Indeed, it is becoming worse at exactly the same time that the U.N.'s Food and Agriculture Organization (FAO) is predicting annual surpluses that will depress farm prices even further.

It is perhaps somewhat surprising to realize that there is widespread hunger in the United States, one of the richest countries in the world. As we approach a population of 240 million, we find that more than 10 million are getting food stamps and that many more are eligible—even though there has been steady economic growth.

Although there are far fewer rural people than urban people, the former are more apt to be poor and hungry than the latter. Family farmers are also leaving the land because of their growing debts and the increasing concentration in the food system. Soup kitchens, food lines, and shelters for the homeless are increasing in number. Among the groups hardest hit are minority youths, migrant farm workers, senior citizens, Native Americans, and women who head households.

The debate over farm and food policy in the U.S. Government continued throughout the year; and even though no significant legislation was enacted, that policy area is expected to get increased attention during the 1988 presidential campaign. But because the stress will be on tinkering with the system and avoiding difficult problems, the prognosis is that concentration will continue in the system and that hunger and malnutrition will continue to increase both in the United States and in the Third World.

MARTIN M. McLAUGHLIN

ANTHROPOLOGY AND ARCHAEOLOGY

Discoveries made in Africa in 1987 have led some researchers to suggest that the species known as *Homo habilis,* believed to be a direct ancestor of modern humans, was more apelike than hitherto thought. A skull and partial skeleton were found in 1.8-million-year-old deposits at Olduvai Gorge in Tanzania by a team directed by Donald C. Johanson of the Institute of Human Origins in Berkeley, California. The skeletal remains are thought to be those of an adult female who stood only slightly more than 3 feet (1 meter) and had long arms relative to her legs. In comparing this new discovery with the remains of an individual of the *Homo erectus* type dating to 1.6 million years ago, some investigators suggest that the great change in size and skeletal form indicates that human evolution happened very rapidly during that 200,000-year interval. Other specialists, however, emphasize the relatively small number of fossil finds of human ancestors and feel that the picture is still far too incomplete to talk about processes of evolution in terms of specific fossils.

In Egypt a team of American and Egyptian scientists supported by the National Geographic Society used Space Age technology designed for studies on the moon to drill a hole and lower a camera into a chamber in the Great Pyramid of Cheops to study a boat placed there 4,600 years ago. A similar boat had been found in 1954 in a nearby chamber, leading scholars to suspect that this one would also contain a boat. The boat excavated in 1954 was in 1,224 pieces; when assembled, it measured 142 feet (43 meters) in length. The drill had to bore through a 5-foot (1.5-meter) piece of limestone to reach the interior. The television camera focused on the piles of wood from the disassembled boat, and also showed inscriptions carved into the walls by the ancient workers. Air samples extracted from the chamber may help scientists learn more about the atmosphere of ancient Egypt and about chemical changes that took place in this sealed environment during the 4,600 years. There are no plans to open the chamber at this time.

In Greece a replica of an ancient naval ship has been constructed and tested. During the 5th and 4th centuries B.C., the trireme played an important role in Greece's naval activity in the Mediterranean Sea. A group of scholars decided to build the ship, based on pictures on Greek pots and coins and descriptions in Greek literature. Modern rowers who tested the replica found conditions cramped and uncomfortable. The crew consists of 170 people, and the ship is some 123 feet (37.5 meters) in length.

The saga of the exploration of the *Titanic* continued in 1987. The great steamship, which sank in 1912 with the loss of 1,513 lives, was rediscovered by a joint American-French expedition in 1985. Dr. Robert Ballard of the Woods Hole Oceanographic Institute directed highly productive dives to the ship, which rests about 2½ miles (4 kilometers) below the surface, some 350 miles (560 kilometers) southeast of Newfoundland. The National Geographic Society, supporter of his work, has published extraordinary photographs from his expeditions. In the summer of 1987, a team of French divers using a deep-sea vessel called the *Nautile* began recovering objects from the wreck, including safes, fine china, wine bottles, jewelry, money, a bronze statue, and a chandelier. The American and French groups who discovered the wreck disagree on how the ship should be treated. The American group feels that the ship should be left untouched as a memorial to those who died in the sinking; French salvagers, on the other hand, are eager to recover interesting and potentially valuable objects from the wreck. A French sponsor of the salvaging expedition said that it intends not to sell the objects, but to establish one or more museums in which they can be displayed.

PETER S. WELLS

Egyptologists used ground-penetrating radar to study an ancient burial pit without disturbing its contents.

© Dvak Arslanian/National Geographic Society

Reappraising the DINOSAURS

by Virginia Morell

W hat I'd like to find about now is a big, ugly bone,'' says Jack Horner as he hunches forward on hands and knees, brushing at the dirt with a small paintbrush. Several fossilized bones, 1 to 2 feet (0.3 to 0.6 meter) in length, lay partially exposed on the hillside, but he dismisses them. "Small potatoes.''

Horner grabs an ice pick and jabs at the hillside, loosening the soil, then scoops away the crumbly earth. A small end of a bone pokes out. Horner exchanges the ice pick for the brush and sweeps away the dirt. "Well," he sighs, "another rib.'' He frowns, squirts a stream of shellac over the exposed bone, and sits back cross-legged, studying the rough hole he and his co-workers have gouged in the soil of this eastern Montana hill.

"We need the head or the pelvis so we can tell if what we've got here is a new dinosaur,'' he says. "I'm pretty sure it's new. No one has ever looked for dinosaurs from this time period [80 million years ago] in North America before, so everything should be new, and we'll have to think up new names.'' Horner smiles at the idea. "New dinosaurs,'' he adds with an even bigger grin, "are neat."

Warm-blooded Dinosaurs

In the past eight years, Jack Horner, curator of paleontology at Montana State University's Museum of the Rockies in Bozeman, has not only uncovered several new species, but entire rookeries of dinosaurs, complete with nests, eggs, and babies—discoveries that have yielded startling new ideas about these giant creatures and how they lived.

Contrary to the long-standing image of dinosaurs as dim-witted reptiles, Horner pictures them as tremendously successful animals that evolved the first social behaviors on earth. He also believes that they were warm-blooded; in the past, most scientists thought that dinosaurs, as reptiles, were cold-blooded. "Horner's discoveries are spectacular," observes William Clemens, a professor of paleontology at the University of California at Berkeley. "It's the first time we've been able to see how members of dinosaur species developed, and Horner's interpretations have certainly influenced my thinking about how they lived."

Unlike many other researchers, Horner does not particularly care why the creatures disappeared. "I want to know what living dinosaurs were like, what they ate, how they cared for their young," he explains. "They were around for 140 million years, and we've been here for only 4 million. So you'd think we might try to understand why they were so successful, instead of concentrating on why they became extinct."

A tall, lanky Montanan, Horner has spent most of his 40 years seeking answers to that question. He found his first dinosaur bone on his father's ranch when he was 8. He labeled the bone "104-A," put it in a box with other fossils, and decided to find more. Since then he has scoured eroded gullies and weathered hillsides across the state.

Egg Mountain

Dinosaurs are so unlike us," says Horner, digging at the earth once more with his ice pick. "We don't even know for sure which are herbivores and which are carnivores." His two student assistants, Phil Peterson and Pat Murphy, work with pickax and shovel above him, literally taking off the top of the hill. By midmorning the trio has uncovered two additional ribs and part of a shoulder blade. Horner decides to visit the site of his most famous discoveries: Egg Mountain.

He climbs into his pickup and heads east on a gravel road that cuts across a golden prairie. Ahead of him lies the Sawtooth Range of the Rocky Mountains. Horner found his childhood dinosaur bone in this same region, but once he began collecting fossils professionally, he devoted most of his time to exploring exposures closer to the Canadian border. Geologically,

New evidence suggests that dinosaurs were warm-blooded animals that, much like birds, lavished attention on their young. At Egg Mountain in Montana, scientists have discovered vast nesting areas used by vegetarian dinosaurs called hypsilophodonts (facing page). Nearby lived gentle duck-billed hadrosaurs, which measured some 30 feet in length. At right, an adult hadrosaur takes its young on a foraging expedition.

Below and facing page: Doug Henderson

Hadrosaur fledglings emerge from eggs (below). The nests, 3 feet wide and 6 feet deep, apparently were scooped out of mud and grass. Among their predators was the terrifying tyrannosaurus (above right), from which the defenseless hadrosaur typically took refuge in shallow waters (left) that covered much of the region.

that area is known as the Judith River formation, and many of the finest and largest dinosaur skeletons come from its beds. Horner, however, was not interested in just another adult dinosaur skeleton; he wanted to understand the dinosaurs' complete life cycle. To do this, he needed babies and juveniles.

"Most people thought dinosaurs grew up at random, sort of like lizards do," explains Horner. "Then, in the 1970s, a few scientists, like Robert Bakker of the University of Colorado, began to make some wild guesses—good wild guesses—about dinosaur ecology and behavior." In two revolutionary papers, published in the British science journal *Nature*, Bakker argued that the dinosaurs were not as reptilian as most experts believed. Instead, he suggested that they were warm-blooded creatures that must have lived far differently than any lizards we know. "One group still lives," he wrote. "We call them birds." About that time, with some luck, Horner found Egg Mountain.

In 1978 he and his colleague, Bob Makela, stopped in at a rock shop in Bynum, Montana, to examine a large bone the owner, Marion Brandvold, had found. She showed them the bone, and then pulled out a coffee can with some pencil-thin bones in it. "I took one look at those and just gasped," recalls Horner. "They were what I'd been searching for years for—baby dinosaur bones." Brandvold took Horner and Makela to the site where she found the bones, and within a week they had uncovered a nest filled with the fossilized skeletons of 15 babies—the first dinosaur nestlings ever to be discovered.

The next summer, while following the surveying markers left on a nearby knoll by a seismic crew, a member of Horner's team stumbled onto a dense patch of fossils. Horner moved his team to this knoll, and over the next several seasons, from 1979 to 1984, they dug and jackhammered nearly 500 dinosaur eggs out of its hard mudstone. In tribute, Horner gave the small prairie hill its rather whimsical name—Egg Mountain.

Dinosaur Family Life

The eggs had been laid by hypsilophodonts, swift-running vegetarians about 10 feet (3 meters) in length. Nearby, Horner also found the nests and eggs of some members of the Hadrosauridae, or duck-billed dinosaur, family. Thirty feet (9 meters) from nose to tail, hadro-

In North America, increased volcanic activity during the Triassic Period did not bode well for the dinosaurs.

saurs were semierect vegetarians with rounded backs, short arms, and ducklike faces. Near Egg Mountain the duckbills laid their eggs in nests, 3 feet (1 meter) wide and 6 feet (2 meters) deep, which they scooped out of the mud and grasses. In some of the nests, Horner uncovered complete clutches, 20 to 25 eggs, neatly arranged in cylindrical patterns; in others, he found the bones of more nestlings. There were also skeletons of juveniles and adults. It was exactly what Horner had been searching for: the first evidence of dinosaur family life.

It was immediately clear that these dinosaurs had not lived like any reptiles we know today, but, as Bakker had suggested, were more like birds. Most reptiles lay their eggs, then abandon them, leaving the young to fend for themselves. The duck-billed dinosaurs, however, covered their eggs with grasses and reeds, then lingered alongside their nests until the warmth of the Sun hatched the eggs. "The hadrosaurs nested in great colonies, like penguins or gulls do, and cared for their young— and that is one of the main reasons, I think, that dinosaurs were so successful," says Horner. "They practiced parental care."

Horner parks the pickup at the bottom of the 50-foot (15-meter) rise that is Egg Mountain, and begins working his way up. At the top he stops to survey the surrounding land and fossil deposits. To his eye the eroded hillside speaks of a world when there was no prairie, and the Sawtooth Mountains were young and newly formed, and only 200 miles (320 kilometers) from a vast inland sea.

Based on an accumulation of fossil evidence from the site, Horner pictures Egg Mountain in the day of the hadrosaurs as an island in a shallow lake upcountry from that sea. Every year, thousands of duckbills migrated there from the coastal plains to nest in a great, honking, teeming colony. Swift, carnivorous dinosaurs called troödonts traveled the upland country in packs, and huge pterosaurs soared among the trees. The lake's waters may have afforded some safety to the waddling, defenseless duckbills. There was also the safety of numbers.

Birdlike Behavior

During the years of uncovering what had transpired at Egg Mountain, Horner found evidence of other birdlike behavior. For example, birds that nest in colonies space their nests at wingtip to wingtip distances. In like manner, 30-foot (9-meter) hadrosaurs set their nests 30 feet (9 meters) apart. Further, the nests of birds that raise altricial young (babies that are helpless) are always littered with eggshell fragments.

"Baby duckbills lived in their nests, and their parents brought them food—berries and grasses," notes Horner. "We know this from looking at the wear marks on the babies' teeth. They had been feeding for some time when something happened to their parents. They were too young to fend for themselves, so they died. But it is very, very rare to find dead babies in the nest because they were well taken care of."

Struck by the duckbills' maternal instincts, Horner named them *Maiasaura peeblesorum*—the latter after the Peebles family that owns the land where he made his finds; *Maiasaura* for "good mother lizard."

"We've found 50 bones per square meter around Egg Mountain," says Horner, "which suggests that in this deposit there are approximately 10,000 dinosaurs. I think they were killed in a volcanic eruption, then transported a mile in a mudflow."

Fast Growers

Rising lake waters sometimes washed over the nesting colonies, engulfing the eggs so suddenly that even the beginnings of life were preserved; inside 22 of the eggs, Horner found duckbill embryos. He now had the complete life cycle, from eggs to embryos to nestlings, juveniles and adults. It convinced him that Bakker is very likely right on another point: dinosaurs were warm-blooded. A baby hadrosaur is 13 inches (33 centimeters) long at birth and grows to 30 feet (9 meters), notes Horner. "If you're born little and have a long ways to grow," he says, "it is selectively advantageous to grow fast—and to do that, you have to be warm-blooded."

Horner thinks he can prove this through a study of the growth rate of the dinosaurs' bones. Such a study, however, requires more than one or two species of dinosaurs. Horner needs more dinosaurs, and once again the complete range, from babies to adults.

It is late afternoon by the time Horner returns to the dig. Phil and Pat have pushed the excavation farther into the hillside. Thick ribs and several vertebrae lie nearby. Pat looks up from his section and says, "We've got the pelvis." Horner flashes a smile and bends down to look. He studies the bone structure for a moment, then stands up.

"Well, boys," he beams. "Looks like we have ourselves a new dinosaur. It's another hadrosaur, but a new species." Horner picks up an ice pick and brush, and sits down cross-legged in the dirt. "Now let's find its head."

The volcanic ashfall that smothered the hadrosaurs also helped preserve their fossils for millions of years.

MARINE
MIRAGES

by Adrienne Mayor

For centuries, sailors in the Mediterranean have described a fantastic panorama of towers, arches, and castles that is sometimes seen shimmering in the mist over the sea between Italy and Sicily. These mirages are called ''Fata Morgana'' because the Crusaders imagined they were the handiwork of Morgan le Fay, the enchantress of Arthurian romance.

Morgan, said to live in a palace under the sea off southern Italy, was famous for her ability to create ''castles in the air.'' According to

Seafaring people spun countless tales to account for the sudden appearance of castles in the sky, misty islands on the horizon, and other marine mirages.

medieval legend, seafarers who mistook her magical mirages for a safe harbor were led far off course and hopelessly lost. A typical account of the mirage, written in about 1500, describes "an array of towers, pinnacles, and columns, palaces with balconies and windows, extended alleys with trees . . . a scene of architectural magnificence" hovering above the horizon until it seems to slowly melt away.

In 1634 in Reggio di Calabria, a port on the tip of Italy's toe, a priest, Father Angelucci, gazed out over the Strait of Messina toward Sicily. Suddenly he saw what he called a "vision of paradise." Angelucci all his life had hoped to observe the by-now-famous mirage, and he strove to describe it scientifically in a letter to his friend Athanasius Kircher, a German archaeologist and physicist. "The ocean which washes the coast of Sicily rose up and looked like a dark mountain range"; against this backdrop "quickly appeared a series of more than 10,000 whitish-gray pilasters," which "then shrank to half their height" and were transformed into "arches like those of Roman aqueducts." Castles with towers and windows also rose above the aqueduct, then the vision shimmered and disappeared.

Kircher, intrigued by the phenomenon, attempted to reproduce the ocean illusion in his laboratory by passing a ray of light through a heated vessel fashioned to mimic the shape of the strait and containing sand from Sicily. Encouraged by the partial success of this experiment, Kircher continued to work in optics. Ultimately, he was able to project on a screen a mirage effect that terrified and mystified audiences. Kircher is credited with the invention of the magic lantern, the precursor of motion pictures—and inspired by optical illusions at sea.

About a century after Angelucci's experience, a friar named Minasi published a dissertation on ocean mirages. Minasi was born near Reggio di Calabria and had seen the Fata Morgana three times. At sunrise, he wrote in 1773, when the sea is calm, the spectator, with the sun behind him and facing the sea, may suddenly see "various multiplied objects, such as numberless series of pilasters, arches, castles well delineated, columns, lofty towers, superb palaces with balconies and windows."

So far, Minasi's description parallels Angelucci's. But 18th-century mirage-watchers tended to invest their visions with action-packed details. Besides cattle and sheep grazing in "delightful plains," Minasi saw "armies of men on foot and horseback, and many other strange figures, all in their natural colors and proper action, and passing rapidly in succession along the surface of the sea." His contemporaries at Manduria in the heel of Italy had described another mirage sometimes glimpsed hovering over the Gulf of Taranto. This illusion also featured animated panoramas, luminous palaces, grazing herds, and cavalry parades, all outlined with an iridescent glimmer.

Ideal Conditions Needed

Although marine mirages were sighted elsewhere, the Fata Morgana of the strait was considered the classic example. A drawing included in Minasi's treatise became the standard textbook representation of an ocean mirage.

There have been many eyewitness accounts and discussions of the atmospheric details of Italy's great illusionary metropolis. Early in the 20th century, a physicist from Reggio di Calabria, V. E. Boccara, made three sketches of the illusion. The first depicts the eerie streak of white mist that often heralds the Fata Morgana. The next shows the phantom city rising out of the sea. The third shows a three-tiered cityscape suspended over the water.

Many writers have concentrated on the ideal conditions for sightings of the famous mirage. They agree that the best time is a hot summer morning, when the air is extremely clear, except for a thin veil of mist obscuring the coast of Sicily. The sea should be calm, with only a gentle northerly breeze.

In 1912 an article in *Scientific American* predicted that one should be able to obtain "good photographs of Fata Morgana . . . without difficulty." Indeed, by 1975 specialists in meteorological optics had successfully predicted and photographed a variety of marine mirages. Meteorologist Alistair Fraser determined the necessary atmospheric conditions, predicted, and then photographed several mirages in Puget Sound of boys "walking on water," ferryboats transformed into "castles," and images of Romanesque arches. According to Fraser, when the flat, evenly lighted surface of the sea is warmer than the air above, the air acts as a magnifying glass, distorting real features of the landscape or a boat into what

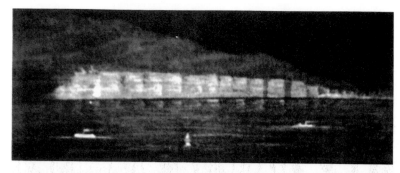

Early in this century, Italian physicist V.E. Boccara depicted the Fata Morgana mirage that occasionally appears in the waters off Sicily. Typically, an eerie streak of mist ushers in the mirage (top). Next, the phantom city seems to emerge from the sea (center). Under ideal conditions, the mirage takes the form of a three-tiered city suspended over the sea (bottom).

Scientific American 106, no. 15 (April 13, 1912)

appears as a mist or fog. Then gentle breezes "sculpt" the blurred image into spectacular castles, cities, mountains, or fancy bridges of the type so ornately described by the Italians.

Luring Sailors

Particularly fanciful descriptions characterize the Irish tales of ocean mirages, called "fairy isles" or "fairy castles." As in the Morgan le Fay legend, they were said to be responsible for beckoning sailors to misadventure. According to Giraldus Cambrensis, who wrote a *Topography of Ireland* in 1187, when a mirage of an enchanted isle appeared, it was the custom to throw a burning coal at it since fire was thought to dispel phantoms. Indeed, many believed that a phantom island could be occupied by mortals if a fire could be started.

To explain the origin of this belief, Cambrensis told the story of a fairy island that appeared off the west coast of Ireland one calm morning. At first, observers thought it was a whale, but as it remained stationary, they decided it was land. Daring youths approached the spot in a boat, but as they drew near, the island vanished. The next day the apparition rose again to mock the sailors. They were able to land on the island only after letting fly an arrow tipped with red-hot steel.

A history of Ireland published in 1636 noted that seamen often encountered enchanted isles as they sailed west. These "temporary" islands were sometimes perceived by people who lived on the western coast, too. In the late 17th century, historian Roderick O'Flagherty recorded that, to inhabitants of the island of Arran in the Firth of Clyde, northeast of Ireland, "often appears visible that enchanted island, called O'Branil, and in Irish Beg-ara." The chronicler describes the place as a "wild island of huge rocks" that occasionally rises in the sea. At times one could also see "a great city far off, full of houses, castles, towers, and chimneys." Suddenly the mirage would become an animated cavalcade of "blazing flames, smoke, and people running to and fro." At other times one saw "nothing but a number of ships, with their sails and riggings" suspended over the ocean. Sometimes, seamen were treated to sights of lively fairs in progress; others saw

great bridges spanning the sky over the sea; one fairy island was more mundanely populated by women busily hanging out laundry.

An Irish memoir written in 1748 told of an enchanted island that could sometimes be seen floating beyond "Giant's Causeway," on the north coast. In the summer of 1812, several sightseers there were amazed to see images of "castles, ruins, and tall spires darting rapidly across the surface of the sea, which were instantly lengthened into considerable height."

Extraordinary Optical Illusions

About 60 years later, over the Firth of Forth (along the east coast of Scotland), in the early summer of 1871, "scarcely a day passed without several instances of atmospheric phenomena of vivid and interesting character." The "extraordinary optical illusions" over the sea were reported in great detail in the sober pages of *Symons's Monthly Meteorological Magazine*. The most spectacular display occurred on a warm Saturday afternoon.

First, an image of Balconic Castle on the Fife coast appeared about 45 degrees up from the horizon. Tiny May Island "suddenly shot up in the form of a huge perpendicular wall, apparently 800 or 900 feet [245 or 275 meters] high." A long row of rocks east of the island "assumed the most diversified and fantastic shapes"; once, they appeared as a "beautiful columnar circle, 20 to 30 feet [6 to 9 meters] high," then

Minasi's 18th-century depiction of Fata Morgana included cattle, sheep, and armies of men on foot and horseback.

Scientific American 106, no. 15 (April 13, 1912)

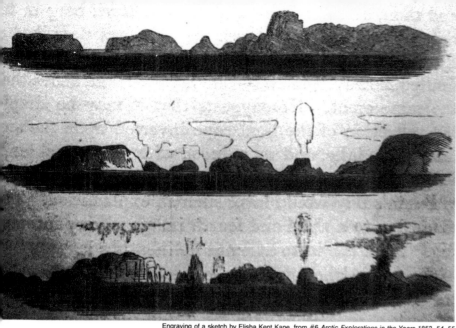

In the 19th century, Dr. Elisha Kent Kane sketched mirages of headlands, islands, and icebergs that he thought were real. Later explorers were confused when the landmasses sketched by Kane did not exist.

Engraving of a sketch by Elisha Kent Kane, from #6 *Arctic Explorations in the Years 1853, 54, 55*

they changed to a grove of trees that rapidly expanded to a "plantation." An arch spanned the trees and the island, then dozens more arches appeared in quick succession; meanwhile, "jagged rifts and ravines" opened in the face of the high wall, and a series of towers, columns, and archways sprang up and disappeared. Witnesses watched this incredibly active panorama for four hours; it ended when the island shrank to a thin blue line above the horizon, and a drenching rain began.

The 1914 *Royal Meteorological Society Quarterly Journal* carried an account of a mirage that appeared off the Cornish coast near Land's End, England. Along the sea horizon suddenly appeared a line of coastal scenery, complete with woods, fields, and hedges. Before long the witness recognized the scene as a reflection of his own location—he was able to identify church spires, a river, and the harbor of Falmouth. Soon he saw Pendennis Head with its castle and military buildings. The mirage lasted for several minutes and was "reversed as in a looking glass and slightly magnified."

Poetic Inspiration

According to legend, submerged in the sea between Land's End and the Scilly Isles was the misty Kingdom of Lyonesse, King Arthur's birthplace and scene of many chivalrous deeds. A haunting verse about this fabled realm was written by English poet Thomas Hardy in 1870: "As I set out for Lyonesse,/ A hundred miles away,/ The rine was on the spray,/ And starlight lit my loneliness."

French legend tells of another ancient submarine city, Ys, which can be glimpsed in the Bay of Douarnenez. This mirage has an aural facet—some travelers say they can hear the tolling church bells of Ys. Edgar Allen Poe might have been thinking of Ys or Lyonesse when he wrote his poem "The City in the Sea," in whose "kingly halls" far beneath the melancholy and serene deep, "the light from the lurid sea / streams up the turrets silently." Some legends of cities that appear to be submerged below the sea could be inspired by what Minasi had classified as "marine" (as opposed to "aerial") mirages. In modern terminology the cities beneath the sea correspond to "sinking" inferior (as opposed to superior) mirages. These refractions occur when the air temperature decreases in relation to the height above the ocean.

Fantastic landscapes shimmering over the sea have inspired other poets—in a famous verse by Wordsworth, a spectacular city with "alabaster domes and silver spires" and "bright pavilions" appears in the sky; "towers with battlements" and "terraces upon terraces" are repeated endlessly, and constantly transformed upon the screen of clouds until the "vapors recede" and the scene vanishes. Wordsworth's romantic description is remarkably like Father Angelucci's dramatic vision.

Many of the supernatural images in the poetry of Samuel Coleridge were mirage-inspired. Coleridge was an avid reader of the memoirs of the early polar explorers, who often encountered mirages. In one of his verses, a mysterious island appears over the sea, its "o'er-hanging cliffs glassed in the ocean," and "warriors coursed o'er the sky and battled in mid-air." And in Xanadu of "Kubla Khan," "high in air a stately palace rose . . . the shadow of the dome of pleasure floated midway on the waves . . . a miracle of rare device / a sunny pleasure dome of ice!" The surreal images of green ice floes, the desolate spires of icebergs, and the dazzling mirages described by the explorers inspired the polar setting, celestial visions, and the ghost ship described in *The Rime of the Ancient Mariner* (1798).

Polar Mirages

In the lonely and vast seas of the Arctic and Antarctic, mirages are common. The dry, dust-free air makes it possible to see for miles, so distances are deceptive. Due to complex atmospheric conditions, the ocean sometimes appears concave, bending upward toward the horizon. In a type of superior mirage that occurs when the air temperature increases with height above the surface, landmasses, icebergs, or ice fields beyond the horizon seem to loom ominously near, or a mountain range far inland may suddenly appear to be on the coast, spectacularly magnified with distinct features.

These "magnification" or "looming" mirages have been recorded in ships' logs around the globe. The *Marine Observer* of 1938 reported that on a regular run of the ship *Hauraki* from Suva to Papeete in the South Pacific,

Tahiti appeared to be only 35 miles (55 kilometers) away—in fact, it was 250 miles (400 kilometers) distant. The next year the captain of the *Morrissey,* traveling between Greenland and Iceland, saw clearly recognizable mountains and landmarks of Iceland that appeared to be only 30 miles (50 kilometers) off, when they were actually 300 miles (500 kilometers) away. From Cuxhaven on the northern coast of Germany, an image of Helgoland, an island with red sandstone cliffs 37 miles (60 kilometers) north, has been observed "hanging upside down" over the sea's horizon. The Royal Meteorological Society has reported such "looming" phenomena from distances of 600 to 2,000 miles (970 to 3,200 kilometers).

In 1818 the British explorer Captain John Ross, searching for the Northwest Passage to China, was defeated by a polar mirage. Sailing up Lancaster Sound, the actual entrance to the Northwest Passage, on his lead ship, *Isabella,* he saw the entire end of the sound blocked by a formidable mountain chain, which he named the Croker Mountains. Dismayed by what was actually the realistic mirage of a continuous landmass, he abandoned his search for a passage to the Pacific.

At the other pole, great controversy arose over the findings of the U.S. Exploring Expedition (1838–42) under Charles Wilkes, and the voyage of the *Erebus* and *Terror* (1839–43) under Sir James Clark Ross, both exploring and

Antarctic explorer Charles Wilkes depicted "nearby" land that actually lay 50 miles farther south than it seemed.

Reproduced in Popular Mechanics 52 (August 1929)

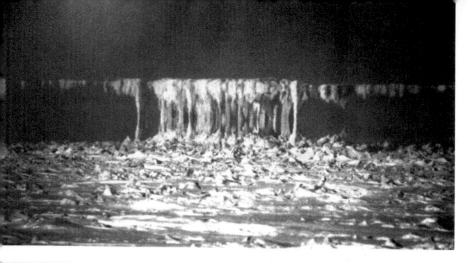

Arctic Fata Morgana can appear when a temperature inversion occurs. A layer of warm air rises above colder air, bending the light rays to create looming apparitions, such as a distant wall of ice (top). Pinnacles, columns, and spires may even seem to materialize from the almost flat terrain (bottom).

Both photos: © Robert Greenler

mapping the Antarctic continent. Ross accused Wilkes of placing along the coast mountains that were 200 miles (320 kilometers) inland, but Ross made similar errors. In some places where he charted the coast, later explorers found only water. Both had been misled by mirages.

New Land

Probably the most famous geographic delusion orchestrated by an Arctic mirage is the case of Robert E. Peary's Crocker Land, "discovered" in 1906. Trying to reach the North Pole, Peary saw a spectacular expanse of snowcapped mountains, valleys, and hills, which he judged to be about 120 miles (200 kilometers) west of his vantage point on the northern tip of Axel Heiberg Island. He again observed the same "land" from Cape Columbia on Ellesmere Island, and mapped it at about 83°N, 103°W. Despite his Arctic experience, even Peary was not immune to the sorcery of the mirage and the yearning it aroused. He wrote that as he gazed at the beautiful "snow-clad summits above the ice

horizon," his "heart leaped the intervening miles of ice." He looked "longingly at this land, and, in fancy, I trod its shores and climbed its summits, even though I knew that that pleasure could be only for another in another season."

Not until 1914 was Peary's error revealed. Financed by the American Museum of Natural History, a party led by Donald B. MacMillan set out in 1913 to explore Crocker Land with sledges and dog teams. MacMillan and Fitzhugh Green set off from Cape Thomas Hubbard over the polar seas made treacherous by blowing snow, "stretching and bucking" thin blue ice, and temperatures of −25° F (−32° C). At last, "this morning Green yelled in through our igloo door that Crocker Land was in sight," wrote MacMillan in his diary. "We all rushed out. . . . Sure enough! There it was as plain as day—hills, valleys, and ice cap, a tremendous land extending through 150 degrees of the horizon." MacMillan crowed, "Great Heavens, what a land!"

No Land

The group pressed on, catching tantalizing glimpses through fog and blowing snow of the "mountain range glittering in the sunshine." After seven days they calculated that they had gone at least 137 miles (220 kilometers) over the polar sea, far beyond where Crocker Land should have been. MacMillan scanned the horizon with binoculars—the sky was now "a deep cloudless blue and all the mist had disappeared." No land was in sight. They had been pursuing a hyperborean looming mirage.

Some historians suggest that "looming" and "magnification" mirages may have helped ancient sea explorers to discover lands that lay beyond the true horizon, enabling them to see over the curve of the earth and use islands as stepping-stones across unknown seas. At least two modern polar explorers used the "looming" effect in this way: Borchgrevink of Norway, in 1895–1899, whose party was the first to land on Antarctica; and Englishman Robert Falcon Scott in Antarctica in 1901–1910.

Optical illusions at sea have inspired countless legends of "lost islands," "castles in the air," "kingdoms in the sea," and "flying ghost ships" around the world. Many of these images appear to be based on recognized mirage phenomena: fairy islands or celestial castles that appear and disappear to tantalize homesick sailors, and ghostly ships sailing the skies, could be attributed to looming superior mirages; and kingdoms in the sea, to inferior mirages. Some scientists suggest that an understanding of ocean mirages may be useful in exploring the atmospheres of other planets, where optical illusions could abound. Atmospheric conditions on Venus, for example, might cause the horizon to appear to bend upward, like the inside of a bowl, creating a looming mirage similar to those encountered in Earth's polar oceans.

Yet the astronauts' psychological reactions to otherworldly mirages will be just as important as their scientific understanding of them. No matter how well we understand the mirage's atmospheric physics, it is the link between the viewer's imagination and the mirage that remains elusive. Interplanetary explorers will do well to remember how Morgan le Fay's "castles in the air" lured seafarers to pursue dreamlands and spelled frustration for mapmakers.

Mirages at sea have always enchanted ocean voyagers, inspired poets, and sparked the curiosity of scientists. The editors of the *Journal of the Optical Society of America* claim that scientists who study meteorological illusions are really "natural philosophers" lured by the "intrinsic fascination" of the mirage, a phenomenon that still bewitches anyone who gazes out over a still sea on a hot summer morning.

Terrified sailors did not understand that inverted images of ships overhead were caused by atmospheric conditions.

Reproduced in Popular Mechanics 52 (August 1929)

The Bettmann Archive

The *TITANIC*'s Legacy to Safety

by Robert L. Scheina

t about one half hour before midnight on April 14, 1912, the British White Star Liner *Titanic* struck an iceberg some 400 miles (645 kilometers) south-southwest of Cape Race, Newfoundland. Two-and-one-half hours later, on the 15th, she carried 1,503 souls to a watery grave in the North Atlantic.

It may come as a surprise to some, but the *Titanic* was not the first such disastrous meeting between iceberg and passenger ship. Some ships survived; the *Corsican* limped into Liverpool with a crushed bow in July 1912 following a close encounter. Others did not; there are the numerous suspected victims like the *Pacific,* which simply disappeared in 1856 without a trace. And yet it took the *Titanic*'s demise to motivate the maritime world to make travel at sea safer, particularly in ice-infested waters.

Worst Maritime Disaster

The *Titanic* tragedy has acquired the aura of the world's greatest maritime disaster. This unenviable distinction resulted from the large number of lives lost (among them numerous distinguished members of society), the attitude of invulnerability falsely based on technological achievements (including the construction of the *Titanic* herself), and the air of inevitability created by many authors. The recent discovery of the wreck, and the endless flow of books and movies, continue to perpetuate the memory of the tragedy.

The sinking of the *Titanic* had a profound influence on maritime laws and regulations throughout the world and improved cooperation among the maritime nations. In the United States, the disaster had an immediate effect.

More than 1,500 passengers perished when the Titanic *sank on April 14, 1912. In the disaster's wake, sweeping new regulations were enacted to improve maritime safety.*

First, a greater control over the wireless—or radio—was sought. The steamship *Californian* was suspected of being only 10 miles (16 kilometers) away from the *Titanic* when she struck the iceberg. The *Californian* might have saved everyone on board the *Titanic* if she had had a radio operator on duty that night.

To improve communications, all U.S. cargo steamships, as well as passenger ships, were required subsequently to carry radios, and an auxiliary power source for electricity was required. The *Titanic* had such a backup system, but most ships did not. Two or more skilled radio operators were to be carried, and one was to be on duty at all times when the ship was under way. In 1912, Congress passed a bill that gave priority to distress and military messages. This was an attempt to control superfluous wireless traffic, which, in the case of the *Titanic*, had complicated the rescue effort. New regulations required effective communication between the ship's bridge and the radio room. Many of these U.S. wireless regulations were given international status at the Berlin Radiotelegraphic Convention of 1915.

Not Enough Lifeboats

The United States also adopted some provisions of the International Convention of Safety of Life at Sea (1914) with respect to lifesaving devices. These provisions were made part of the U.S. Seaman's Act of March 4, 1915, and related to the number and character of lifesaving devices carried on board ships.

The *Titanic* carried only enough lifeboats for half of those on board. This was standard operating procedure for the large passenger ships of that day and was not unique to the *Titanic*. The erroneous logic held that if a ship such as the *Titanic* were involved in a collision with another ship, surely one of the two would remain afloat, and passengers could be shuttled to that surviving ship by the lifeboats from both vessels. Even the most naive landlubber might challenge this logic by asking, What if both ships did go down?, or, How many lifeboats does an iceberg carry?

Tragically, most of the lives lost on board the *Titanic* could be attributed to the shortage of lifeboats. Ironically, the night was clear and the sea smooth. The weather conditions were so ideal that even overcrowded lifeboats manned by inexperienced passengers remained afloat.

The Seaman's Act of March 4, 1915, also provided for the certification of "able seamen" and persons qualified as "lifeboat men." A

The Titanic *expeditions revealed that the ship sank because the iceberg forced apart—rather than gashed—massive steel plates on the starboard bow. The ship broke into two parts before sinking 12,000 feet to the ocean floor.*

Painting by Pierre Mion, © National Geographic Society

Lifeboat drills now are required on all oceangoing vessels. At a designated signal, passengers don flotation jackets and report to their assigned lifeboat stations, where trained crew members instruct them on emergency procedures. Many Titanic fatalities would have been avoided if the ship had been equipped with enough lifeboats to accommodate all the passengers.

number of the *Titanic*'s lifeboats were not adequately crewed. And had the weather been more typical of that found in the North Atlantic, many more lives would probably have been lost.

Preventive Measures Sought

But as the 1912 *Annual Report of the Bureau of Navigation* noted, "The profound feeling aroused in the U.S. by the loss of the British steamship *Titanic* on April 15 did not find expression in radical legislation difficult or impossible to administer, but readily concurred in the sentiment of other nations in favor of an international conference for the consideration of means to prevent the recurrence of such disasters." In layman's language, this says that no laws were passed that affected how a ship was to be built. Although the White Star Line, owner of the *Titanic,* argued that she had been engineered and built to the highest standards possible, her sister ships, the *Olympic* and *Britannic,* were structurally altered as a result of the accident. U.S. legislation significantly affecting how a ship was to be built would not become law until 1936, the result of the *Morro Castle* disaster.

The world's public was stunned by the *Titanic* disaster, and the governments immediately sought means to cooperate to avoid any recurrences. The most important gathering was the International Conference on Safety of Life at Sea in 1913–1914, which convened at London on November 12, 1913. Ice and the *Titanic* were the dominant topics at the conference. On January 20, 1914, the representatives of 13 maritime powers signed a convention that provided for

After the Titanic *sank, the ship's owners added an inner skin to her sister ships,* Olympic *and* Britannic, *and raised the height of their watertight bulkheads. Surprisingly, no laws concerning ship building were passed as a result of the* Titanic *disaster.*

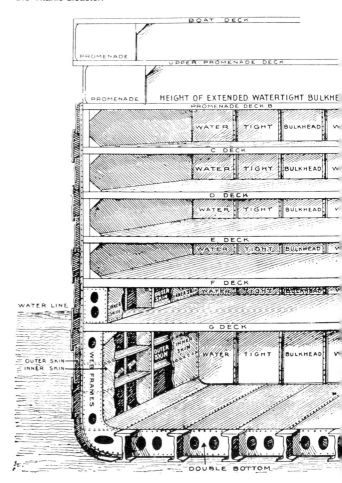

"the inauguration of an international derelict-destruction, ice-observation, and ice-patrol service, consisting of two vessels, which should patrol the ice regions during the season of danger from icebergs and attempt to keep the trans-atlantic lanes clear of derelicts the remainder of the year."

Ice Patrol Initiated

The United States was asked to manage this triple task, the expense shared by the 13 countries. Because the convention would not go into effect until July 1, 1915, Great Britain, on behalf of several of the countries, asked the United States to begin at once. In fact, two U.S. naval scout cruisers had patrolled the danger area through 1912 following the *Titanic* disaster, and, in 1913, two revenue cutters had been used. On February 7, 1914, President Woodrow Wilson officially asked the Revenue Cutter Service, the predecessor of the Coast Guard, to begin immediately the international ice-observation and ice-patrol service.

Each year since 1914, with the exception of the U.S. war years of 1917–18 and 1942–45, the Coast Guard has maintained the International Ice Patrol. The duties of the patrol are to find and to keep daily track of icebergs and field ice, determining their set and drift, and report this information to the world. Ice observation generally begins in March and ends in August, but the patrol is maintained whenever there is thought to be a significant threat to shipping. The patrolled area, about the size of Pennsylvania, is in the general region of the Grand Banks off Newfoundland. In the latter part of the ice season, April to July, the area is blanketed with fog, created by atmospheric conditions at the confluence of the Gulf Stream and the Labrador Current, which adds to the danger.

The need for the International Ice Patrol was reinforced by events that occurred during World War II when the patrol was suspended. The British *Svend Foyne* collided with an iceberg off the southern tip of Greenland on March 19, 1943, and went down. All 145 persons on board were rescued. There were, in addition, many other collisions of ships and icebergs during the war. Fortunately, no others sank.

Badly Shaken Convoy

On May 27, 1945, the ice almost caused a disaster that would have rivaled that of the *Titanic*. Allied convoy ON-303 was plying across the Atlantic on course for America. For five days,

Photos: US Coast Guard

In 1914 the International Ice Patrol was formed to warn ships of danger from icebergs in the North Atlantic. "Bombing" an iceberg with dye (above) is one method the patrol uses to more easily identify a particular iceberg and record its movement (below).

thick fog had limited visibility. At 7:10 P.M. the british frigate *Chelmar* reported to the convoy commodore on board a freighter that a surface craft was sighted on the starboard bow of the convoy. A few minutes passed, and the frigate corrected the report—it was a growler (a small iceberg). At 7:18 P.M. the *Chelmar* warned, "Large iceberg!" A 15-second blast belched forth from the horn on board the commodore's ship, which meant, "Turn left, an emergency." No ship responded. Again the horn blasted, and finally horns responded with acknowledgment of the order. The warning had been received, and the turn was being executed. But how many of the 83 merchantmen and 80 escorts understood the warning and endeavored to avoid each other in a thick fog? The radio tapped out the telegraph message in hopes of informing all ships. The commodore could not see in the fog; had the convoy executed the turn? The new course was radioed in plain language, and all engines were ordered stopped.

Within 15 minutes, 20 ships had collided with one another, some more than once, and four had struck the iceberg. Miraculously, none sank. Two factors prevented a catastrophe. First, the convoy was making 9.5 knots (11 miles, or 17.5 kilometers, per hour), about one-half the speed of the *Titanic* when she met her fate. Second, the commodore perceived that a collision with ice was a greater danger than one among the ships traveling on a similar course;

The Titanic's *legacy to safety is commemorated each April by laying a wreath near the site of the disaster.*

US Coast Guard

he had immediately ordered the emergency turn in spite of almost total lack of visibility caused by the fog. The following day, May 28, the badly shaken convoy passed over the site where the luxurious White Star liner had gone down.

Ice Patrol Backup

World War II accelerated the development of electronic aids to navigation such as loran (*long-range navigation*) and radar (*radio detecting and ranging*). These devices have the potential to make transit of ice-infested water safer, but they have not replaced the International Ice Patrol. Loran permits ships to more accurately fix their own positions and those of icebergs reported by the patrol in any weather condition. Before loran existed, ice-patrol cutters and the transmitting merchant ships were at times fog-bound for days. Their position had to be determined by dead reckoning and radio-direction-finder bearings. This was the best technology available to man in the 1910s, '20s, and '30s, and it left much possibility for error.

Radar can detect ice, but not to the degree of efficiency needed. Most icebergs ride very low in the water and are often hidden from radar by the sea clutter, or the constant movement of the water. Also, ice absorbs much of the energy emitted by the radar, reflecting back only a small portion. Thus, the radar screen registers the size of an iceberg as being much smaller than it is in reality.

A Legacy of Life

A chilling reminder of the force of nature and the brashness of man occurred on January 30, 1959, when the *Hans Hedtoft* radioed that she had struck an iceberg and was sinking. A severe storm prevented the rescue ships from arriving on the scene for several hours. When they did arrive, they found nothing—not even debris. The *Hans Hedtoft* had gone down with 55 passengers and 39 crew members. This ship was on the return half of her maiden voyage, and had been especially reinforced to operate in ice-infested waters. She was equipped with all of the modern aids to navigation, including loran and radar. The *Hans Hedtoft* sank outside the area covered by the International Ice Patrol.

Not one ship has been lost to ice within the patrolled area except during war, at which time the patrol was not being carried out. This record, and the lives saved through better regulation of the radio and lifesaving apparatus, are the legacy of the *Titanic*.

THE EIGHTH WONDER OF THE WORLD.
THE ATLANTIC CABLE.

"Heart's Content, July 27th 1866.
I hope that it will prove a blessing to England, and the United States,
and increase the intercourse between our Country & the Eastern Hemisphere."
Your faithfully
Cyrus W. Field.

Washington, July 29th 1866.
To Cyrus W. Field, Heart's Content:
May the Cable under the sea tend to promote harmony between the Republic
of the West and the Governments of the Eastern Hemisphere.
Andrew Johnson.

The Cable Under the Sea

by James R. Chiles

O n January 8, 1815, American troops under Andrew Jackson won a great victory against an attacking British force at the Battle of New Orleans. Sharpshooters and cannon behind well-defended positions brought down the staid redcoats by the hundreds, until the famed British discipline broke. The only problem with this success was that representatives of the two belligerents had signed a peace treaty in Belgium two weeks earlier, and only formalities remained before ratification.

The extracurricular battle wasn't surprising, because information between continents never moved any faster than a ship at sea. Tramp freighters cruised from port to port hunting cargoes, because they had no way of knowing where freight had piled up. American newspapers got their news from Europe by two-week-old mail or from arriving passengers. But in 1854 a small number of visionaries undertook

The two hemispheres became forever linked with the successful laying of the transatlantic cable in 1866.

In the early days of the telegraph, some colleges offered special courses to train students as operators.

to change all this with a telegraph cable bridging 2,000 miles (3,200 kilometers) of the North Atlantic.

Invention of the Telegraph

To no single person or country belongs the credit for the telegraph. Electric telegraphy began with the invention of practical batteries in 1800. Early approaches used a multitude of wires. Some used 26, one for each letter, with tiny sparks, needles, or cork balls nudged by a charge for indicators. The greatest advance, about 1830, was the application of electromagnetic theory to the apparatus. In America, Samuel F. B. Morse seized upon magnets to devise a system using a simple open-or-closed key to transmit, and a receiver that printed the dots and dashes of his simple code on a strip of paper. He used only one wire, with the ground serving to return the current.

In 1842, just two years after he got his patent, Morse laid an experimental underwater line across New York Harbor to Governors Island. It wasn't the very first water crossing, but his one-wire design was well suited for submarine telegraphs, which required an absolute minimum of wires. Landlines could use crudely insulated or even bare-metal wires, but submerged cables required excellent and expensive insulation to function properly.

Eleven years after Morse's patent, the English succeeded in laying a cable across the English Channel. That cable used another invention fresh out of the patent office: a German

cable-coating machine invented in 1847 and first applied to electric cables used for detonating harbor mines. The inventor drew on a new type of insulation, gutta-percha.

Gutta-percha, a distant relative of rubber, had just reached the West. It came from an obscure tree that grew only in the jungles of Malaya, Borneo, and Sumatra. Condensation and coagulation of the milky fluid of the tree yielded a rigid, strong material. Water didn't hurt it. Its insulating qualities even improved in cold, deep water. In fact, its greatest enemies would prove to be sun and air. For the next 70 years, nothing could match it for submarine cables.

A Spark Kindles

With this basic technology available, people began pondering the possibility of sending messages across the Atlantic. The first to act was a British engineer, F. N. Gisborne, who started with the modest plan of faster communication between the United States and Newfoundland. By getting the latest information to and from European packets stopping at Newfoundland, his company would slash several days off the information transit time. An America-bound message, just off the boat from London, would start south on a telegraph across Newfoundland. A carrier pigeon would cross the Cabot Strait to relay it to a telegraph station on northern Nova Scotia, which would pass it on to New York City.

But surveying a route 400 miles (650 kilometers) long across the wilds of Newfoundland and laying the first 40 miles (65 kilometers) of wire proved so expensive that Gisborne had to go to New York for more venture capital. A fellow engineer introduced Gisborne to the wealthy businessman Cyrus Field. They met on a winter night in 1854.

Field's adventure began that night. After Gisborne described the Newfoundland project, Field returned home and consulted a large globe in his study. He realized that the first transatlantic cable would have to cross Newfoundland. Why not stretch Gisborne's cable on to Europe? He wrote to the leading experts on telegraphy and oceanography. The replies were encouraging. Samuel Morse came to New York to see Field, and explained why he believed an electric impulse could get through such a cable.

The Navy's oceanographic authority, Lt. M. F. Maury, replied to Field after consulting a recently completed survey of the North Atlantic between Newfoundland and Ireland. The sea bottom was mostly level, he found, not too deep, and covered with a sediment that would be easy on cable housings. He couldn't be much more specific because the soundings had been taken 50 miles (80 kilometers) apart. But it was enough for Field, who immediately started gathering fellow investors and effectively assumed control of the company. Over the next 13 trying years, he would cross the Atlantic more than 40 times, suffering from seasickness on each trip.

Enormous Undertaking

To the early Victorian mind, the project was enormous. Leading electrical scientists disagreed about how a submerged 2,200-mile (3,500-kilometer) wire would behave and how much power would be needed. Morse himself vastly overestimated the carrying capacity of the

Cyrus Field raised the funds for the first transatlantic cable and personally supervised its laying.

Chicago Historical Society

cable, and therefore its profitability. But he was much closer to the truth than the astronomer royal, Sir George Airy, who believed that the cable would neither sink to the bottom nor conduct messages.

Field's Atlantic Telegraph Company gave its British cable manufacturers—cable wasn't being made in America yet—a paltry four months to manufacture the line, because American backers were anxious to do all the laying during the relatively calm summer months of 1857. Specifications for construction and materials were loose. The two companies working on the outer coverings forgot to check with each other about how to spiral the metal strands, and discovered when it was too late that they had laid them in opposite directions. The mistake required an elaborate splice to keep the cable from unwinding underwater.

The first Atlantic cable, which took three attempts in 1857 and 1858 to lay, consumed 367,000 miles (590,000 kilometers) of iron wire and 300,000 miles (480,000 kilometers) of tarred hemp. At the heart was a single conductor, seven strands of copper. (The Atlantic Ocean, a much better conductor than the impure copper used, would return the electrical current.) William Thomson (later Lord Kelvin), a director of the company and a renowned physicist, strongly urged using a heavier copper conductor, but expediency won out. And the cost cutters had the support of Morse and Michael Faraday, who wrongly believed that a thicker conductor would require more current. Surrounding the seven-strand copper core were three layers of gutta-percha, covered in turn with tarred hemp. The outermost layer was made of iron strands, for tensile strength.

Laying the Cable

One hundred and twenty crewmen, working for three weeks, loaded 2,500 tons (2,300 metric tons) of cable aboard two steam-driven ships. One was the frigate *Niagara*, The U.S. Navy's biggest ship. The other was the Royal Navy's *Agamemnon*. The plan was for the *Niagara* to begin laying its cable off Ireland; halfway across, it would splice to the British vessel, which would continue to Newfoundland. They kept in constant touch with the station at Ireland, checking the cable for continuity. Thomson and his group were able to locate faults in the thin cable (about the diameter of a garden hose) by using a Wheatstone bridge, a recent British electrical invention, to measure the resistance of the cable between the ship and the break, and converting that figure into miles.

There was something hypnotic, no doubt, in the sight of the black cable slipping into the ocean and connecting the ship with land far over the horizon. Here was the first human track upon the ocean. But 300 miles (480 kilometers) out of Ireland, the brakes on the *Niagara*'s paying-out mechanism grabbed too firmly, and the thin black line broke and vanished beneath the waves. The ships returned to England and discharged their cargo at Plymouth. The company ordered 700 more miles (1,125 kilometers) of cable and rebuilt the cable-handling machinery. Further, it was decided that next time, cable laying would begin in midocean, to allow splicing under controlled conditions.

In June 1858, the flotilla met for a rehearsal session in the Bay of Biscay, and then set out once more. A storm along the way nearly sank the *Agamemnon*—which had 250 tons (225 metric tons) of cable unwisely stored on the main deck, repeatedly causing the vessel to roll 45 degrees off the vertical—but the ships made the rendezvous. Before they could complete the difficult splice, the cable broke twice, first at the *Niagara*'s machinery, where a second splice was made, and then on the seafloor, where a third splice followed. Finally, 300 miles (480 kilometers) later, it broke again at the *Agamemnon*'s stern, and the ships returned to England. Field and Thomson reported to the company's directors in London. The board chairman suggested the company sell the cable and quit. A vice-chairman resigned. But under Field and Thomson's influence, the board voted to try again immediately, while the crews and cable were still available.

Cause for Celebration

The third expedition was a temporary success. The gentlest possible handling of the cable kept it intact across the ocean. On August 10, 1858, for the first time ever, the British Empire had instantaneous contact with its lost colonies. The celebrations started almost immediately, and reached such a height in late August that New Yorkers accidentally burned the cupola off their city hall with bonfires and fireworks. Speakers hailed Cyrus Field as "Cyrus the Great," and compared the cable to the discovery of America and the invention of the printing press. The company's chief engineer was knighted.

On September 1, at the peak of excitement, the cable stopped working. Measurements showed that about 270 miles (435 kilometers) off Ireland, the copper core was now open to the ocean. It had worked for one day short of a month. It had passed about 400 messages, most of which were between telegraph operators trying to straighten out garbled telegrams. Queen Victoria and President Buchanan had exchanged greetings.

The public and press immediately heaped abuse on the cable company. Some charged fraud. But the experts knew a great hurdle had been passed. An Atlantic cable definitely could be made to work. It would save vast amounts of money; a single message to Canada canceling the movement of two British army regiments to England had already saved the Crown a quarter of a million dollars.

Commissions met to examine the failure. The reason was a combination of manufacturing defects, handling damage during the three expeditions, and injury to the insulation from excess voltages. The latter had been the unauthorized inspiration of Dr. Edward Whitehouse, the project's first electrician, who wired together batteries to put 2,000 volts across the cable (he needed the high currents to operate a printing receiver of his own design). The company banished him from the project. Not only did high voltages damage the cable, they charged it up like a huge capacitor, and this charge interfered with the passage of the pulses.

The Marine Galvanometer

In fact, just a few volts was sufficient to get a clear signal through the cable. What made the weak currents practical was a supersensitive receiving instrument that Thomson had invented in early 1858 after noticing how slight movements of his monocle bounced light around. The device's only moving part weighed less than one five-hundredth of an ounce.

Thomson's "marine galvanometer" was small enough to sit on a tabletop. Current from a telegraph wire passed through a coil of fine copper wire. The coil's magnetic field applied a twisting motion to a tiny iron magnet suspended inside from a silk thread. A mirror attached to the magnet reflected a thin beam of light from an oil lamp across the table. The light, flashing to the left and right of a zero point, indicated the dots and dashes of Morse's code. It took two operators to work the receiver: one to watch the light and call out the letters, and another to write down the message. It raised the transmission speed by about tenfold over old methods.

Cable, payed out from a storage area below deck (right), is lowered from the stern of the Niagara (above), the U.S. Navy's largest ship at the time. The 1857 expedition ended prematurely, however, when the cable broke 300 miles from Ireland.

Both illustrations: Culver Pictures

Another Attempt

But by 1865, the Atlantic Telegraph Company had reawakened. After two years of war, the British and American governments decided the cable was more necessary than ever before. Field returned to England and rounded up old acquaintances and financiers. In 1864 contracts went out for a stronger cable, a little more than an inch (2.5 centimeters) in diameter, with a conductor three times heavier. The outer iron wires would be galvanized against corrosion. It would be built in one piece 2,700 miles (4,350 kilometers) long.

And 5,000 tons (4,500 metric tons) heavy. There was only one ship on earth to transport and lay such a cargo: the *Great Eastern*. It was a product of an era when a single engineer could design and build with equal success tunnels, bridges, railroads, and a whole new class of ship. In this case the engineer was Isambard Kingdom Brunel, already famous for his Great Western Railway. He had designed the *Great Eastern* to transport 4,000 passengers to the East Indies without recoaling. The 22,500-ton (20,400-metric-ton) iron vessel first saw water in 1858 amid extravagant press notices. Everything about it was grandiose, from its 60-foot (18.3-meter) paddle wheels to the six great masts. It was five times bigger than the next largest ship of the era, and nothing would outweigh it until the *Lusitania* in 1906.

Another Setback

Modified with cable tanks and handling machinery and loaded with the new cable, the *Great Eastern* left England in June 1865. Three times the electricians detected faults in the cable just after it had gone overboard. Each time the crew recovered the cable by laboriously transferring an end to the bow and winching it up. On the last recovery, 600 miles (965 kilometers) from completion, the cable chafed and broke. It came to rest 2.5 miles (4 kilometers) down. The captain started dragging for the cable end by steaming over it at right angles with a grapnel attached to 5 miles (8 kilometers) of wire rope. Four times the crew hooked the cable, and four times the rope or its shackles broke under the weight.

The next year, the company started again, with 1,900 miles (3,000 kilometers) of cable, better machinery, and a stronger grappling rope. In July 1866, the cable was complete, to be immediately joined by a second cable when the *Great Eastern* recovered the broken 1865 cable and spliced it to a new section.

Success at Last

"The world changed that day," says Dr. Vary Coates of Congress' Office of Technology Assessment (OTA) and coeditor of *The Transatlantic Cable of 1866*. "Some major assumptions changed forever. Before the cable the State Department closed down at 5:00 P.M. every Friday and opened again Monday morning. After the cable they had to have someone available twenty-four hours a day."

The public waited a few weeks to see if the cable would hold up—it did—and then the honors and banquets began, although never at the frenzied pitch of 1858. Congress voted a medal of thanks to Field. The queen knighted four more of the British personnel.

For businesses, the cable represented a long stride toward a global economy. Even at a cost of $5 to $10 per word, customers queued up immediately. One of the first was Lloyd's of London, which used the cable to report the movements of ships in harbor. Owners of tramp steamers could now locate potential cargoes by telegraphing harbor agents and directing their

ships to ports. Commodity and stock speculators used the cable to smooth out price differences between the continents. Banks used it to transfer money instantaneously for international business purchases, reducing the risk of nonpayment and making credit available to smaller firms. Businesses cut their inventories, knowing they could quickly order more goods from overseas. The editor of the *Times* of London had called the cable "a great bore," but the major news organizations "simply couldn't compete without it, once it became available," says Coates. During the Franco-Prussian War of 1870, a team of reporters from the *New York Tribune* kept their readers in daily contact with the fighting.

Transatlantic Telephone

No transatlantic telegraph cables were laid after 1928. Radiotelephone service began on the shortwave band in 1927 between stations at Lawrenceville, New Jersey, and London. Signals curved around the earth by bouncing off Heaviside's ionosphere, which meant that on some days the only way to be understood was to bellow. Sunspot activity could shut down the system altogether. And limits on the capacity of the system meant a person could wait hours for a call to go through.

At about this time, Bell Telephone considered laying a telephone cable with the capacity of exactly one conversation, but decided to wait for more powerful technology. The wait paid off. In 1956 AT&T, the British Post Office, and the Canadian Overseas Telecommunications Corporation successfully laid the first transatlantic telephone cable. It could carry 36 voices one way; a second cable was required for the other direction. This was a coaxial cable that worked in essentially the same way as the coaxial cable between the wall and your television set, dividing the 36 voices across a bandwidth 240 kilohertz wide. It required several innovations. One was the repeater, a vacuum-tube amplifier with as many components as a radio set, spaced at 20-mile (32-kilometer) intervals across the Atlantic. Because it is difficult and expensive to raise a submarine cable from 2-mile (3.2 kilometer) depths, the tubes inside had to be extremely reliable. (AT&T used a 20-year-old tube design.) Also, each repeater could be only 3 inches (7.5 centimeters) in diameter, and had to be flexible enough to pass through the cable-laying machinery. Designers divided components into separate sausagelike tubes, reinforcing the 8-foot (2.4-meter) string with steel rings. The outer covering was polyethylene, an extremely durable white polymer discovered in Britain shortly before World War II. One of its many advantages was that it was distasteful to the teredo worm, a marine borer responsible for injuries to many gutta-percha cables.

Cables Abandoned

This cable, TAT-1, was retired in 1978. Today all 25 transatlantic telegraph cables, as well as three old telephone cables, have been abandoned to the deep. (The last telegraph cable expired in 1965.) There are currently nine working transatlantic telephone cables. These cables split the message traffic with satellites hovering 22,300 miles (35,880 kilometers) over the equator. Cables and satellites together moved approximately 212 million phone calls, plus telex and telegraph messages, between America and Europe in 1985.

Optical Fibers

Now an entirely new type of transatlantic cable, labeled TAT-8, is under construction. It will be the first transatlantic cable to use optical fibers, piping pulses of laser light. (Alexander Graham Bell himself first studied the transmission of telephone conversations via beams of light. He even invented a working model, using a selenium photo detector, and was so enthusiastic about it that in 1880 he wanted to name his infant daughter Photophone. He considered the photophone his greatest invention.)

From Tuckerton, New Jersey, TAT-8 will cross the ocean to branch into two lines serving both Britain and France. During summer 1987, AT&T buried a 100-mile (160-kilometer) length of TAT-8 in the mud of the continental shelf, using a sea plow dragged by the cable ship, with the robot sub *Scarab* available when the plow couldn't handle the terrain. A sea plow is a heavy framework of steel tubing that slides along the bottom, cutting a 2-foot (0.6-meter)-deep trench and feeding in cable coming down from the ship. Television cameras inform the engineers of any obstacles or problems. The chief purpose of the burial is to prevent fishing trawlers from snagging the line with their bottom-dragging nets. Steel armoring wires, wrapped around the polyethylene, also help defend the cable against fishing gear and small dragging anchors.

There's another hazard on the continental shelf: sharks. AT&T has discovered from ear-

AT&T Bell Labs

Modern transatlantic cables incorporate optical fibers, which transmit telephone conversations via light pulses. The cables are buried in trenches dug in the ocean floor by means of a sea plow dragged by a cable ship.

lier trials off the Canary Islands that sharks will occasionally grab a section of fiber-optic cable and try to bite through it; something about the line's electromagnetic field appears to trigger a feeding reflex. (The earlier copper-cored cables never attracted sharks.) The solution: a double layer of tooth-resistant steel tape atop the armoring wires. The deep-sea portion of the cable, which AT&T and partners unrolled in 1987, won't require armoring or burial. Virtually nothing can damage it down there.

The high cost and high technology of TAT-8 are a reminder that getting information across the ocean is still a huge undertaking. Transatlantic cables have always demanded the most reliable communications technology. When their owners cut the shore ends and abandon them to the ocean, it's not because they've completely worn out, but because new cables with enormous capacities have taken over. The owners of TAT-8 plan for only 25 years of service. They know it will still be in good condition after that period, but they also know something bigger and better will come along.

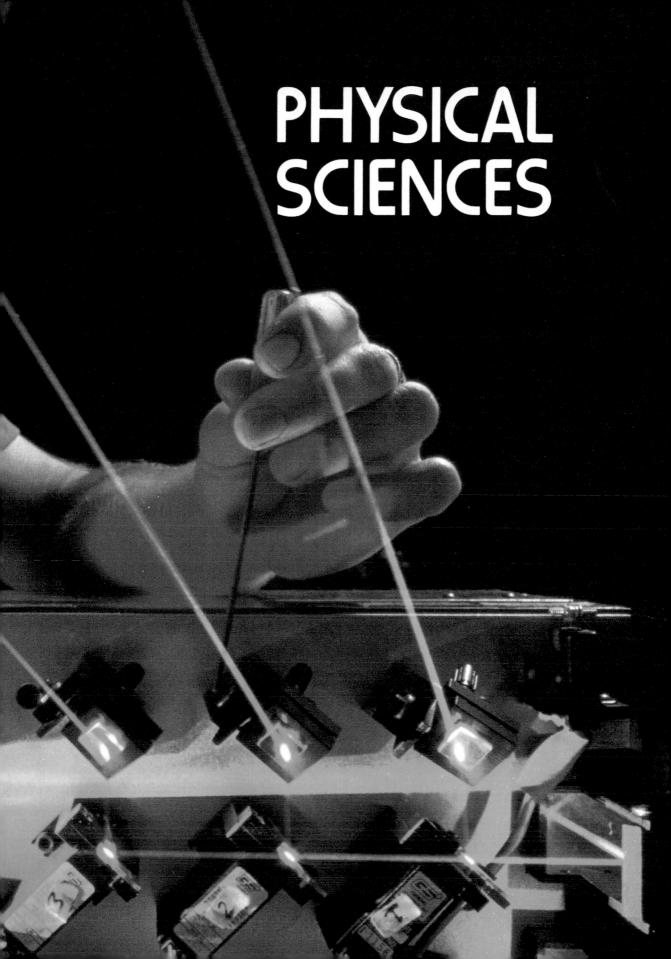

PHYSICAL SCIENCES

NBS researchers use a block to demonstrate the "impact echo" technique, a nondestructive method of detecting flaws in concrete structures.

REVIEW OF THE YEAR

PHYSICAL SCIENCES

PHYSICS

Scientists at the Argonne National Laboratory, Argonne, Illinois, announced the development of the world's first electrical motor based on the unique properties of high-temperature superconductors. Until recently, superconductors had to be cooled with expensive liquid helium to about $-420°$ F $(-251°$ C). The new motor is made of ceramic material that becomes superconducting at $-290°$ F $(-179°$ C), allowing it to be cooled with inexpensive liquid nitrogen. Although the motor produced negligible power, and is too small for practical use, it demonstrated for the first time that such motors are possible.

In a more theoretical breakthrough, researchers found evidence for the existence of a sixth fundamental force of nature. The original four forces—gravity, electromagnetism, the strong force that holds the nucleus of an atom together, and a weak force that causes some atoms to decay radioactively—were joined recently by a fifth postulated force, which counteracts gravity. Evidence for a sixth force, found by physicists at the Hanscom Air Force Base in Massachusetts, appears to be an additional, attractive force that slightly increases the effect of gravity beyond that predicted by Newton's laws of physics. The fifth and sixth forces might force theoreticians to build new models of gravity.

Another facet of subatomic physics—the law of lepton conservation—was upset by the complementary observations of researchers from the University of South Carolina and the Pacific Northwest Laboratory of Richland, Washington, and the University of California at Irvine. The law states that the number of leptons (lightweight or weightless particles) emerging from an atomic reaction must equal the number entering into it. The work provided evidence that a particle called a majoron is released during an extremely rare form of radioactive decay called two-neutrino double-beta decay. During ordinary beta decay, a neutron decays into a proton by the release of a neutrino and an electron. The production of majorons as a third particle released from the reaction of two neutrons during double-beta decay seems to overthrow the law of lepton conservation, and to herald a new realm of nuclear phenomena.

The mass of neutrinos at rest, formerly considered to be zero, appears to be much less than the recent estimates that gave the particle a tiny mass, according to studies of neutrinos emitted by a supernova detected in 1987. Physicists at Cornell University, Max Planck Institute for Radioastronomy, and the University of Wuppertal, in West Germany, found that the observed release of neutrinos from the supernova was pulsatile (of or marked by pulsation), with a period of 8.9 milliseconds. Using the period to estimate time of flight between the supernova and Earth, they estimated that the mass can be no greater than 0.2 electron volt, much smaller than previous estimates.

The discovery that subatomic particles called muons can catalyze the fusion of deuterium and tritium nuclei at room temperature, rather than the millions of degrees needed by conventional methods, suggests that a "cold-fusion" approach to nuclear energy could someday become a reality. Earlier predictions postulated that a muon could catalyze only a single such fusion reaction. But researchers from the Los Alamos (New Mexico) National Laboratory, Brigham Young University (Provo, Utah), and the Idaho National Engineering Laboratory at Idaho Falls showed that muons actually catalyze an average of 150 fusions. Although this figure is still a long way from the 1,200 fusions per muon necessary to sustain an energetically practical process, the possibility that muons could be produced economically prompted physicist Marshall Rosenbluth at the University of Texas (Austin) to begin studying the possibility of a cold-fusion reactor.

Borrowing technology used by dolphins and submarines, researchers at the National Bureau of Standards (NBS) developed a nondestructive method to detect flaws in concrete. Called "impact-echo," the technique measures the reflection from flaws of sound waves produced by the impact of a steel ball. Impact-echo appears to be both easier and cheaper to use than other techniques, such as X rays, gamma rays, and drilling.

The ongoing revolution in the study of fire, fire safety, and fire fighting advanced further with the development of the Cone Calorimeter, which predicts how much heat an object will release if it burns. Developed by the NBS, the device helps to predict the course of a fire, and its effects, by measuring the amount of oxygen consumed by a sample of the material, the time it takes for the material to ignite, and the amount of soot and smoke produced.

CHEMISTRY

Chemists using extremely short laser pulses probed the sequence of molecular events that occurred during simple chemical reactions. Ahmed H. Zewail and his colleagues at the California Institute of Technology (Caltech) in Pasadena used femtosecond (10^{-15} second) pulses to monitor the atomic activity that takes place within trillionths of a second during the dissociation of cyanogen iodide into iodine and cyanide, and the interaction between hydrogen and carbon dioxide to form carbon monoxide and hydroxyl. The group first initiated reactions by pumping high-energy laser pulses into a mixture. Subsequent "probe" pulses were absorbed by molecules in various stages of the transformation from reactants to products. These various transition stages of the reactions reemitted the light—a process called laser-induced fluorescence. The researchers were able to determine the velocity of reactions, and the identity of the transition-stage molecules, bond lengths, and other chemical features that change during the evolution of the reaction.

The study of magnetism also was given a boost as teams from around the world continued development of organic materials that are ferromagnetic, i.e., that become magnetic at low temperatures when unpaired, spinning electrons line up. Researchers at Ohio State University in Columbus constructed a lattice in which iron-containing decamethylferrocene molecules transferred electrons to tetracyanoethylene molecules, leaving each component with unpaired electrons. At temperatures below 5° K (about $-250°$ F or $-268°$ C), the electron spins aligned spontaneously, and the compound behaved like a ferromagnet. Soviet and Japanese workers also made progress in the development of organic ferromagnetism, which now joins conduction and superconductivity as electronic properties formerly associated only with inorganic materials.

A 20-year, worldwide search for chemical reactions that can power visible-light lasers ended at the Georgia Institute of Technology in Atlanta. Visible-light lasers powered by chemical reactions are not only simpler to operate than those dependent on electrically excited materials, but they are also potentially very powerful, and are likely to be more compact. The Georgia scientists energized thallium atoms by colliding them with excited molecules formed by reactions between ozone and silicon or germanium. When the thallium atoms were subsequently stimulated to emit their radiation in a coordinated fashion, they produced pulsed-light amplification. The team also produced a less powerful, but continuous, light amplifier based on the reaction between three-atom sodium clusters and atoms of halogens, such as chlorine.

Chemists at Carnegie-Mellon University in Pittsburgh, who were studying chemical models of a light-sensitive molecule important in the process of vision, stumbled across a compound that can make any object practically invisible to radar. The compound, called ATRSBS, absorbs radio waves and dissipates the energy as heat.

Chemists at Ohio State University synthesized a molecule that looks like a three-bladed propeller. Called propellahexaene, the molecule consists of three six-membered, carbon-based rings, and flips back and forth between right- and left-handed forms.

At the University of Illinois (Urbana-Champaign), researchers used an ultrasonic cleaning bath to turn nickel powder into a better catalyst for certain chemical reactions. Shock waves created by the collapse of bubbles formed by the ultrasonic bath stripped off the protective oxide coating that forms on nickel, exposing more of its surface. This greatly improved its catalytic activity in adding hydrogen to organic compounds called alkenes, a reaction widely used in the chemical industry.

MARC KUSINITZ

Ian Worpole/Discover Magazine, Family Media Inc.

The World's
BIGGEST
Machine

by Arthur Fisher

T hrow deep."
    That's the red-lettered message on
a sign tacked to a bulletin board in a
Lawrence Berkeley Laboratory building high
above San Francisco Bay. And that's what President Ronald Reagan, quoting pro quarterback
Ken Stabler, said at the end of a meeting to discuss the pros and cons of building the SSC, or
Superconducting Super Collider: "Go for the
big one."

    Big it is. Bigger than those wonders of the

ancient world, the Pyramids of Egypt and the
Colossus of Rhodes. When it is completed in
1996, the SSC will be (assuming Congress goes
along with the administration's proposal and
votes for the necessary funds—$4.4 billion in
1988 dollars) the largest particle accelerator
ever built, dwarfing Fermi National Accelerator
Laboratory's (Fermilab's) Tevatron, in Batavia,
Illinois, and the European Center for Nuclear
Research's (CERN's) Large Electron-Positron
Ring, now being built near Geneva, Switzerland. At a site yet to be chosen, the SSC will
consist of a racetrack-shaped tunnel 52 miles
(84 kilometers) in circumference, 10 feet (3
meters) in diameter, and buried at least 30 feet
(9 meters) underground.

    Inside the tunnel, two rings of supercon-
ducting magnets—some 10,000 of them, strung
like pearls on narrow, evacuated particle-beam
pipes—will focus and guide two beams of protons traveling in opposite directions. The protons race around their tracks millions of times,
getting an extra jab of radio-frequency energy
with each circuit, until they are traveling at
nearly the speed of light. At special chambers

called interaction halls, the opposing beams will cross over and collide with an energy 20 times greater than any before achieved: 20 trillion electron volts (TeV) per beam, for a total of 40 TeV. Massive detectors will record and analyze the debris left by these titanic collisions.

Government Rationale

Why have particle physicists been clamoring for such a monster? Why does it have to be so much bigger and more powerful than any other accelerator? Wouldn't something only one-half its size—still a big jump upward—have sufficed? And why has an administration opposed to "budget-busting" decided to back the SSC, even in the face of complaints from other scientists that it will divert too much money from other worthwhile projects?

The administration's rationale was given by John S. Herrington, secretary of the Department of Energy (DOE), in announcing the president's approval in February 1987. He termed the decision "a momentous leap forward for America and science and technology. . . . The Super Collider holds the potential for a new generation and a new revolution in science, education, technology, and commerce. Like Apollo, it will have spinoffs, discoveries, and innovations that will profoundly touch every American. . . . Once again, this nation has said there are no dreams too big, no innovation unimaginable, and no frontiers beyond our reach."

The particle physicists' reasoning can be put less grandly: they are stuck. Without powerful new experimental tools, they cannot progress beyond their present theories of the nature of matter and energy, space and time. To understand why, consider how we got to the so-called Standard Model of particles and forces.

Atom Smashing

The route to that model has been paved with some 30 years of experimental data from accelerators. Just as the telescope is the basic tool of the astronomer, and the microscope of the biologist, the accelerator serves the physicist as a way to look inside the atom. It does this with what is inside a Swiss watch: bang two of them together, and see what comes out. Physicists have been banging atomic particles together with ever-increasing force in the instruments designed for that purpose—accelerators.

Until about 20 years ago, all accelerators were of the type known as fixed-target, in which a beam of speeding particles smashes into a stationary target. New technology brought the advent of colliders, in which two counterrotating beams collide head-on at designated points. The advantage of the collider design is that almost all of the kinetic energy borne by the two particles goes into creating new kinds of matter, whereas in the fixed-target design, most of the single particle's energy is wasted in contributing to the forward motion of the collision products. The difference is tremendous. The useful energy of the SSC will be 40 TeV, the sum of its twin 20-TeV colliding beams. If one of these beams were simply aimed at a fixed target, the useful energy would be only 0.2 TeV.

And the energy level is crucial. Because matter and energy are interchangeable in the nuclear domain, the more massive a particle, the more energy is needed to create it in the innards of an accelerator. One salient example: particles called the W's and the Z were predicted long before they were actually created and identified in 1983, at the Super Proton Synchrotron at CERN. They were simply too massive to have been seen until that collider crashed beams of protons and antiprotons together with a total energy of 630 billion electron volts (BeV).

The discovery of the W's and the Z—called intermediate vector, or force-carrying, bosons—confirmed a prediction of a theory unifying two of the fundamental forces in nature, electromagnetism and the weak nuclear force, and more or less capped the Standard Model.

Going Deeper

On a recent visit to Fermilab, I asked Leon Lederman, the facility's wise and witty director, about the status quo and the need to go beyond it. "If you summarize all the physics up to a certain energy level," he told me, "it is called the Standard Model. Briefly, it says the world's fundamental building blocks are six quarks and six leptons and their antiparticles. The quarks and leptons seem to fall naturally into three families, grouped according to their properties. Then there are four forces that govern how these particles combine and interact: electromagnetism, the strong nuclear force, the weak nuclear force, and gravity. In turn, these forces are carried by other particles: photons, gluons, and the W's and Z. Gravity we don't know much about . . . but there's hope.

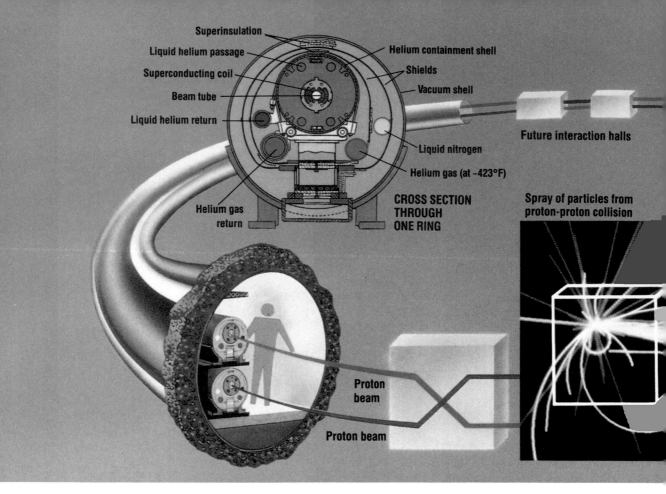

Superinsulation
Liquid helium passage
Superconducting coil
Beam tube
Liquid helium return
Helium gas return

Helium containment shell
Shields
Vacuum shell
Liquid nitrogen
Helium gas (at –423°F)

CROSS SECTION THROUGH ONE RING

Future interaction halls

Spray of particles from proton-proton collision

Proton beam

Proton beam

The SSC will enable physicists to study the composition of subatomic particles by smashing apart protons in high-speed, head-on collisions. The collisions will occur between two beams of counterrotating protons (red and green lines), each traveling in a separate ring consisting of a narrow evacuated pipe surrounded by liquid helium cryostats for cooling and by superconducting magnets. Two types of magnets will be used: dipoles, which bend the beams, and quadrupoles, which focus them. (A cross section of one ring through a dipole is shown at upper left.) After being accelerated to 1 trillion electron volts (TeV) by a linear accelerator and three booster rings (not shown), the protons (130 trillion per ring) will enter the main rings. There, they ultimately will be accelerated to 20 TeV by radio-frequency quadrupoles in millions of circuits around the SSC. The beams collide in one of four interaction halls. A computer simulation of one such collision is shown superimposed over an interaction hall. The colored tracks indicate the paths of different particles.

"So that's the Standard Model. It identifies the fundamental building blocks. It provides a powerful new mathematical formulation, known as gauge-symmetry theory, for the four basic forces. And it takes a giant step—the formulation of the electroweak theory—in the 50-year search for a unifying principle. It incorporates the two earlier revolutionary theories of the 20th century, the quantum theory and special relativity. And it accommodates all the data coming out of all the accelerators that have ever been built since the Leaning Tower of Pisa. So it is a very powerful synthesis. You can write all the rules down in a couple of pages.

"All of this has brought us to a new level of understanding of physical laws. And yet, the

Standard Model has ticking away in it some very dramatic incompletenesses, some serious defects. For one thing, it does not account for the masses of the quarks and leptons, or for the pattern of apparent families of particles. Why are there three families? Are there any more?

There is also much uneasiness, said Lederman, because a good theory should be essentially simple. The Standard Model contains about 20 parameters—numerical values that are just there rather than being predicted by theory. "Designing the world this way," Lederman said, "the Creator would have had to set 20 dials carefully at seemingly arbitrary values."

There is an even more serious defect, said Lederman. The carriers of the weak nuclear

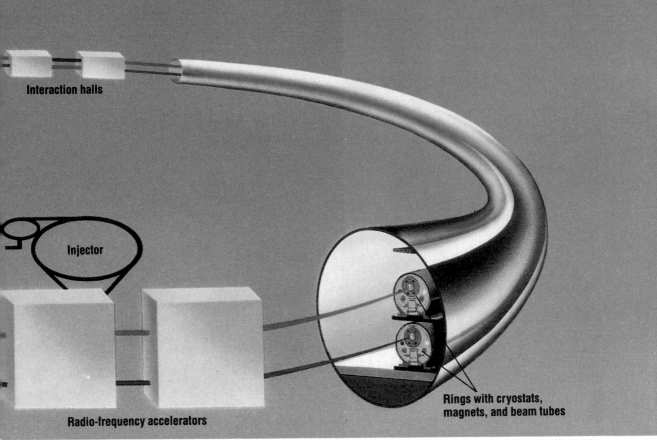

Interaction halls

Injector

Radio-frequency accelerators

Rings with cryostats, magnets, and beam tubes

force, the W and Z bosons, are very massive—100 times more so than the proton. But gauge symmetry—essential to the unification of forces—implies that the force carriers have zero mass, as does the photon. Current unification theory holds that at some enormously high energy regime, such as the one that reigned in the first instants after the Big Bang, all the forces were symmetrical, and all their carriers massless; but at lower energies the symmetry became broken. Just how does the symmetry break?

"This apparent breaking of symmetry is one of the most unhappy elements of the Standard Model," said Lederman. To get around it, to provide a symmetry-breaking mechanism, theorists invented an as-yet-undetected particle called the Higgs boson, named for Dr. Peter Higgs, now at Edinburgh University in Scotland. The Higgs boson hypothetically is the carrier of yet another force, which acts on the W and Z particles to give them large masses. Its properties are "delicately chosen," said Lederman. "The Higgs mechanism is very awkward. . . . It could be said that it is a rug under which is swept our ignorance of the meaning of structure

or lack of structure for an elementary particle. The Superconducting Super Collider is specifically designed to confront the Higgs theory with decisive data."

The "Top" Quark

How? Theory predicts that the Higgs boson, if it exists, cannot have a mass greater than 1 TeV. "Something has to happen at 1 trillion electron volts," said Lederman. "New physics has to be there to account for this business that we lump together and call Higgs." Then isn't it overkill to design the SSC with an energy of 40 TeV?

The answer is no, for the numbers are deceiving. The energy actually available to create new entities depends on the particles that are colliding. "In a machine that accelerates electrons and positrons and causes them to collide in head-on collisions, that number is very easy to come by," Lederman told me. "It is simply the sum of the energies of the two counterrotating beams. But the situation is different with a proton, which is a complicated object, not a single pointlike particle like an electron. A proton is made up of three quarks that are held together

Dipole superconducting magnet assemblies, like this one at Fermilab, will help protons follow the contour of the SSC.

One useful analogy is to think of a proton-proton collision as banging together two beanbags rather than two billiard balls. The energy level of the SSC was chosen to ensure that the "beans" would collide with an energy of at least 1 TeV. At this level the door to new physics, now locked, springs open. Investigators will be seeking out, in addition to the Higgs boson, the "top" quark, which the Standard Model predicts but which has never been detected with certainty. "There is a very rich spectrum of particles proposed by our friends who developed supersymmetry theory," Lederman said. That theory demands heavy particles with Runyonesque names like "winos," "sleptons," "Higgsinos." Their appearance or nonappearance in the SSC may allow physicists to learn which of several competing post–Standard Model theories is the correct one.

"On the other hand, we may be in for a tremendous surprise," Lederman said. "Some totally new and unexpected picture of nature may emerge."

Why So Big?

So much for the reasons the SSC needs to be so powerful. Why does the SSC have to be so enormous?

Because protons carry an electrical charge, they can be accelerated by an electromagnetic field such as radio waves. Protons in the SSC will be accelerated by radio frequency fields. Each passage through such a field slightly boosts their speed and therefore their kinetic energy. To achieve very high energies, the protons must receive millions of such kicks, which means they must travel along a closed path, usually a circle or racetrack-like oval. (To accelerate protons to 20 TeV in one straight pass would require a tube more than 600 miles—965 kilometers—long.)

And that's the problem. Like any other moving object, protons and all other particles obey Newton's Law of Inertia: they want to move in straight lines. To confine them within a closed curve, their paths must be bent by powerful magnets. And the higher the energy of the particle beam, the more "rigid" it becomes—the harder it is to bend it along a curved path. So for a given magnet strength, the higher the energy of the protons, the greater the path's circumference must be; increasing the circumference reduces the sharpness of the bend.

In fact, the 52-mile (84-kilometer) circumference chosen for the SSC is a trade-off

by gluons. So when you accelerate a proton, you are carrying with it the baggage from lots of other things, and the proton's energy is actually shared among those things."

The thing that creates new physics, said Lederman, is the collision of these constituents of the proton and antiproton—a quark-quark or gluon-gluon collision. And that energy is only a fraction of the total, a fraction that varies in complex ways.

between size and magnet design. Original proposals had the circumference at anywhere between 50 and 100 miles (80 and 160 kilometers). The larger circumference would have saved money in magnets, but the collider would not have fit at many of the suggested sites (some 20 states are eager for the SSC to be in their territory), and a larger tunnel would have cost more to excavate and build. The racetrack shape, with its straight passages, is simply more convenient for experimental purposes than a circular layout.

Such decisions have been the concern of a band of scientists and engineers called the SSC Central Design Group. After the administration's go-ahead was announced, I visited the group's director, Cornell University physicist Maury Tigner, at SSC headquarters. It is on the grounds of Lawrence Berkeley Laboratory, high above the main University of California, Berkeley, campus, at the end of a long, hill-climbing street appropriately named Cyclotron Road. Ernest O. Lawrence invented the cyclotron, first of the modern breed of accelerators, in 1930, for which he was awarded the Nobel Prize. It was 5 inches (12.7 centimeters) in diameter.

Tigner's office was down the hall from the bulletin board with the "Throw deep" sign. It was filled with the usual stacks of files, documents, and books, with one slightly incongruous note: sandwiched between an engineering handbook and a physics text was a volume of the poems of Wallace Stevens. Finding a "resonance" in some of the harder poems, Tigner said, was a challenging and satisfying intellectual experience.

Equipment similar to that slated for use at the SSC, including miles of specially designed cable, found its first application in the less powerful particle accelerators at Fermilab in Illinois and CERN (below), outside Geneva, Switzerland. At the SSC, the superconducting niobium-titanium wire cable for the magnetic coils, made in a custom-designed machine (right), is brought together from separate spools, drawn through a guide, twisted, and flattened.

Both photos: © Kevin Fleming

At Fermilab (above), which now has the highest-energy accelerator in the world, scientists use bicycles to get around (left). The racetrack-shaped SSC will be some 13 times larger than the accelerator at Fermilab, and more than 20 times as powerful.

Historical Continuum

So, of course, is particle physics. "We regard the field," Tigner told me, "as part of a continuum that stretches back in history—part of the effort to understand the world around us, one of man's premier intellectual and cultural activities. We've been using accelerators to do science ever since the late twenties and thirties, when Cockcroft and Walton and Ernest Lawrence showed us how to make instruments that achieved a resolving power of almost nuclear dimensions.

"Since that time, this science has always been big science, requiring major resources. So the followers of this trail have always had to organize themselves to share the resources, much as astronomers do with their telescopes. As the needed instruments have become bigger and more expensive, they've become fewer and fewer in this country and around the world, and the time needed to plan them and bring them to reality has grown longer and longer." (The United States had 22 modern accelerators in 1953; now there are four.)

I asked Tigner about the genesis of the SSC. "We can trace it back to the early seventies, when people began to understand that the accelerators then in existence were only going to go so far in giving us access to the energy that was needed to press beyond our understanding. Even then, the Standard Model was pretty much in place, and we were already beginning to perceive its problems—the many fundamental questions left unanswered. We knew the energy domain we would have to leap to if we were to escape the limits of this model in its explanation of the fundamental physical entities— if indeed there are such things—and the forces that govern them.''

Supercooled Magnets

In 1978, Tigner continued, there was an international meeting of physicists at Fermilab, and the next year in Geneva, at which a number of possibilities for the distant future were discussed, among them a 40-TeV proton collider. ''At that time,'' Tigner said, ''we knew that we would have to use superconducting-magnet technology to achieve the desired energy.''

A superconducting magnet is one whose coils are wound with a superconductor—a material that loses all resistance to the flow of electric current when cooled sufficiently, generally to temperatures close to absolute zero (−459° F or −273° C). The magnets used in all accelerators but one use ordinary copper windings, whose resistance generates great quantities of heat, which must be conducted away by water. They also consume gigantic amounts of electrical power. Fermilab's 400-giga-electron-volt (GeV) machine incurred $14 million in electricity costs in just 26 weeks in 1982.

Even more crucial, the field strength of the magnets—and thus the energy level of the accelerator—is limited in conventional magnets to about two tesla. In superconducting magnets using the best superconductor (for this purpose) available—niobium-titanium—the field has an upper limit of 15 tesla. The worth of such supermagnets has been abundantly proved since 1983 in the main ring of Fermilab's Tevatron—the world's only accelerator using superconducting magnets. The Tevatron uses 150,000 pounds (68,000 kilograms) of niobium-titanium.

The SSC, with its 10,000 magnets, will use much more of this material, which was once considered fairly exotic. I asked Tigner whether any of the newly discovered, even more exotic high-temperature superconductors now causing a great stir might have any influence on the final design and cost of the SSC

''We're following this development with great interest,'' Tigner said. ''If it should turn out to be useful, we would adopt it so fast you'd think we invented it. But that seems very iffy, mainly because there is no evidence now that these materials could carry a sufficiently great current density in the presence of high magnetic fields. The currents carried are 100 to 1,000 times smaller than in present superconductors such as niobium-titanium.

''Furthermore, these materials are ceramics. We'd have to find ways to form them into the very fine filaments necessary in a superconducting magnet. And there are other technical problems.

''But suppose your fairy godmother handed you this stuff today with all the problems resolved. What kind of impact would it have on the SSC? Probably not much. Being able to operate at a somewhat higher temperature, say 30° K [−405° F or −243° C] instead of 4° K [−452° F or −269° C], would just not save that much in refrigeration cost.''

Finding a Home

In 1983, with the necessary superconducting-magnet technology successfully demonstrated, an SSC group was invited to headquarter at Lawrence Berkeley Laboratory. ''Before that,'' Tigner said, ''it had been almost like organizing a pickup softball game—pretty spontaneous.'' As a result of a study conducted in 1984, the DOE gave a contract to the Universities Research Association, a consortium of 56 research universities, to carry out a detailed design-and-cost study and form a special organization to do the job—the Central Design Group. ''We'll probably stay at Berkeley,'' Tigner said, ''until we move on-site in 1989.''

Finally, I asked him about the criticisms of some scientists that the SSC will divert money and talent away from equally or more important research. One such critic is the radio astronomer and physicist Arno Penzias, a Nobel laureate. ''The Super Collider's capital cost,'' he has written, ''will clearly squeeze capital expenditures for other sciences.''

Here is Tigner's response: ''None of us for one moment would want to press on with this great wave of discovery in particle physics if it were to come out of the hides of other scientists. We may be parochial in certain respects, but we have a deep respect for science as an entity; to make a huge advance in one part of it at the expense of others would be a bad mistake. We are very happy to see that the SSC is viewed in the administration as going forward in the context of a big increase in the other sciences—for example, the National Science Foundation budget is targeted for doubling in the next five years. We are very anxious that other scientific areas that are ripe for progress should be supported. ''If our country and culture fail to make such investments, then we are doomed to decay.''

SUPERCONDUCTORS
GET DOWN TO BUSINESS

by Anthony Ramirez

Courtesy AT&T

Superconductors—materials that offer no resistance to electrical flow—repel external magnetic fields. The superconducting material above, cooled by vaporous liquid nitrogen, forces a magnetic cube to float above it.

After months of rising excitement, the big breakthrough came in May 1987 at IBM's sleekly sinuous Thomas J. Watson Research Center in Yorktown Heights, New York. Scientists had been making astoundingly rapid progress with the quirk of nature called superconductivity, which enables some materials to carry electricity at low temperatures with virtually no loss of current.

In February, researchers had fashioned superconductors that worked at $-283°$ F ($-175°$ C), a temperature high enough to use cheap liquid nitrogen as a coolant instead of far more costly liquid helium. But the superconductors appeared to carry too little current to be commercially practical—until an IBM team led by vice president Praveen Chaudhari showed that their capacity was a hundred times greater than anyone had demonstrated before. Then, a scant two weeks after the IBM announcement, researchers at the University of Houston raised the going temperature for superconductivity once again—this time to $-54°$ F ($-48°$ C), which

one scientist cheerfully called "room temperature if you open your window in Alaska." The twin advances suddenly transported a sunburst of remarkable uses from tantalizing fantasy to the realm of serious possibility.

Relatively soon, perhaps in a few years, an array of promising electronic applications could ensue: superconducting computer chips, medical scanners, and ultrasensitive detectors to probe the earth for minerals or transmit defense communications in deep space. Further along could come a world transformed by superconductors in almost unimaginable ways—ultrafast computers, hyperefficient power plants, 300-mile (480-kilometer)-per-hour levitating trains, and, ultimately, clean, safe, and plentiful energy from nuclear fusion.

Marathon Efforts

All of this seems much closer to reality than it did even a few months back. Companies like AT&T, Bell Communications Research, Westinghouse, and General Electric, long frustrated in their quest for commercially usable superconductors, are mustering platoons of scientists for marathon lab sessions. Other research squadrons are being speedily deployed at Du Pont, Corning Glass, and GTE, which have done little or no work in superconductivity but are skilled at fabricating the exotic ceramic materials that the new superconductors are made of.

Shoji Tanaka, a leading researcher in superconductivity at the University of Tokyo in Japan, estimates that as many as 600 physicists in Japanese universities and 100 researchers at Japanese companies are hurrying to commercialize the new materials. He says such companies as Toshiba, Hitachi, Sumitomo, Mitsubishi, and Furakawa are hard at work on superconductors. Labs in France, West Germany, Britain, Taiwan, China, the Soviet Union, and other countries are also charging ahead.

The leader for now is IBM. In its May 1987 breakthrough, the company transmitted a strong electric current through a tiny superconductor thinner than a human hair. Such "thin films," already shown to work in principle in ultrasensitive detectors, will be crucial to connections on computer chips. IBM believes it can eventually match that achievement in larger-scale applications, which could include wire, flexible tape, cables, magnets, and other widely used commercial products. If it succeeds, licensing fees for the technique could add significantly to profits.

In from the Supercold

It's hard to exaggerate the progress that's been made in superconducting over the past 18 months; such frenzies of discovery are rare in the cautious, painstaking world of scientific investigation. In that short time, superconductivity has come in from the supercold. Exploring the phenomenon once required liquid helium, which is scarce, expensive at $11 a gallon, and a nuisance to handle. Many of the new superconductors use more plentiful liquid nitrogen, which costs 22 cents a gallon, requires less refrigeration, and is so user-friendly that it can be carried around in a Styrofoam cup. The latest materials, developed by physicist Paul C. W. Chu and his Houston colleagues, appear somewhat unstable but display the earmarks of superconductivity at about the temperature of dry ice. The new materials are generally easy to make and retain their superconductivity in magnetic fields much more powerful than the old materials could tolerate—an important property, since magnets are crucial to many superconductor applications.

The remaining barriers to commercial superconductors appear less formidable than the problem of current-carrying capacity that IBM seems to have largely solved. The toughest obstacle: the new materials are brittle, much like Necco wafers, and therefore hard to form into useful shapes. They are also "anisotropic," meaning that they transmit current better in some directions than in others. Twisting, looping, or compressing them into a wire may reduce the amount of electricity they can carry.

How Does a Superconductor Work?

The basic science of superconductors begins with the simple fact that the flow of submicroscopic electrons making up an electrical current meets resistance as it collides with the ions and atoms of the conducting material. The higher

Superconductor temperature measurement. When discovered, a material that exhibits superconductivity at room temperature will find nearly limitless applications.

© John Madere

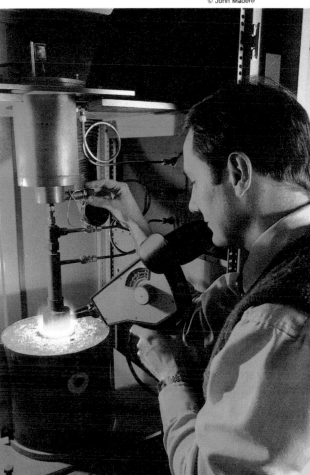

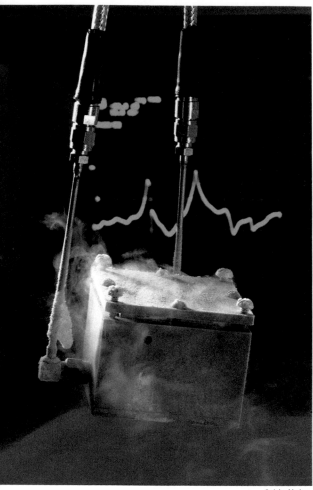

© John Madere

Plentiful and inexpensive, liquid nitrogen cools the experimental superconductor inside the casing to −320° F.

Scientists first found that some substances act as superconductors at temperatures near −459.7° F (−273° C)—absolute zero—the point at which all molecular motion, and therefore all resistance, stops. In 1911 the Dutch physicist Heike Kamerlingh Onnes discovered that frozen mercury loses all resistance at the temperature at which helium changes from a gas into a liquid, about −452° F (−269° C). By 1973, using alloys of metals like niobium and germanium, scientists had succeeded in nudging the critical temperature, the point at which a material shows a sharp drop in electrical resistance, only to −418° F (−250° C).

The turning point came in January 1986, when an unconventional insight struck Karl Alex Muller and Johannes George Bednorz of IBM's Zurich research laboratory. They tested substances so electron-poor that they normally don't conduct at all: compounds of lanthanum, barium, copper, and oxygen. Fired as ceramics, they are similar to the substances found in oven-proof cookware. Bednorz says that since he and Muller were novices in superconductivity, "We were free to try something crazy."

Out of hundreds of mixtures, one showed zero resistance at a record-breaking −400° F (−243° C). After a group at the University of Tokyo led by Tanaka confirmed Bednorz and Muller's breakthrough, an international race was on. By the end of 1986, the Tokyo group, along with researchers at AT&T's Bell Labs and the Institute of Physics in Peking, had raised the critical temperature to −388° F (−233° C). In February 1987, researchers at the University of Houston and the University of Huntsville, Alabama, led by Houston's Chu, got a whopping rise in critical temperature to −283° F (−175° C), comfortably above the −320° F (−195° C) boiling point of liquid nitrogen.

"The Woodstock of Physics"

The March 18, 1987, meeting of the American Physical Society in New York City turned into a frantic crush of 3,000 scientists from a dozen countries, all trying to learn about the latest advances. "The Woodstock of physics," Michael Schluter of Bell Labs called it. Since then the stampede has been on, especially for headlines. Rushed and incomplete work has created misleading impressions. At the "Woodstock" meeting, Bertram Batlogg, a Bell Labs researcher, proudly brandished a flexible electrical tape made from the new materials. A truly flexible tape could be used for magnetic coils or

the temperature, the more energy the resisting particles have and the more likely they are to get in the way. It is as if a man tried to walk through a boisterous New Year's Eve crowd in Times Square. He may get through, but he will raise a sweat doing it.

In a properly cooled superconducting material, electricity encounters almost zero resistance, so that a current can travel great distances without dissipating energy. It is as if the Times Square pedestrian not only walked unimpeded, but was also picked up by the crowd and carried when he got tired. According to the prevailing explanation of superconductivity, the crystal structure of the superconducting material forces the electrons to form orderly pairs, eliminating wasteful electron scattering.

INSULATOR

In materials with extremely high resistance, such as rubber or glass, electrons are tightly bound to atoms and cannot be jostled loose to sustain a flow of current.

CONDUCTOR

In materials with lower resistance, some electrons are loosely bound and form a current when voltage is applied. Resistance is a measure of the energy lost in the form of heat from electron collisions.

SUPERCONDUCTOR

When materials become superconductive, all resistance disappears because electrons are bound into pairs, which move in step with each other, avoiding collisions. Current flows with no energy loss.

for electrical transmission lines. "I think our life has changed," proclaimed Batlogg. But there is one big problem with the Bell Labs tape: when it's flexible, it doesn't superconduct; and when it superconducts, it isn't flexible.

As it does in an ordinary conductor, a current flowing through a superconductor generates a magnetic field—the principle underlying electromagnets. But if the magnetic field becomes too powerful, it quenches the superconducting flow. Until IBM's advance in May 1987, the new superconductors could withstand huge magnetic fields applied to them, but couldn't themselves generate a large field because they carried too little current. Now they may be able to generate large magnetic fields without shutting off the superconductive flow.

What makes the IBM breakthrough so remarkable is not merely how quickly it happened but its wide applicability. IBM passed a current through a thin film in such a way that it could probably turn the same trick in a thicker application. When a current rushes through a superconductor, it produces troublesome eddies. If allowed to careen through the current like tiny tornadoes, they disrupt flow and weaken current-carrying ability. Junk particles and defects de-

liberately introduced into the ceramic attract the eddies and pin them down. In principle, says Chaudhari, the research team leader, IBM could do the same thing with larger applications that it does with thin films. He won't give the exact recipe; that's patent-lawyer country.

Some of the earliest thin-film applications may be computer chips that marry semiconductors to superconductors. Superconductors probably won't substitute for silicon or gallium arsenide in chips, but they could replace the metals that connect chips together. Superconducting circuits communicate with each other faster than semiconductor circuits do, because they use less energy and generate less heat, so they can be crammed together more tightly than silicon-based circuits. Higher-performance computers would result, and office-size supercomputers could be shrunk to the size of shoe boxes.

But that doesn't mean superconducting supercomputers will arrive soon, Chaudhari cautions. "Those two supers in a row sound appealing, I know," he says, but major difficulties remain with both cost and design.

Easy-to-Use SQUIDs

Other thin-film applications on the near horizon include cheaper and easier-to-use versions of tiny, ultrasensitive detectors called SQUIDs, for

A computer-generated model of a high-temperature superconducting crystal shows the barium (green), yttrium (silver), copper (blue), and oxygen (red) atoms.

IBM Research

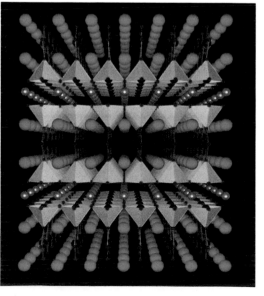

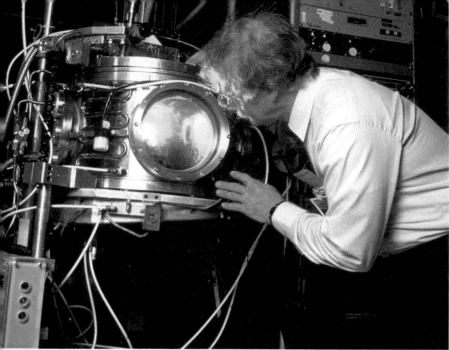

The inherent brittleness of superconducting materials has impeded their use in many applications. But now, in a process developed by IBM, superconductive materials in the "green state" (not yet having achieved final hardness) can be deposited in a thin layer on objects of a variety of shapes. IBM's Gerald Cuomo (above) observes a sapphire substrate being so coated.

superconducting quantum interference devices. SQUIDs have applications ranging from defense to medicine and geology. Scanners that measure magnetic activity in the brain will become smaller and cheaper, says William Black, senior vice president of Biomagnetic Technologies, which now makes them using helium-cooled superconductors. The skull distorts electric currents, but magnetic waves pass through it

IBM scientists have "grown" a thin superconducting film that mimics the orientation of its substrate.

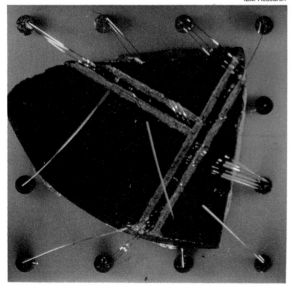

undisturbed. The magnetic waves of, say, schizophrenics or cancer patients may contain important diagnostic information. Unlike imaging scanners that use large magnets to probe the body, brain-wave scanners passively measure the body's own faint magnetic fields. They're faint indeed: about one-billionth of a gauss, a measure of magnetic strength. (Refrigerator-door magnets run more than 100 gauss.)

Stanford physicist Theodore Geballe, an expert in thin films, says SQUID-based sensors will be able to analyze the dim magnetic fields within the earth to find deposits of oil or minerals. The military sees a variety of uses for SQUIDs: the Navy wants SQUID-based equipment to detect the magnetic stirrings of Soviet submarines hidden deep within the ocean. The Air Force is interested in high-frequency radar and other sensor and communication systems in space, where they are necessary to Star Wars, the Strategic Defense Initiative. Liquid-nitrogen superconductors would make those systems smaller and reduce their power requirements. Computers on the ground would have to analyze billions of bits of information about thousands of incoming missiles and mobilize defenses in an instant. A superconducting computer might be capable of a trillion calculations a second, compared with a mere billion for the fastest Cray supercomputer, says Dallas Hayes, an official at the Rome Air Development Center near Boston, Massachusetts, which is overseeing a signal-processing project.

Levitating Trains

Further down the line are commercially viable magnetic trains, hyperefficient power plants, and, perhaps, nuclear fusion. A Japanese prototype superconducting levitating train already travels at up to 300 miles (480 kilometers) per hour. It works on the familiar principle that like poles of a magnet repel; powerful magnets repelling powerfully can lift a train. But since the magnets on the Japanese train are cooled with liquid helium, heavy compressors are needed to keep the costly coolant from evaporating. Cheap liquid nitrogen would help make a magnetic train lighter and more economical.

Researchers at Westinghouse are working on electric-power generation through superconductors that would more than double the usable output of conventional generators, according to research director John Hulm. Transmission lines would send the electricity great distances with virtually no loss, compared to the 8 percent lost today in transmission and distribution, the Electric Power Research Institute estimates. Superconductors could save hundreds of millions of dollars in fuel and other costs annually, says the industry group. Magnetic containment fields also could store electricity essentially forever, notes Hulm of Westinghouse. Utilities now dissipate unused power every night when customer demand slackens.

Such containment fields, or bottles, also will be needed for nuclear fusion generators that could produce electricity more safely and cheaply than conventional nuclear power plants. The generator's plasma, a boiling mixture of hydrogen isotopes, would be so hot—hotter than the surface of the sun—it couldn't touch any surface; only a magnetic bottle could hold it. Helium-cooled superconductors, costly and troublesome, now power magnetic bottles and the pulsing magnets that heat the plasma in experimental fusion reactors.

East-West Competition

With such promising applications, it is no wonder that Japan's Ministry of International Trade and Industry (MITI) is swinging into action. Japan has progressed to "a respectable level" in the superconductivity race, says an official at MITI's Office for Basic Technology for Future Industries. U.S. scientists were impressed with the University of Tokyo's methodical confirmation of the initial discovery of the new superconductors at IBM Zurich.

Alarmed by the possible threat of Japanese

© Kaku Karita/Gamma Liaison

The Japanese have designed prototype trains that levitate over tracks by means of superconducting magnets.

dominance of yet another high-tech industry, Senator David Durenberger, a Minnesota Republican, has sponsored a bill to establish a presidential commission to coordinate superconductivity research and development, as Japan's MITI does. The prospect of such bruising competition makes some top Japanese scientists uneasy, especially in view of the two countries' strained trade relations. "Much too political, much too political," says the University of Tokyo's Tanaka of the Durenberger bill. "Superconductivity is like a precious stone in the earth. We must develop it very carefully. It must not be dominated by one person, one company, or country."

With a scientific and commercial free-for-all busting out around the world, however, Tanaka's noble sentiments may be lost in the race to commercialize superconductors—especially since the first few laps have gone cleanly to the United States.

Titanium
the
Magnificent

by James R. Chiles

The stuff is everywhere: in the sand on the beach, in the dirt in your backyard. Most of it is used as a common compound for everyday purposes, such as making the page in your hand opaque enough so that you do not see the printing on the other side. But some goes through a metallurgical hell of arc furnaces and leaping electrical currents to be purified into the most glamorous metal in the world today.

On Lenin Avenue in Moscow stands a 40-foot (12.2-meter)-tall statue of Yuri Gagarin, first man to orbit the earth. It is a monument to more than the man: it is made of cast titanium, the metal without which the Space Age would never have gotten off the ground.

This most modern of structural metals, the fourth most abundant in the earth's crust, begins with very old ore. I first encountered it in its raw form resting in ancient sands in northern Florida. Through thousands of years of metallurgical history—from the first cold-working of native copper, through the sculpture and spearheads of the Bronze Age, and on into the ages of iron and steel—these black sands had waited. Even when chemists discovered the element almost 200 years ago in European deposits, titanium was locked in a chemical embrace so tight that no one knew how to separate it from the ore.

Tough to Refine

Titanium's day was coming, though. Advancing technology meant engineers were demanding more and more from the traditional metals, and finally even the best alloys were no longer good enough. Then, just as the radial aircraft engine began to give way to the turbine with its extraordinary requirements of lightness and strength, an Austrian scientist figured out how to refine titanium economically. Fifty years later, we have yet to exhaust its potential.

Extracting titanium from its ore sands requires heroic measures. First, titanium-bearing sand is run through gravitational and electrostatic separators, where long blue sparks flicker in the dark, ozone fills the air, and electrons crawl on your skin. The concentrated ore is treated with chlorine to make titanium tetrachloride, a clear liquid that, when exposed to air, produces a dense white vapor used for tracer bullets, skywriting, and naval smoke screens.

Titanium ranks high among metals in strength, corrosion resistance, and cost. In Western Australia (left), Florida, and elsewhere, titanium ore occurs in sand and dirt, from which it is extracted and purified.

Next, stainless-steel tanks are loaded with magnesium or sodium and welded shut. Titanium tetrachloride is fed into the tank through a pipe. Two days of heating and distilling yields chloride of magnesium or sodium and about 8 tons (7.2 metric tons) of dull gray titanium "sponge," which collects on the walls of the tank like brittle fungus. After the tank cools down, workers cut it open and break out the sponge with chip hammers. The process is hard on the tanks; one I saw was so blackened and sagging, it looked like a locomotive boiler after a train wreck.

Hydraulic presses crush the sponge into huge electrodes for vacuum-arc furnaces, which consolidate and purify the metal into cylindrical ingots for shipment to manufacturers. Working the pure metal is no piece of cake, either. Years ago a trade journal commented that "trying to fabricate titanium by conventional means is like trying to catch a barracuda with a bent pin." Even today the best way to bond titanium to another metal is blast welding: lay down a sheet of the second metal, a sheet of titanium on top, and then a low wooden box of explosives. Find a place to hide, and set off the blast, welding the sheets together.

Myriad Applications

Titanium—named for the Greek giants who once ruled the earth—is tough to make and tough to work, but for some purposes, nothing else will do. Aboard the SR-71 Blackbird, the world's fastest plane, the thin titanium skin holds its strength even when Mach-3 air friction fires it to 800° F (425° C). It's practically nonmagnetic, so submarines with titanium hulls can slip by magnetometers designed to pick up conventional steel-hull subs. A tough and transparent oxide layer gives the metal immunity to many acids and other corrosives that would burn holes in lesser metals.

The pure metal isn't something you'll find in the hardware store, but chemical combinations of titanium with other elements are all over the marketplace. The vast majority of the 991,000 tons (900,000 metric tons) of titanium metal and oxides consumed in this country in 1985 went into pigments, and also to unsung industrial uses like welding rods and additives for steelmaking.

The aerospace industry uses about three-quarters of the titanium mill products in this country. The F-15 fighter is about one-third titanium by weight, the B-1B bomber about one-

© Michael Freeman

PHYSICAL SCIENCES   301

Only a chiphammer can remove the distilled titanium "sponge" that collects on the inside of the tank where it formed.

quarter. The Boeing 747 uses it for massive undercarriage frames that withstand the rigors of landing. Because of its resistance to creeping when under centrifugal force, titanium is excellent for turbine blades and rotor disks in jet engines. That many modern planes can't fly without it explains why, as of 1985, the United States had 36,000 tons (32,700 metric tons) of raw titanium metal in its National Defense Stockpile, plus an equal amount of high-grade ores. Geologists have staked out another 8 million tons (7.2 million metric tons) of accessible titanium, mainly in New York and Florida.

Mineral City

The mining of titanium in Florida began by accident. George A. Pritchard and Henry H. Buckman, a pair of prospective prospectors, had found titanium ore—then worth $18 to $80 a ton—in a sample of Florida beach sand sent to them in Indianapolis. They did not have enough money to follow the lead to Florida, however, until Pritchard was injured in a streetcar accident and Buckman's car was involved in a wreck. Armed with insurance settlements of nearly $1,000, the pair reached Florida in 1915. They found the richest sand near what is now Jacksonville Beach and began mining. In 1922

After grinding excess metal from a titanium hip joint, the part is roughed to help it form a strong bond to bone.

the National Lead Company bought Mineral City, as the operation had come to be known, but by 1932 mining ended as richer ores were found elsewhere. The Mineral City clubhouse became the core of a golf club and resort operation. A committee decided to choose a more appropriate name, and settled on Ponte Vedra after seeing the name of the Spanish town in a newspaper dateline. When a raft-load of German saboteurs left their U-boat to land on Ponte Vedra Beach in 1942, residents had already turned to tourism. Today the site is solid condominiums; the only suggestion of the old mine is the world-class golf course, artistically carved out of piles of titanium-free waste sand.

Currently America's titanium ore comes from only two mines, both near Jacksonville, Florida. Together they produce about one-twentieth of the world's supply of ore. I paid a visit to the smaller of the pair, operated by Associated Minerals (USA) Inc. The mine occupies the Green Cove Springs Deposit, a low, pine-covered ridge that was prime beachfront property half a million years ago. Beneath the shallow topsoil is sand mixed with dark organic silt, about 30 feet (9 meters) deep. Most of the sand grains are the common quartz variety, but 3 percent are compounds of zircon, titanium, iron, and various rare earths.

Mine manager John Glover—Australian, like his company—drove me down sandy roads to see the diggings. The operation imitates the company's previous beach mines on Australia's east coast. Working in a temporary lake, a green dredge scoops up the ancient sands with a large bucket wheel, creeping back and forth along a quarter-mile (0.4-kilometer) face. Hourly it passes 1,000 tons (900 metric tons) of harvested sand back to a concentrating barge. The concentrator uses water flow and gravity to cull out most of the lighter, waste sand.

At the main plant, electrical and magnetic separators parcel the mineral sands into rutile, ilmenite, and other metal ores. Shift supervisor Lorell Sweat led me down a narrow passage between electrostatic separators. It was like moving through a huge bug zapper. I was careful to walk down the exact center of the passageway after Sweat told me that sparks occasionally reach out into the catwalk to snap a worker. The current is just powerful enough, he said, "to make you mad at the world."

Even at Mach 3 the titanium skin of the world's fastest plane—the SR-17 Blackbird—withstands air friction.

© Michael Freeman

Alvin's titanium hull helped the submersible resist deep-sea pressures during the Titanic expeditions.

One kind of titanium ore emerging from this plant, the brownish red variety called rutile, is excellent for making metal. For economic reasons, though, the plant's output currently goes to pigment—a much bigger market than metal. All of the titanium metal produced in this country begins with foreign ores, mostly from Australia, Canada, and Sierra Leone. The refining process, which involves corrosive chemicals and high-voltage electricity, is difficult and costly, and milling and forging the reluctant metal is equally challenging; titanium cuttings try to weld themselves to tool bits, and the metal will react with practically anything when heated to melting. These accidental combinations are nearly always brittle and worthless.

Finicky Element

Lockheed found just how difficult titanium can be when the company developed the SR-71 back in the 1960s. Some of the first parts were so brittle that they shattered if dropped to the floor. Wing panels spot-welded in summer failed early, while those welded in winter lasted indefinitely; it turned out there was more chlorine in the water used to wash parts in summer, and chlorine and titanium don't mix. A titanium bolt could be ruined by an assembly worker using a steel wrench plated with cadmium.

Working with titanium is a finicky business, as seen at Precision Castparts Corporation. A complex of metal buildings wedged into the residential suburbs of Portland, Oregon, PCC specializes in a small but profitable corner of the aerospace industry: titanium castings for jet engines. It uses the lost-wax process: a Sumerian bronze worker of 3,000 years ago would recognize virtually every step.

Steve Waters, titanium sales manager, walked me through the plant, explaining how to make a "fan frame" for a jumbo jet engine. (A fan frame is a set of interconnected rings about 6 feet—2 meters—across.) It begins with a hollow aluminum mold of the part to be cast. Pumps inject a special wax into the mold. The wax hardens and emerges a pale green. Workers trundle the delicate wax models down hallways to tables where other workers add other delicate wax parts and smooth out any irregularities. Each model now has a number and a dossier. Robots take over, alternately dipping the models into ceramic slurries, spraying them with sand, and letting them dry. Repeated many times, this process builds up a thick shell around the wax. A trip into an oven melts out the wax and fires the mold, which will be good for exactly one titanium fan frame.

Pouring titanium into the shell requires a furnace closed to the outside air. When cool, hammers, saws, and water jets strip the shell from the casting. Ready to fly? Hardly. Furnaces heat-treat the casting. Acid baths slim it. Fluorescent dyes highlight surface cracks; X rays reveal hollows inside. Inspectors write all over the casting with felt-tip pens, flagging defects for repair work. Arc welders remove surface flaws. Heat and high pressure fill interior voids. Then X rays to check the repairs. More welds. More X rays. Several months after starting life as a wax mold, the titanium part clears the shipping department. Waters showed me a fan frame that had passed all the final exams. I handled it gingerly; the price, Waters said, was "considerably over" $50,000.

The same reasons why designers are willing to pay a premium for titanium in the air apply to research in deep water. Many deep-sea submarines have pressure spheres and hulls of titanium: the French *Nautile,* the Japanese *Shinkai 2000,* and the American *Sea Cliff* and *Alvin.* *Alvin* was recently prominent as the vessel that visited the *Titanic* at 12,500 feet (3,800 meters).

The deepwater advantages have not escaped the Soviets; their "Alfa" class attack submarines have a double hull of titanium. Alfas are the deepest-diving military submarines: reportedly, they can go to below 3,000 feet (900 meters), versus about 2,000 feet (600 meters) for steel-hull subs.

About a quarter of the titanium milled for industry does hard labor as tubing and tanks in water desalination plants, chemical refineries, generating stations that use seawater to cool their boilers, and food-processing factories. Acidic foods like orange juice will often take on a metallic taste from processing vats, but not if the vats are made from titanium.

Remarkable Nitinol

As if titanium's combined assets of strength, light weight, and corrosion resistance are not enough to earn it status as the miracle metal, then certainly the remarkable feats of nitinol, a nickel-titanium alloy, are. First developed at the U.S. Naval Ordnance Laboratory in 1958, nitinol exhibits what metallurgists call the "shape memory effect": bend a wire of it into a desired shape, heat it, cool it, and then straighten it. Upon reheating, the wire will rapidly twist itself back to the original configuration that was heated, exerting a force of almost 100,000 pounds per square inch (70 million kilograms per square meter).

Nitinol is already found in lightning-

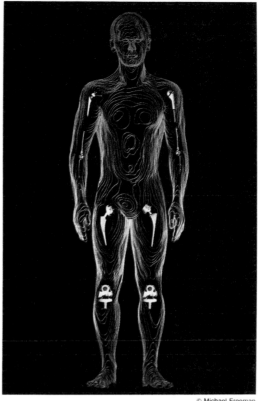

Prosthetic joints made from titanium alloy are strong, lightweight, and compatible with living tissue.

response fire detectors, springy wire for orthodontic braces, and weldless pipe joiners. Engineers hope to use it as the "muscles" for robotic limbs and hands. Medics think nitinol could have special uses for persons with a ballooned artery (aneurysm) or weak walls. A thin wire would be heated to memorize a tight, coiled shape at body temperature. After insert-

Spherical tanks constructed of titanium alloy held the onboard fuel supplies for Skylab during its space missions of the 1970s.

ing the straightened wire into the artery via a tiny catheter, it would recoil to form a strong, rigid lining. Even the brassiere industry is looking to replace the steel supports in its garments with nitinol so that, after washing, a bra will return to its original form when it hits the critical temperature—that of a warm body—for the shape memory to spring into action.

A High-Performance Aura

The medical community has long been a user of titanium. Eye surgeons use tiny instruments machined from titanium because "it's lighter than stainless steel, and it never rusts," says Daniel Wilson, a Texas ophthalmologist. The importance of light weight is that the surgeon can work longer before his hand gives way to the tremors of fatigue. Titanium also appears in bone screws, jaw implants, the Jarvik-7 artificial heart, casings for heart pacemakers, implanted drug pumps, and artificial joints from shoulder to ankle.

The same thin, transparent layer of oxide that protects titanium against corrosion in the human body has drawn artists with a technological bent. Using electricity or heat, it's possible to selectively thicken this oxide layer, "painting" the metal in a limited but vivid range of colors. The artist can make yellows, browns, blues, greens, pinks, and purples.

I tried the electrical method in my backyard, running one wire from a transformer to a titanium plate, and the other wire to the metal ferrule on my paintbrush. I dipped the paintbrush in a jar of ammonium sulfate solution; when I touched brush to metal, the liquid in the brush tip sputtered like frying bacon, a thin vapor rose, and rich colors appeared magically on the shiny gray surface. Which color I got depended on the voltage and on how long I left the brush in place.

Attention, hobbyists: caution is advised. I burned out the windings in my transformer on one attempt, and severe electrical shock is only a slip of the wrist away. "I've had a couple of shocks," recalls Edward de Large, a British artist living in California. "One knocked me off a typist's chair when I inadvertently connected myself to the transformer."

Jewelry, sculpture, and a few consumer items are probably as close as most people will come to the metal. Nikon offers a camera with a titanium frame, and Porsche Design sells pens, watches, sunglasses, electric shavers, and lighters with titanium components. Scattered through the sports marketplaces are titanium bicycles, tennis rackets, water skis, connecting rods for racing engines, and golf clubs. Kathleen Soltow, vice president of a Michigan forging company, keeps a couple of titanium wrenches in her briefcase for demonstration purposes. "It sounds silly, but since they're noncorrodible, we think they're fabulous in marine work, or for mechanics who have to travel. A toolbox is terribly heavy."

Silly, perhaps, but many a backyard hobbyist might like a titanium crescent wrench. When he goes to retrieve it from the neighbor who borrowed it, he'll be able to point it out every time: it's the one that's supernaturally light and strong, and so rust-free it almost glows in the dark. These virtues are why, in the 40 years since it left the furnace in quantity, titanium still shines in its high-performance aura. It's the metal that designers reach for when nothing else will do.

© Michael Freeman

Not just high-tech anymore: titanium's elegant silvery luster and high-performance properties add a touch of class to watches, eyeglass frames, and other consumer goods.

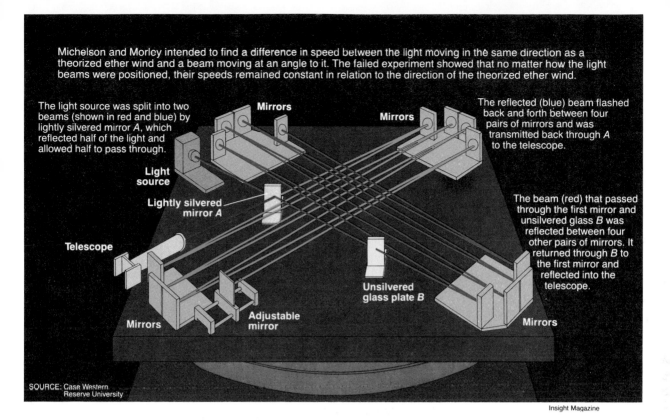

Michelson and Morley intended to find a difference in speed between the light moving in the same direction as a theorized ether wind and a beam moving at an angle to it. The failed experiment showed that no matter how the light beams were positioned, their speeds remained constant in relation to the direction of the theorized ether wind.

The light source was split into two beams (shown in red and blue) by lightly silvered mirror *A*, which reflected half of the light and allowed half to pass through.

Mirrors

Mirrors

The reflected (blue) beam flashed back and forth between four pairs of mirrors and was transmitted back through *A* to the telescope.

Light source

Lightly silvered mirror *A*

The beam (red) that passed through the first mirror and unsilvered glass *B* was reflected between four other pairs of mirrors. It returned through *B* to the first mirror and reflected into the telescope.

Telescope

Unsilvered glass plate *B*

Mirrors

Adjustable mirror

Mirrors

SOURCE: Case Western Reserve University

Insight Magazine

A MOST ENLIGHTENING EXPERIMENT

by John Holmes

They couldn't believe it. Albert A. Michelson and Edward W. Morley, arguably America's two foremost scientists, had spent much of 1887 working to put the finishing touches on what most scientists thought was a virtually complete understanding of the laws of the universe.

Michelson, a physics professor at Cleveland's Case School of Applied Science, and Morley, a chemistry teacher at that city's Western Reserve University, were trying to prove the existence of ether, a mysterious, invisible gas that scientists long had believed permeated the universe and perhaps even existed in spaces occupied by solid objects. The two had devised what is now widely considered one of the most famous, sophisticated, and important experiments of all time, and they had failed.

Their surprising failure shocked the global scientific community and shattered the views of universal laws that scientists and scholars had held since the time of Sir Isaac Newton. And though they didn't know it at the time, their experiment also cleared the path for several major developments of modern physics, most notably quantum mechanics and the theory of relativity. These revolutionary theories explain the laws and elements of the universe and such concepts as space, time, and causality.

"I think it was the most important experiment ever performed. It is deeper and more important than Ernest Rutherford and the atom or Gregor Mendel and his peas. If [Michelson and Morley] had gotten a different result, mankind's view of space and time would be completely different," says Philip Taylor, a physics professor at Case Western Reserve University (the two schools federated in 1967). The university is spending much of the year commemorating the experiment's centennial.

UPI/Bettmann Newsphotos

Case Western Reserve University Archives

In 1887, Albert Michelson (left) and Edward Morley (right) sought to prove the existence of a theoretical light-carrying medium then called ether. Although the experiment failed, it led to a new understanding of light's properties.

Luminiferous Ether?

Before the 1880s, scientists had proved that light behaves in some respects like ripples in a pond or sound waves in the air. "A wave needs a medium to carry it," Taylor explains. "You can't have sound if there is no air to carry it. If you throw a pebble into a pond, you see the ripples going out. But if there is no water, there are no ripples."

Therefore, scientists believed, light also must move through a conductor of some kind. At the time, most agreed with the hypothesis that this medium was luminiferous (light-carrying) ether. "Their idea was that if the earth goes around the sun through this ether, then there must be an ether wind. And if there is an ether wind, it ought to bend the light waves," Taylor says. "They thought light waves ought to be carried downwind faster than they go upwind."

At that time, "the ether theory was almost universally accepted," says John Stachel, a physics professor at Boston University, and the editor of Albert Einstein's collected papers. "Michelson and Morley hoped to prove the existence of ether by measuring its effect on light," so they built a finely tuned instrument with which they hoped to compare the speed of light moving in the same direction as earth's orbit around the sun with the speed of light mov-

ing perpendicular to the orbit. If the ether affected the movement of light as they suspected, their device would show that light moving perpendicular to earth's rotation travels slightly slower than light moving in the same direction as the rotation.

Experimental Protocol

The pair devoted about $2,000 and worked for months in a secluded basement laboratory to perfect their device. The plan was this: they would fire a beam of light at a thinly silvered mirror that would split the beam, allowing half the light to pass through, and sending half of it off at right angles. The beams would ricochet among a series of 16 mirrors, and later reunite as a single beam visible through an eyepiece.

Light waves, like other waves, have detectable crests and troughs, and if the beams hit the eyepiece at precisely the same time, their crests and troughs would be arriving in phase and easy to pick out. If the beams traveled at different speeds and arrived slightly out of sync, the patterns of the split beams would be blurred or indistinguishable.

The scientists were able to study the beams in such great detail thanks to an optical interferometer Michelson had devised. In a time when many scientific measurements were still rough, and sometimes even primitive, the instrument functioned with a precision that astounds scientists even today. "They built a simple apparatus to measure something one part in 100 million," says Taylor. "That was an incredible accomplishment 100 years ago."

Before they began, the pair was convinced the beam traveling in the same direction as earth's orbit would arrive at the eyepiece first. But it did not, and no matter how they rotated the device, the result was always the same: the two beams of light always struck the eyepiece at exactly the same moment. Thus, it became obvious that light was impervious to the earth's movement through space.

Even with Michelson's amazing interferometer, the work was extremely tedious, meticulous, and demanding, and the researchers had to stand constant vigil to protect the device from even the least extraneous interference. The strain wore hard on the affable, easygoing Morley, and eventually broke the stern, obsessive Michelson, who had a nervous breakdown several weeks into the project.

Baffled by Results

"They were very disappointed [in their results]. The notion of ether had been part of the conventional wisdom so long that they assumed the problem must be in their experiment," Taylor says. "They thought perhaps what happened was because they did the experiment in a basement, and that maybe the walls would carry the ether along with them. They thought maybe they ought to repeat the experiment on the top of a mountain, where there would be no restrictions on the flow of the ether." But for a number of reasons, they never did.

"The scientific community was baffled by the results," Taylor explains. "These were the two strongest scientists in the United States. Michelson measured the speed of light with more precision than anyone else had ever done it," and in 1907 became the first American to win the Nobel Prize in Physics. "Morley had measured the composition of air with more precision than anyone else. So nobody doubted them; no one thought they had fouled up. Everyone accepted [their finding] as being a fact of nature, though no one could quite understand it."

In fact, many researchers continued to press the notion that ether existed in some form or fashion, primarily because "so many were still so attached to a mechanistic outlook. There was ordinary matter and there was ether, and if you could understand the two and their interactions, you could understand everything. It was very

With evidence suggested by the failed Michelson-Morley experiment, Albert Einstein (center) was able to develop his theory of relativity, which links matter to energy. Albert Michelson is standing at front left.

California Institute of Technology Archives

seductive," Stachel says. "Another reason was the nature of light. At that time the idea was that a wave had to have some medium in which to propagate. And based on mechanical knowledge, that seemed almost irresistible."

Among the scientists most intrigued by the experiment was Albert Einstein. In 1905, as he was perfecting his special theory of relativity, Einstein used the experiment as evidence that the speed of light is constant but that time and space are relative. That work eventually helped lead to his famous $E = mc^2$ equation that links matter to energy.

Years later, Einstein told Michelson: "It was you who led the physicists into new paths, and through your marvelous experimental work paved the way for the development of the theory of relativity." Even so, Michelson and Morley remained deeply troubled by the unexpected result of their work, and were never fully comfortable with Einstein's radical interpretation.

A Major Stepping-stone

In retrospect, most physicists now view the experiment as one of a series of stepping-stones that together constitute the birth of modern physics. "One reason for that is just the sheer precision with which the experiment was performed. They set extremely high standards by which future experiments would be measured,"

Taylor says. "A second is that it was really the first crack in the structure [of our knowledge of the laws of the universe], and eventually the whole structure had to be modified. They really changed the way science was done."

They also helped change the rules governing who conducts frontline scientific research in that they were among the first truly professional scientists. "Before then, the game was largely played by amateurs who had the money to support their own experiments," Taylor says. "You had to have enough income to support your work."

That began to change as the industrial revolution matured and more firms hired scientists strictly for research and technical work. At approximately the same time, several of the major U.S. universities began to emerge as sites for significant scientific study and research. The experiment and the changes that followed also forced European scientists to take their U.S. counterparts seriously for the first time.

"People still look back at that experiment and consider it a failure because they didn't get the result they expected. But the experiment wasn't really a failure," Taylor says. "It's like a guy in Texas who drills a well looking for water but strikes oil instead. Michelson and Morley didn't realize it at the time, but that is what they had done. They had hit pay dirt."

Mt. Wilson Observatory, Pasadena, CA

The huge stellar interferometer designed by Michelson was formerly used at the Mount Wilson Observatory in California to measure the diameters of stars.

THE 1987 NOBEL PRIZES
Physics and Chemistry

by Elaine Pascoe

R esearch in the hottest areas of chemistry and physics—molecular recognition and superconductivity—brought Nobel prizes to five U.S. and European scientists.

The award in chemistry was shared by Charles J. Pedersen and Donald J. Cram of the United States and Jean-Marie Lehn of France. Working separately, they pioneered in the development of molecules that can recognize and bind selectively with other substances, in some cases mimicking chemical reactions that are vital to life processes. Among the potential applications of their work are the creation of artificial enzymes, precision methods of detecting and removing toxins from soil and water, and highly targeted methods of delivering drugs.

The award in physics went to K. Alex Muller of Switzerland and J. Georg Bednorz of West Germany, who, working at the International Business Machines (IBM) research laboratory in Zurich, Switzerland, succeeded in 1986 in producing superconductivity at temperatures higher than ever before. Their work touched off an avalanche of research by other scientists, leading to further breakthroughs and the opening of what some observers have termed a new era in electricity. A notable aspect of the Nobel award was the speed with which it followed the research.

The Prize in Chemistry

Pedersen is credited with making the initial breakthroughs in the field of molecular recognition. In the 1960s, while working as a research chemist for Du Pont in Wilmington, Delaware, he discovered quite by chance a compound that could dissolve caustic soda in organic solvents such as benzene and ether. Studying the compound, a cyclic polyether, he uncovered the mechanism involved: the compound contained six oxygen atoms that bound to sodium and hydroxide ions in the caustic soda, loosening their electrostatic attraction and causing the soda to dissolve.

Pedersen called his compound a crown ether for its coronetlike shape. It and similar compounds found immediate use in transferring metal ions, such as sodium and potassium, into organic solutions, where they could be used in various chemical reactions. And by tailoring crown ethers to suit different sizes of metal ions, chemists were able to detect and separate specific metals from mixtures. They could, for example, remove toxic substances such as cadmium, lead, and radioactive strontium from tissue samples.

Cram and Lehn took the research a step further. Lehn, a professor of chemistry at the Université Louis Pasteur in Strasbourg, France,

Charles J. Pederson shared the Nobel Prize for chemistry for his discovery of compounds called crown ethers.

AP/Wide World

Donald J. Cram, a winner of the Nobel Prize for chemistry, poses with his wife and a model of a "host" molecule.

created three-dimensional crown ethers by replacing some of the oxygen atoms with nitrogen and adding successive polyether rings, so that the resulting compound was like a stack of plates. The new compounds could bind still more selectively with metal ions, and were also capable of recognizing biological substances, such as the neurotransmitter acetylcholine. The discovery created the potential for the production of artificial enzymes.

Cram, then a Du Pont consultant, likewise recognized that crown ethers could be altered to mimic the actions of enzymes, including those vital to life processes. He coined the term *host-guest chemistry* to refer to the new field of research—molecules such as the crown ethers act as "hosts" for metal ions and other molecules, which are "guests." Among his achievements was the creation of new host molecules, in the shape of spheres and hemispheres, that could bind more strongly to their guests.

Together, the work of the three scientists brought chemistry into the realm of biology and other sciences. Its potential for the development of artificial enzymes has important implications for medicine and industry. The precision with which the various compounds can separate substances may lead to improved ways of detecting and removing environmental pollutants.

Charles J. Pedersen was born in 1904 in Pusan, Korea, and went to the United States to study chemical engineering in the 1920s. He received a bachelor's degree at the University of Dayton and a master's in organic chemistry from the Massachusetts Institute of Technology (MIT), and in 1927 he began his career at Du Pont. He remained there 42 years, retiring in 1969, and produced his Nobel-winning work in the last years of his career.

Donald J. Cram was born in 1919 in Chester, Vermont, and received a doctorate from Harvard University in 1947. He then joined the faculty as a professor of chemistry at the University of California at Los Angeles (UCLA), where he has remained. He is considered a researcher with international influence, and is known as a tireless worker who often develops his ideas with three-dimensional models of molecules.

Jean-Marie Lehn, who was 48 when he received the Nobel, was born in Rosheim, France, and earned a doctorate in chemistry from the University of Strasbourg in 1963. He became a professor of chemistry at the Université Louis Pasteur in 1970, and in 1979 he also began to teach at the College de France in Paris. He is considered by many to be France's leading chemist.

Jean Marie Lehn shared the Nobel Prize for chemistry for work that may allow the production of artificial enzymes.

The Prize in Physics

Until the breakthroughs of 1986, superconductivity was considered a dormant research field. The phenomenon had been discovered in 1911 by Heike Onnes, a Dutch scientist. He found that electrical resistance disappeared when mercury was cooled to near absolute zero ($-273°$ C or $-459°$ F, the temperature at which atomic motion ceases). Later researchers produced superconductivity in other metals. But in each case the temperatures required were so low that the superconductors had no practical use—the highest temperature at which superconductivity could be produced was 23 Kelvin ($-250°$ C) in niobium-based alloys.

Bednorz and Muller decided to focus on nickel and copper oxides. After two years of experimentation, they tried a lanthanum-barium-copper oxide and, in 1986, succeeded in producing superconductivity at about 40 Kelvin. The temperature was still too low to be practical, but their work touched off renewed interest in the field. Within a year, other researchers had produced and confirmed superconductivity in related ceramic materials at temperatures above 90 Kelvin. Since materials can be cooled to this temperature using cheap and widely available liquid nitrogen, practical superconductors became a real possibility for the first time.

The elimination of resistance opened new possibilities for electricity. Current could not only be transmitted without energy loss, but also stored, in power loops where it would travel around and around until needed. Without the heat created by resistance, computers could be reduced to pocket size and operate faster than ever. More powerful magnetic coils could be produced, as well as electric motors that would rarely need recharging. And because superconductors repel external magnetic fields, they could be used to reduce friction in machinery and to power high-speed magnetic levitation (maglev) trains. While these uses remain largely in the future, the Nobel committee credited Bednorz and Muller with the "systematic work, deep insight, and experience of structural problems" that made the superconductivity breakthroughs possible.

Karl Alex Muller, 60 when the award was made, earned a doctorate in physics at the Swiss Federal Institute of Technology in 1958. He joined the IBM Zurich Research Laboratory in 1963, and in 1982 became an IBM fellow, a position that allowed him to pursue his own research projects.

J. Georg Bednorz, who received the award at the age of 37, was born in West Germany and received his undergraduate degree at the University of Münster. Like Muller, he earned a doctorate at the Swiss Federal Institute of Technology, and then, in 1982, joined IBM's Zurich lab. His knowledge and skills were key factors in the production and testing of the new ceramic material used in the superconductivity project.

Georg Bednorz (left) and K. Alex Muller shared the Nobel Prize for physics for discovering the superconductive properties of a compound at the "high temperature" of $-400°$ F. Their breakthrough touched off an explosion of new superconductivity discoveries.

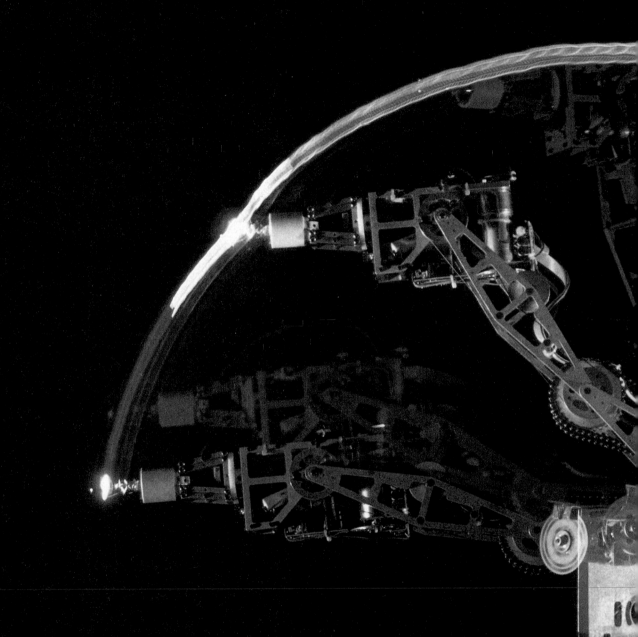

TECHNOLOGY

Edward Lallo/NYT Pictures

In computer-automated checkout lines, the description and price of each item passed over the scanner appear on a video display screen. Customers can summon human assistance by touching the screen.

REVIEW OF THE YEAR

TECHNOLOGY

New technologies for everything from defense to entertainment were in evidence in 1987. Among the highlights of the year were a new solar-powered car, improved automated bank tellers, and flat-screen television.

TRANSPORTATION

The General Motors Corporation's Sunrayer, a one-passenger vehicle powered entirely by the Sun, trounced the competition in the 1,950-mile (3,140-kilometer) Australian transcontinental World Solar Challenge race in November, outdistancing the closest of its 24 competitors by about 600 miles (965 kilometers). GM has no plans to produce a solar car for consumers, but the company's engineers said that useful spin-offs might be expected—such as solar cells to operate a car's radio, lights, and other accessories when the engine is turned off. (See also "Running on Sunshine," page 160.)

While solar cars weren't yet in dealer showrooms, consumers did see another new development: four-wheel steering. Two Japanese manufacturers, Honda and Mazda, unveiled models with rear wheels that turn side to side rather than remaining fixed as the car turns. The idea is to improve the vehicles' handling, but the technology is complex: at low speeds, the most benefit is gained when the front and rear wheels turn in opposite directions, to shorten the turning radius; at high speeds, all four wheels should turn in the same direction, to facilitate lane changes and other maneuvers. To accomplish this, Mazda uses an electronic system and Honda a mechanical one, based on the degree that the front wheels turn. Other manufacturers were said to be studying four-wheel steering, but some (including General Motors) questioned whether the improvements in handling were worth the costs.

For air travelers, 1987 was a year of frightening near misses. A plan to require electronic anticollision devices on commercial jetliners took a step forward in March, when the first such device was tested on a normal passenger flight. The equipment transmits radar signals that are bounced back by the air-traffic transponders aboard other planes. It then displays the other planes' relative positions and altitudes on a cockpit screen, sounding a warning when evasive action is needed.

BUSINESS AND CONSUMER

Bar codes, the patterns of lines that allow supermarkets to ring prices automatically with optical scanners and take inventory at the same time, are finding wider use in industry. Automobile makers in particular are adopting the codes as a way of keeping track of inventory and charting the progress of parts through manufacturing. Meanwhile, supermarkets are expanding the technology. One chain has introduced self-checkout lanes, in which consumers scan their own purchases. Another new system allows price changes to be made instantaneously throughout the store: shelves carry liquid-crystal price labels instead of the usual paper ones, and the liquid-crystal display changes in response to a signal transmitted by a central computer.

Since their introduction a decade ago as a way of cutting labor costs, automatic teller machines have been popular with banks but less so with customers. This has prompted designers to rethink the machines, looking for ways to make consumers feel more comfortable with them. Already incorporated in some machines are color graphics, "swipe" readers for bank cards (so that the machine doesn't swallow the card), fewer circuit boards (reducing breakdowns), and greater cash capacity. Industry sources predict that the applications will be limitless—automatic tellers will handle stock transactions, open accounts, and take loan applications.

ENTERTAINMENT

The first practical flat-screen color monitor, with improved brightness, contrast, and color fidelity, was introduced by Zenith in 1987, and the firm said it planned to incorporate the new screen in some of its color televisions in 1988. Conventional color tubes have convex screens, which contribute to glare and picture distortion but were necessary to accommodate the shadow mask, an essential part of the tube. The shadow mask is a layer of metal pierced with tiny holes; beams fired by an electron gun at the back of the tube pass through it and are directed to color phosphor dots that are painted on the inside of the tube's front panel. Conventional masks are curved to keep them from distorting in the heat generated by the electron beams.

Zenith engineers adopted an idea first developed for military avionics: they produced a flat screen of extremely thin foil and kept it under

Four-wheel steering provides better handling, greater stability, and easier parallel parking and U-turns.

Reprinted from Popular Science with permission © Times Mirror Magazines, Inc.

tension by bonding it to a piece of glass. The new screen holds its shape so well that more powerful (and hotter) electron beams can be used, permitting a brighter picture. This in turn allows the use of darker glass, for more contrast; and the flat screen can be coated on both sides with antiglare materials. The foil screen is etched with half a million tiny holes, improving resolution.

DEFENSE

Research for—and debate on—the U.S. Strategic Defense Initiative (SDI), the space-based antimissile defense system proposed by President Reagan, continued in 1987. In April a panel of leading physicists cited enormous technical obstacles to the plan, which is also known as Star Wars. The panel stopped short of saying that workable versions of the laser and particle-beam weapons that are an integral part of the proposed system could not be built, but it concluded that the necessary technologies would have to improve by factors of 100 to more than 1 million. The panel also disclosed that many of the orbiting weapons platforms that make up the system would require nuclear reactors, and its report said that it was "highly questionable" whether a space-based system could survive an attack against it. The Defense Department termed the panel's conclusions "unduly pessimistic."

CRIMINAL JUSTICE

New electronic devices are lightening the workload for overburdened probation and parole officers by allowing them to monitor the whereabouts of their charges from a central location. The most common of these devices are wrist and ankle bracelets that transmit encoded signals to a receiver in the offender's home, which then sends the information over telephone wires to a host computer. If the offender strays more than 150 feet (45 meters) from the transmitter, the signals stop. The idea for the system came from Judge Jack Love of Albuquerque, New Mexico, who spotted a similar device in the comic strip "Spiderman" in 1979. Another system uses voice identification: a computer telephones the offender at set intervals and matches the voice with a record held in its memory. Telephone systems that transmit black-and-white still pictures on 3-inch (7.6-centimeter) screens also are coming into use.

With some 1.9 million people living under probation or some form of supervision, overworked law enforcement officials have generally welcomed these systems. In 1987, 45 agencies were using electronic devices to monitor more than 1,000 people. But as the systems have come into wider use, critics have raised questions about their reliability and their constitutionality.

ELAINE PASCOE

317

RELAUNCHING THE AIRSHIP

by John Barber

The air is hot and choppy as pilot Michael Young steers the Fuji airship over the northern suburbs of Milwaukee toward Lake Michigan. Thermal currents surging upward buffet the 164-foot (50-meter)-long blimp, transforming its passage into a rollicking elephantine ballet. Young wrestles with the helm as if it were an exercise machine, pumping and twisting while the ship pitches and yaws toward the calmer air over the blue-green lake in the distance. That is what chief pilot Trevor Hunt calls "basic aviation." When you fly a blimp, adds copilot Stephen Tomlin, "you actually have to fly. It's not a case of 'wheels up, flaps up, coffee up.'" Simply getting the airship across town violates the rule printed on a plaque above the instrument panel: "Aerobatic maneuvers are not approved." The exercise—intended to display Fuji signs—is all part of the rebirth of lighter-than-air aviation.

Going with the Past

It was 50 years ago that the golden age of dirigibles ended with the fiery explosion of the zeppelin Hindenburg at Lakehurst, New Jersey. But last month the U.S. Navy revived the tradition when it awarded Airship Industries Ltd. (AI), the British company that owns and operates the Fuji ship, $264 million to build a better blimp for military surveillance. By showing that the apparently antiquated dirigible has a place in modern battle, the contract breathed life into dozens of plans for airships in modern transportation. They range from craft to compete with helicopters in logging to trucks for carrying freight past the ends of roads. Said airship advocate Rowland McFarlane, retired deputy minister of transport in Alberta, Canada: "Maybe it's time to say, 'To hell with the future, let's get on with the past.'"

The U.S. Navy's vision of that future includes a fleet of 50 airships, each about 400 feet (122 meters) long and containing 1.5 million cubic feet (42,000 cubic meters) of lighter-than-air helium, eight times as much as the Fuji airship. The reason it wants to build such ships now, more than 20 years after scrapping its original blimp fleet, lies in the threat of modern sea-skimming missiles. That became clear first in 1982, when a French-built Argentine Exocet missile sank the British destroyer HMS *Sheffield* in the 1982 Falklands War, and again in May 1987, when two Iraqi Exocets disabled the USS *Stark* in the Persian Gulf. The missiles are all but invisible to shipboard radar as well as that carried by airborne warning and control system (AWACS) airplanes. But airships can scan above a fleet with much more sensitive equipment and can stay aloft for days as op-

Airships—long overlooked as a plausible means of transportation for people and goods—soon may become a common sight over American cities.

Airship Industries

posed to hours. They themselves will be protected both by the fleet and also by the use of so-called Stealth technology to make them difficult to detect.

Composite Car

The innovations perhaps most responsible for Airship Industries' winning of the Navy contract are the ship's car, which is made of lightweight composite materials instead of metal, and its twin cowled propellers, which can pivot in order to push the ship up or down as well as forward. During takeoff, a cumbersome process in most blimps, the vertical thrust of the Fuji ship "just blows it off the ground."

The awarding of the contract to a British firm came as a surprise to most Americans, who have long equated Ohio-based Goodyear Tire & Rubber Company with airship technology. Although Goodyear has built more than 300 airships since 1911, only three survive, essentially serving as floating advertisements over sports stadiums. In March 1987, Goodyear's chances

of securing the Navy contract were further diminished when it sold its aerospace division to Loral Corporation in New York City to defend itself against a takeover bid. Nevertheless, Goodyear is now completing construction of a new airship that will have many of the same capabilities as those made by AI. And indeed, Goodyear officials tried to assert their preeminence in the airship field by suing Fuji Photo Film U.S.A. Inc. for trademark infringement last year, claiming that blimp advertising is Goodyear's exclusive right. The suit was recently settled privately out of court. But in the meantime the British firm put nine advertising airships into service in the United States, Britain, Japan, and Australia, home of the company's majority owner, former America's Cup defender Alan Bond.

Eye-catching Advertisements

Bond's company leases one ship and its 18-person crew for about $350,000 per month. But the novelty of blimps makes them irresistible to some advertisers. When not operating controls, blimp pilots often pass time waving back to their audience. Copilot Tomlin recalls a day that he spent on a British beach when one of AI's billboard blimps floated into view. "Everybody looked up," he said, "and everybody who had a camera took a picture." AI broadened its business when it launched a regular sight-seeing service, with $200 tickets for a one-hour flight over San Francisco on May 6, 1987—exactly 50 years after the *Hindenburg* crash.

The company's success in making blimps pay their way has inspired the small but committed band of airship advocates who previously had only their dreams to console them. But in fact, the airship dreamers are far from satisfied by visions of skies cluttered with helium-filled

Constructing airships from composite materials instead of metal makes them lighter and more fuel-efficient.

advertisements or even military surveillance platforms. Instead, they envisage the world transportation system made over by new kinds of heavy-lift airships. So far their record of achievement has been spotty, with most projects petering out for lack of funds after the construction of large-scale models. But the faith still burns bright. "Many people start these things, then they fall apart," said Alberta's McFarlane. "But I think it is ready now. The time is right for the true renaissance of the dirigible."

"The *Hindenburg* Syndrome"

The first obstacle confronting those attempting to bring about that renaissance is what they call "the *Hindenburg* syndrome." Usually, the syndrome takes the form of simple skepticism. It emerged last summer when inventor Frank Piasecki attempted to launch his revolutionary *Heli-Stat* airship not far from the New Jersey site where the *Hindenburg* crashed. The *Heli-Stat*, comprising four surplus helicopters connected by a steel framework to a 1950s Navy surplus blimp, failed catastrophically on a test flight, killing one crewman and injuring four others. The U.S. Forest Service had invested $33 million in the machine, designed to lift logs from remote sites.

Despite such events, airship advocates say that the *Hindenburg* crash is now irrelevant. They point out that modern ships filled with inert helium could not burn like the *Hindenburg*, which used hydrogen because at the time the United States would not surrender its helium monopoly. They also blame the sobbing, hysterical reporting of radio newsman Herb Morrison, whose broadcast of the *Hindenburg* explosion, recorded live, is a classic monument to the power of electronic media. Morrison initiated a modern myth when he declared, "There's not a possible chance of anybody being saved." But in fact, 61 of the 97 people aboard the *Hindenburg* walked away from the wreck. Declared John Tansowny, an investment director with the Alberta government and director of Lighter Than Air International, a group devoted to promoting the airship cause: "If we had had an excited cameraman in a dinghy watching the *Titanic* going down, we probably wouldn't be using boats now."

Zeppelin Fever

One thing seems clear: the Lakehurst crash overshadowed the remarkable achievements of the great German zeppelins. When the 776-foot

(237-meter)-long *Graf Zeppelin* first appeared over New York City in 1928, it created a sensation, quickly nicknamed Zeppelin Fever, that spread wherever it traveled. Over its nine-year career, the famous craft covered a remarkable 1,053,000 miles (1,684,800 kilometers) safely, and made one nonstop 6,973-mile (11,220-kilometer) trip from Germany to Japan. It flew over pack ice in the High Arctic and through tropical cyclones. As a passenger ship, it made 63 round trips between Germany and Rio de Janeiro, Brazil, averaging 95 hours one way—about 10 days better than the fastest liners.

The 804-foot (245-meter) *Hindenburg*, launched in March 1936, was the most advanced and luxurious rigid airship ever built—a "great floating palace," according to Morrison. It had hotel-like lounges, and cabins for 72 passengers, and even a 112-pound (50-kilogram) aluminum piano. Passengers balanced coins on edge to test the company's claim that it offered "the quietest and most comfortable means of transportation known." There is no record of any passengers becoming airsick.

The job of protecting ships from cruise missiles requires no aviation technology fundamentally different from that employed in the past. By contrast, conventional blimps are ill-suited to hauling heavy cargo. The main problem is ballast transfer. If an airship is made sufficiently buoyant to carry a heavy load, an equal weight of ballast must be taken on at the same time as the cargo is unloaded. The alternative would be venting helium to reduce lift, which would prevent the ship from picking up more cargo elsewhere before returning to its home base. And even without cargo, airships require extensive ground support—the small Fuji blimp uses an 11-person ground crew to take off and land.

The Flying Golf Ball

Those logistical problems would defeat one of the prime attractions of airship transport—the ability to operate in remote, relatively inaccessible areas where establishing and maintaining ground-service facilities are difficult. Mainly for that reason, those who envisage cargo airships—"the banana freighters of the 21st century," according to one advocate—have been forced into devising novel and in some cases radical designs.

Many of those radical designs have emerged in Canada. Perhaps the best known is

In 1937 the golden age of airships came to an abrupt end when the dirigible Hindenburg, *the largest airship ever built, crashed in flames at Lakehurst, New Jersey. Modern airships would not burn like the* Hindenburg *because they use inert helium gas for flotation rather than highly explosive hydrogen.*

© Ruth Kaplan

The doughnut-shaped Hystar *airship has a central fan that blows downward for extra lift in vertical takeoffs.*

the airship being developed by the Magnus Aerospace Corporation of Ottawa, the Magnus LTA-20—better known as the flying golf ball. The Magnus consists of a spherical bag of helium with a fuselage slung beneath it on two curving arms. "It has never been done before," says Magnus aviation researcher Dennis Hughes. "No one has ever seen a round airplane." The helium is intended to support the weight of the ship, while helicopter-like rotors will provide most of the cargo-carrying capacity. Apart from its shape, the most innovative aspect of the ship is the fact that it spins to generate extra lift. Aerodynamically, this is known as "the Magnus effect," after H. G. Magnus, the German physicist who first described it.

Magnus Aerospace built a 22-foot (6.7-meter)-diameter model of its ship in 1982 and tested it for a year. Now Hughes says that the company is planning a 65-foot (19.8-meter) prototype that will lift one ton. He added that

the design's main advantage is that "with a sphere there is no such thing as a crosswind." But technical difficulties with the Magnus ship forced organizers of the Canada Pavilion at Expo 86 to cancel its scheduled appearance in Vancouver, British Columbia. They replaced it with a model of a flying saucer. Also known as the Hystar airship, it was designed by Vancouver's George Ninkovich to solve the problem of lifting timber out of remote sites. The Hystar consists of a doughnut-shaped ring filled with helium surrounding a central fan that blows downward to provide extra lift. The 15-foot (4.5-meter), radio-controlled model flown regularly at Expo proved so successful that Hystar received inquiries about using similar craft for promotional work. Ninkovich said that he has since built more than 12 of them and that they have helped him to finance a 55-foot (16.7-meter) manned model designed to lift one ton. It is now undergoing flight tests.

Aerodynamic Miracle

So far, the only experimental modern airship ever to lift more than a ton is the bizarre Cyclo-Crane, built by AeroLift Inc. of Tillamook, Oregon. To many, the 1985 maiden flight of the 190-foot (58-meter) Cyclo-Crane, lifting a microbus in its cargo sling, represented an aerodynamic miracle. Like the Hystar, the Cyclo-Crane was designed to replace heavy-lift helicopters in logging. It resembles a blimp, except for the four large wings projecting from its center. In flight the craft spins around its long axis, passing air over the four wings, which can be adjusted either to lift the craft up or press it down.

Unlike the LTA-20s and the Hystars, which contain just enough helium to loft their own weight, the Cyclo-Crane is so buoyant that when it is not loaded, the wings must be kept moving to hold it down. A crash due to engine failure would be as novel as its design. "Unlike a lot of construction cranes that fall down and kill people," said AeroLift vice president Robert Phillips, "this one falls up."

The Cyclo-Crane's life began auspiciously seven years ago with $3 million invested by a consortium of three Vancouver logging companies: MacMillan Bloedel Ltd., Pacific Logging Ltd., and British Columbia Forest Products Ltd. But AeroLift is "struggling with a lack of resources," according to Phillips, searching out investors to finance a ship with a payload capacity of 13 to 16 tons.

Hybrid Craft

Phillips' problem is one of those facing the new generation of airships. But when one model proves fatally flawed, there is usually a new one available. The one currently filling that role is the work of a West German engineer based in Edmonton, Alberta, and financed mainly by a Vancouver mining company. Juergen Bothe began working on airships in 1978 for the West German government, which was investigating a role for airships in Third World transport. He concluded that blimps were "too ancient a technology," and he devised a hybrid craft instead. Bothe said that hard scrutiny from independent experts has proved his Helitruck "significantly superior" to any other new design. "This is not the renaissance of the airship," he added, "but the birth of a new type of aircraft."

On paper the Helitruck is a formidable machine. A combination of lifting devices—including helium, stubby wings, helicopter-like rotors, and the bulbous fuselage itself—enables it to take off from a short runway when fully loaded with a maximum 10 tons. It can fly at speeds of 275 miles (442 kilometers) per hour. Its rigid shell design is based on the sleek, streamlined form of a dolphin, but its dimensions—140 feet (42.7 meters) long by 110 feet (33.5 meters) wide—bring it closer to the shape of a pregnant goldfish. Still, what it trades off aesthetically, the Helitruck more than gains with a cargo hold three times the size of the hold in a de Havilland Dash 7.

Above: Aerolift, Inc.; below: © Ray Giguere

The extraordinarily buoyant Cyclo-Crane—the first airship capable of lifting over a ton—could replace heavy lift helicopters in logging operations.

Juergen Bothe, a West German engineer, holds a model of his hybrid craft, the Helitruck. By combining features of airships, airplanes, and helicopters, the Helitruck will be able to take off from a short runway carrying up to 10 tons and fly as fast as 275 miles per hour.

Bothe says that he sees two main roles for the ship: providing short-haul, door-to-door cargo service in industrial areas, and functioning as "a truck where there are no roads." He says that extensive studies suggest that there is indeed a market niche awaiting the Helitruck. "I am firm in my belief that once you could show this model, you would have a mini-revolution in transportation," he declares, adding that he needs only $25 million worth of financing to build one.

Not a Pipe Dream

The search for that money is what brought the 43-year-old inventor to Canada. He has found a supporter in Vas Rotgans, president of Mandrell Mining Ltd. in Vancouver. Rotgans, whose company develops and markets new mining technology, recently set up Bothe with an office and a Cyber 180-130 scientific computer in Edmonton. The two chose Edmonton because of Alberta's interest in airships, dating from the 1970s, when McFarlane was deputy minister of transport. Now retired, he is an avid supporter of Bothe, whom he calls "a brilliant engineer." Bothe says that he came to the province partly because of its "political interest" in airships, adding that government encouragement as well as financial support are necessary for the success of the project. And for his part, Rotgans says: "We want something that is not a pipe dream but an economic tool with a specific function. A lot of people dream of floating in air, which is nice, but it doesn't pay."

Photographs of Reality

That attitude is common. In fact, it is a characteristic of many latter-day airship advocates that they dismiss potential competitors as mere dreamers. One man whose vision is particularly broad is Leslie Vivian of L. R. Vivian Associates Ltd., a Toronto, Ontario, firm that publishes technical manuals. Vivian has developed an elegant plan for deploying Bothe's Helitrucks in the Canadian North. The system would involve large standardized containers fitted out as prefabricated houses, snowmobile repair shops, and medical centers. Vivian says that the Helitruck would allow the building of entire towns and industries in the roadless North, adding that it could pick up and move containers wherever they were needed—creating what he calls "tumblewood industries." Vivian says that his plan sets him apart from what he calls "the concept dreamers who failed because they established no legitimate applications."

Still, few can make the same claims as Airship Industries vice president George Spyrou, who introduced himself at a Vancouver conference last fall by declaring: "I shall not show you drawings of dreams, but photographs of reality." For now there are fewer factors than ever before preventing some new aviator's dream from taking off and flying.

Passenger accommodations in an airship's gondola resemble those of an airplane. The main thrust of airship technology, however, seems to be toward cargo-carrying and military applications.

THE MUSIC OF HIGH TECH

by Terri Thompson

In the 1960s, composer Walter Carlos created a sensation with a recording he called *Switched-On Bach*. Using one of the first music synthesizers, devices that electronically mimic a variety of musical instruments, Carlos spent months creating sounds, recording the music bit by bit, and editing together thousands of snippets of tape. The result: a top-selling album of electronically produced classical compositions that sounded as if they were played on a harpsichord—sort of.

From Bach to rock, musical technology has changed since then. Carlos still flouts convention: he's had a sex-change operation and now is called Wendy. But electronic music is no longer the stuff of the avant-garde. These days, anyone capable of playing a keyboard instrument can be a one-man band. For only hundreds of dollars, today's electronic instruments will respond with sounds respectably close to those of a concert grand piano, a whole orchestra, a vast choir, or just about anything that the player can dream up.

Sax and Violins

With a technique called digital sampling, the sound of a car door slamming or a dog barking can be turned into music that can be played at any pitch. These sounds are captured and stored as numerical values on floppy disks; to clone

Stevie Wonder uses digital sampling to electronically produce sounds quite close to those created instrumentally.

sounds, the sampler merely recalculates the numerical values. Flip a switch and you can "sample" patches of existing recordings. If you don't like it as a violin, punch a key and it's a saxophone. If you want to see it as sheet music, print it with a personal computer.

Artists ranging from Stevie Wonder to French composer-conductor Pierre Boulez are embracing the new technology. Instead of practicing in soundproof rooms or painstakingly copying sheet music a note at a time, musicians wearing headphones are sitting at music workstations that bear a greater resemblance to a control panel at NASA than to musical instruments. Indeed, the new technology is revolutionizing the way music is played, composed, studied—and enjoyed.

Even New York City's Juilliard School, the most respected conservatory in the United States and a bastion of classicism, has embraced high tech. The school opened its first electronic studio this fall, thanks to donations of synthesizers and music editing equipment from Yamaha International Corp., a leading producer of new music technology. "It's the wave of the future," says Dean Bruce MacCombie. "Better to get involved with it than to pretend it doesn't exist."

It exists, all right. Sales of electronic keyboards and related equipment jumped more than 40 percent last year, to $1.3 billion, according to the American Music Conference, a nonprofit organization that promotes music participation by amateurs. In 1986 Americans bought 2.6 million electronic keyboards—twice the number sold in 1985 and more than five times the 1984 total. They also bought 350,000 synthesizers in 1986, compared with 220,000 in 1985. That's because the plunging cost of the computer power needed to make electronic systems work means they are affordable to more people. At the same time, escalating labor and material costs have caused prices for acoustic pianos to nearly double over the past five years. Last year just 166,555 new pianos were sold, compared with 282,172 in 1978.

Today an estimated 25 million people in the U.S. play keyboard instruments. And thanks to the new musical technology, predicts Robert Moog, the first to use a keyboard rather than knobs and dials on a synthesizer in the early 1960s, "musical activity on the part of amateurs will increase."

Despite the pioneering development in the U.S., it took the Japanese to make the market sing. Composer Larry Fast, who has been creating synthesizer music for 20 years, remembers working on a synthesizer that used a mainframe computer and cost $2 million when he was a researcher at AT&T Bell Laboratories in Murray Hill, New Jersey, in the 1970s. But in 1983 Yamaha swept into the U.S. with its DX7. The portable keyboard did everything the monster at Bell Labs could—and sold for $2,000. Today, for a mere $400, "you can get a Yamaha synthesizer with features that were lacking in the DX7," says Fast. And other foreign manufacturers, including Casio, Akai, Roland, and Korg, now share the market with Yamaha.

Steinway Sound

The U.S. is not completely out of the picture, however. Although Moog's original company folded in 1977, he has joined forces with Raymond C. Kurzweil, a computer scientist and entrepreneur, who has put his small Waltham, Massachusetts, company, Kurzweil Music Systems Inc., at the forefront of electronic music. While many developers of electronic instruments concentrated on adding new sounds to composers' vocabularies, Kurzweil set out to reproduce faithfully the sound of traditional instruments and the response of high-quality piano keyboards.

In 1983 Kurzweil introduced its prototype of the Kurzweil 250. Instead of using analog circuits, like those in the first electronic synthesizers, this new generation of musical instrument has gone digital. To create the sound of, say, a key on a Steinway piano, it simply calls from its computer memory the sound of that note and reproduces it through speakers. To all but the most discerning, the sound is very close to the real thing.

But that system—and similar ones from Ensoniq, E-mu Systems, Lowrey Industries, Oberheim Electronics, Sequential Circuits, and Yamaha—can do far more. They sound just as good mimicking a violin, a flute, or a massive chorus. And they can do all those things at once. A musician can "layer" sounds on top of one another, so a single keystroke can simultaneously produce the same note sounded by a guitar, piano, or a full string section. Or, with a so-called sequencer function, the musician can play a part on one instrument and store it, then add another part while the first part is being played back, and so on, gradually creating a full orchestra.

But it's not just the individual instruments that are driving the revolution in music. It is an

© Gili Melamed

A student digitally composes music in the electronics studio newly opened at New York City's Juilliard School.

industry standard known as MIDI, short for Musical Instrument Digital Interface. While companies trying to automate factories still can't agree on protocols that will let their dissimilar equipment communicate, in 1983 music makers agreed on MIDI. It allows a musician to hook up synthesizers, electronic drums, and organs to a single keyboard and connect the entire system to a personal computer, regardless of the manufacturer. MIDI—the conduit through which all the signals pass from one instrument to another—facilitates music composition in ways almost inconceivable a few years ago.

With MIDI, all the information can be stored in digital form in the computer's memory, rather than on recording tape. So the composer can manipulate it in ways that were unheard of a few years ago. Play a tune on the keyboard, and the written notes appear on the computer screen. Change a note on the screen, and the computer plays back the corrected ver-

© John S. Abbott

An Orchestra in an Apartment

Iris E. Gillon is a thoroughly modern musician. A concert pianist and composer trained at the Juilliard School, she begins and ends each day playing the piano. Her cramped Manhattan apartment functions as both a studio and classroom and houses the usual tool of her trade: a Steinway grand. But it also contains electronic keyboards, synthesizers, sequencers, a drum machine, and the pièce de résistance, a personal computer.

An innovator by nature, Gillon entered the electronic age of music in 1981, when a student suggested that she use a computer to write her compositions, which run the gamut from full operatic works to rock and pop film scores. Quick to see the possibilities, she learned how to program and began developing software to produce her manuscripts.

Today Gillon composes music with the aid of a Casio electronic keyboard hooked up to a Macintosh computer and a Yamaha sound generator. By using synthesizers, which replicate the sound of virtually every instrument in a 55-piece orchestra, and a sequencer to "layer" each part, she can play a full symphonic score on the keyboard, and the computer prints it out.

The cost of all the high-tech paraphernalia: less than $6,500. The time to churn out a typical score: a few hours.

Gillon insists that the technology hasn't changed her creative process. But instead of taking days or even weeks to write a full orchestral score, she leaves that drudgery to the computer. Perhaps best of all, she doesn't need an orchestra to "proofread" the composition. By feeding it through her synthesizers, she can hear any glitches. Correcting the pitch or rhythm is a matter of a few keystrokes, so there are no surprises when the orchestra assembles. That can mean huge savings in studio time.

Fully aware that the new electronic age is putting fellow musicians on unemployment, Gillon says she remains committed to the "live" performance. But she also is incorporating into her scores the sounds made possible by the latest generation of synthesizers and digital samplers—from the chirping of birds to the roaring of motorcycle engines. She plans to have at least four synthesizers in her orchestra.

Even the acoustic-piano sound produced by some of the newer electronic pianos is getting remarkably close to the real thing, says Gillon. Today's electronic keyboards not only are attracting a new breed of musician, but also may be bringing more back to traditional instrument-playing. "My synthesizer students eventually turn to study in piano," she says.

Despite her taste for the avant-garde, Gillon isn't about to give up traditional piano. "There is no replacement for a great instrument," she says. "My piano has a spirit, and that cannot be reproduced."

sion. Don't like the tempo? Have the computer change it. Or alter the key, or change the violin part to a flute. Nor does the composer have to be adept at the keyboard. A saxophone player, for example, can hook up a so-called "wind-controller" and play music into the system, then tell the computer to play it back through the synthesizer. Or MIDI can turn the sound from the saxophone into an entire orchestra.

Miami Heist?

Professional musicians quickly saw the potential in linking instruments to computers. Since the MIDI standard was introduced, sales of computer hardware and software based on MIDI have shot up to about $500 million, and the market is expected to double within the next three years. The latest generation of personal computers from Apple, Atari, Commodore, and IBM accommodates the technology. Many brands of musical software are available for $50 to $500. And the five top manufacturers of synthesizers

In the 1960s, Robert Moog introduced a synthesizer operated by a keyboard rather than by dials and knobs.

Courtesy Robert Moog

are building MIDI into all but their lowest-priced instruments.

Such changes are not without controversy. The biggest battle centers around the so-called digital sampling technology. These devices are so adept at stealing others' sounds—even styles and human voices—that composers soon will have at their disposal unlimited electronic "sidemen" stored on computer chips. Put Beverly Sills singing a high C into the memory, for instance, and a digital sampler can play it back as a high D, or any other note. Hit two keys at once, and you hear two Beverly Sills. Play a few notes in sequence, and you have Sills singing a melody she never sang before.

Professional musicians have taken the issue to court. David Earl Johnson, a struggling percussionist, is suing the producers of "Miami Vice," claiming the theme music of the popular TV show rips off his conga sound. Johnson says that the composer of the score with the pulsating beat had sampled his conga playing at a recording session and later used his sound without compensating him. To protect his latest record album, Frank Zappa has taken the precaution of copyrighting against sampling.

Now that entire orchestras can be replaced by synthesizers, some worry that thousands of musicians may be put out of work. Others fear that music as an artistic endeavor will stagnate as the new crop of musicians becomes ever more dependent on technology.

Most, though, believe new technology is giving musicians unprecedented creative tools. After all, what past composer could invent new instruments at will, make music from any sound, and hear their compositions just seconds after they were written?

"We want to revolutionize music making," says Jeffrey G. Gusman, R&D manager at Yamaha Communications Center Inc. in New York City. "We are supplying the artist with the tools he needs." Even Bruce A. Stevens, president of venerable piano maker Steinway & Sons, believes "there is a world of opportunity for the use of computers" in music. Nor does he expect it to put him out of business. He is convinced that after musicians learn how to play an electronic keyboard, they'll want to upgrade to a fine acoustic piano.

No one is happier with the new wind blowing through music than Wendy Carlos. It will lead to "a lot of alternative styles," she says. "This is the first time I've felt I haven't needed to apologize for producing electronic music."

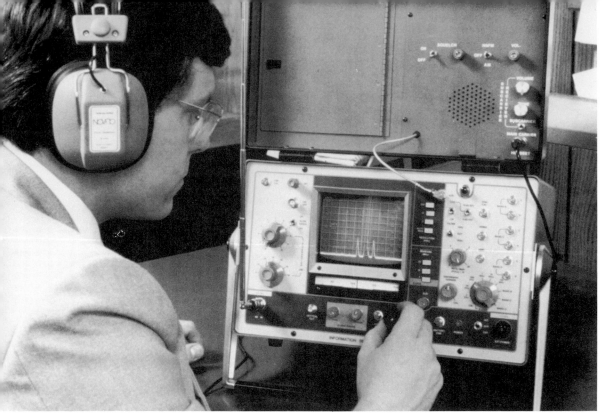

Popular Science

Electronics experts have devised radio-frequency scanners with which to monitor transmissions sent by bugs.

ELECTRONIC ESPIONAGE

by John Free, Naomi Freundlich, and C. P. Gilmore

A bug—a tiny microphone that can be hidden almost anywhere—is but one in a startling arsenal of devices used today to spy on personal enemies, competing companies, and other world powers. Such devices played a major role in the recent spying controversy between the United States and the Soviet Union. Much was written about the resultant diplomatic skirmishing. But little has been said about the devices themselves, their incredible capabilities, and the astonishing technology on which they are based. Almost nothing has been written about how some of the most interesting equipment works.

The Veil of Secrecy

Nobody wants to talk about bugs. The Central Intelligence Agency (CIA) and National Security Agency (NSA) refused to be interviewed. Private companies were also wary; several pro-spective sources hung up when they learned why we were calling.

Despite such problems, we were able to dig out some surprising facts. Among them:
• Bugs can be made almost any size. The smallest we actually saw was a tiny electret microphone just 3/16 inch (4.7 millimeters) across at its largest dimension. The security expert who gave it to us wouldn't say where he got it.
• Bugs are widely available. Tiny ones undoubtedly used in industrial espionage can be bought openly in some European and Asian cities, though they're as illegal there as here. Easily available even here, however, are wireless microphones smaller than a cigarette pack. They have legitimate uses, but also can be used for bugging.
• Bugging experts use dozens of methods to keep their devices from being detected, from planting them in electronic equipment to wiring

them with the latest in fiber-optic technology. The Soviets planted thousands of false bugs in the now-infamous U.S. embassy in Moscow to confuse sweeping attempts.

• While the CIA and Federal Bureau of Investigation (FBI) undoubtedly bring the latest in electronics technology to bear in acquiring supersmall, difficult-to-detect devices, surprisingly sophisticated bugs are relatively easy to build. We obtained plans for the so-called "martini olive" bug that received considerable publicity several years ago. It can be built in any reasonably equipped electronics workshop by anybody with even a moderate amount of electronics knowledge.

• Sensitive information in computers is easy to steal; a $500 device can tune in on any unprotected computer at ranges of perhaps 1 mile (1.6 kilometers) and reproduce anything appearing on the computer's screen.

• People who don't want their conversations bugged rely on frequent sweeping of sensitive areas. We saw a demonstration of several kinds of advanced equipment used in this effort.

Bug Types

Bugs—devices designed to eavesdrop surreptitiously on conversations—come in three basic forms. First are units that contain both a microphone and a small transmitter. They are hidden in a room and transmit a signal to a nearby receiver. If such a unit is tied into a power source— room electrical wiring or a telephone line, for example—it can transmit indefinitely. And the wiring may also be used to route signals from the bug to distant points.

Second are microphones. They can be extremely small, and hidden almost anywhere. But they require wires—which can be smaller than a human hair—to conduct the signal to a listening post outside the room. Finally, there are passive devices, which sit silent and unobserved, that can transmit room sounds when stimulated by a radio signal from outside.

Bugs can be very small—small enough to be built into a fountain pen or stuck into a small hole in the wall, the binding of a book, or elsewhere. Harry A. Augenblick, president of Microlab/FXR, tells of one clever design. "This is a picture-hook bug," says Augenblick, pointing to a 1-inch (25-millimeter) long, ¼-inch (6.4-millimeter)-diameter spike with a picture hook on its flat end. "First you use a tool that punches a hole in a wall, then you slip the bug in. After you hang the picture back on the

wall; you wouldn't know for years that somebody had changed your picture hook."

An investigator who insisted on anonymity showed us a transmitter about the size of a book of matches. "With its battery pack, this one will transmit for nine days," he said. "You can throw one of these in a trash can and retrieve it later." How far can such bugs transmit? "A matchbook-sized device can have a range of a quarter-mile [0.4 kilometer]," says Frank G. Mason, president of a Fairfield, Connecticut, security firm that bears his name.

The variety is endless. A bug can be slipped into a telephone handset. Merely picking up the handset supplies telephone line voltage to the bug, which then transmits anything said into the mouthpiece to a nearby receiver. "We once got a call from a guy who said every time he picked up his telephone, his television picture went blurry," said Rob Muessel of Information Security Associates in Stamford, Connecticut. "We never found out what that meant because he didn't hire us. But there was probably a transmitter planted inside his phone."

Similar bugs can be designed to send out signals all the time—even when the telephone is thought to be inoperative. "Wires are often put in telephones for nonexistent intercoms or speaker phones," says Mason. "So there is a spare pair of wires." If someone intent on bugging can get to a terminal board in that building, he can wire the spare pair so that the microphone in the telephone sends a voice signal to the terminal even when the phone is on the hook. "In government agencies where the phones must be replaced quite often," Mason says, "they test phones before new ones are put in, and find that eight out of 10 phones are 'hot on the hook.'"

The Martini-Olive Bug

Another astonishing fact is how easy it is to build very small—and very effective—bugs. A San Francisco security expert named Hal Lipset won momentary fame some years ago as the man who had bugged a martini olive. In our research, we obtained plans and directions on how to build the infamous martini-olive bug.

The plans call for hollowing out opposite ends of a small copper cylinder with a lathe, then carefully mounting in the two cavities about a dozen tiny parts—transistors, resistors, capacitors—available from any electronics-supply house. The instructions describe how to cut apart a standard alkaline battery and use parts of it to construct a very small battery. Finally, a disk made of foil serves as a microphone. The instructions say the unit can be made in several sizes, including one in which the finished device is approximately ½ inch (12.7 millimeters) in length and slightly less than that in diameter. It will transmit at a frequency of 600 megahertz.

How do you make it look like an olive? "A case may be formed around the unit with fiberglass putty and molded to any desired shape," the instructions conclude. The antenna is disguised as a toothpick in the olive!

The most interesting bug we saw falls into the second category: microphones. The bug, a miniature electret microphone, would need thin wires leading to a receiving station. That would be no problem for someone with access to the target room; we were told that the "wires" can actually be two lines of metallic paint on a wall, which are then covered by regular paint. Such an installation is almost impossible to find.

A practical *electret* wasn't devised until 1925. An electret is made by polarizing certain waxes or plastics with high voltage: one side has a strong positive charge; the opposite side of the electret material has an equally strong negative charge. An electrical potential is permanently "frozen" into the material. Practical applications of electrets for microphones became possible with the development of low-noise transistors and suitable dielectric—nonconducting—materials.

Just how small bugs can be is unknown. Frequently, news reports speak of "pinhead-sized" bugs. Yet there is no evidence that bugs that small really exist. It seems at least possible that they do not, and that the pinhead estimate is the result of logical confusion. The electret mike contains a tube on one side through which the sound enters. The hole is approximately the size of a pinhead. Thus, it is possible that the smallest bugs are not themselves pinhead-sized, but require a pinhead-sized hole in the wall through which they pick up sound. Says Mike Russell of Sherwood Communications in Southampton, Pennsylvania: "Microphones are usually found in ceilings or mid-level in the wall. They're usually behind the wall, with a tiny hole the size of a pencil point drilled through."

Cleaning Up the Premises

While companies are reluctant to talk about bugging, they're often happy to talk about their antibugging activities, which are legal, and which, indirectly, reveal a good bit about bugs, too. For example, Microlab/FXR's Augenblick gives a demonstration of the company's SuperScout—a $25,000 bug detector the company says is used daily by 53 lesser world governments and hundreds of large companies.

It looks like a cross between a vacuum cleaner and a beach-variety metal detector. The body of the device is a briefcase-sized receiver, and attached by long electrical cords is an adjustable boom with a flat, vacuum-cleaner-like head on its end that functions as an antenna. Augenblick slings it over his shoulder.

"We will find your little tape recorder whether it's on or off or even if you take the batteries out of it," he promises. Moments before, out of his presence, the tape recorder has been hidden on the lower shelf of the office coffee table under a stack of magazines.

He switches on the detection device, a nonlinear junction detector. Augenblick has explained the operating principle earlier. "Normally, if I sent a signal out around this room, it would bounce off everything, and the signals coming back would all have the same frequency as the one that went out," he explains. "But semiconductors such as transistors and diodes are nonlinear devices in which current flows more readily in one direction than in the other. That means that when SuperScout transmits at exactly 1 gigahertz, any semiconductor nearby will generate harmonics—that is, it will send back signals in exact multiples of the original frequency—1, 2, and 3 gigahertz, for example."

He methodically sweeps the head of the antenna up and down the office walls, across bookshelves, over furniture, and finally across the floor—all the while keeping an eye on the needle at the top of the shoulder-slung portion of the device.

Then he begins sweeping over the coffee table. The monitor needle swings to the right, and he grins. "There it is!" he exclaims triumphantly.

Nonlinear junction detectors can be misled—especially if electronic equipment containing semiconductors is anywhere nearby. "In the beginning we did some very crude things," says Augenblick. "An operator conducting a sweep of former Israeli Prime Minister Golda Meir's office literally tore down her office wall and found nothing. There was just a simple radio in the next room."

Although a nonlinear junction detector

Above: Popular Science; all others: © J. P. Laffont/SYGMA

Electronic bugging devices can be concealed in the most commonplace items. The Soviet Union alleged that the transmitter wired into a brick (above) from their embassy in Washington was planted by American spies. At right, a small bug wired into a light switch uses AC lines for both power and transmission.

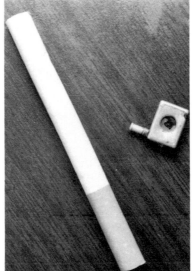

Some more ingenious hiding places. A wireless microphone can fit easily into a cigarette pack (above). Some modern transmitters are hardly as big as a cigarette (center). Miniaturized bugs can fit even into a ballpoint pen (far right). The drop-in transmitter at right replaces the microphone in a telephone receiver. The device transmits radio signals when the phone is in use and derives its power from the telephone lines.

A nonlinear junction detector uses microwaves to find semiconductor-containing transmitters and recorders.

such as the one Augenblick demonstrated can find just about any bug containing semiconductors if used with sufficient care, it is expensive and tedious to use. Thus, many persons debugging a site use a device called a scanner, which detects RF (radio-frequency) signals from bugs instead of the circuits inside the bug. Naomi Freundlich saw one in action at Information Security Associates in Connecticut. She reports:

"Rob Muessel turns a knob on the VCR-sized receiver; at each click, he homes in on radio-frequency signals. 'This instrument can scan signals from 20 kilohertz to 1,000 megahertz—1 gigahertz—and up into the 7- to 8-gigahertz microwave range,' he says. At one point the scanner screen dances with a whole mountain range of blue peaks, stronger than any we have seen yet. 'What are you picking up now?' I ask excitedly, imagining us picking up secret transmitted conversations. Muessel turns some dials, and a particularly large peak appears on the screen. But instead of satisfying my voyeuristic tendencies, strains of Simon and Garfunkel's song 'The Boxer' come through.

We have accidentally stumbled across the FM mountain range.

"'That's all that's really involved in using this device,' says Muessel. 'You just tune through and listen.' Tuning through and zeroing in on some of the larger peaks, we pick up ham radio, cellular telephones, and even the repetitive staccato sound of transmitted data from pocket pagers.

"Then Muessel sets up a transmitter in the room. Even when there is no sound, there is a peak on the scanner screen. 'We sometimes use a steady sound source,' says Muessel as he turns on a high-pitched beeper. As the transmitter signal pulses in time with the beeper, I hear the regular sound in my earphones. I also listen as we pick up the same pulsating peak at exactly two and four times the frequency of the original.

"The RF scanner can also be used to detect hidden video cameras. 'If we had a closed-circuit TV monitor, we could hook up a television receiver and display video signals,' says Muessel as we pass a large peak from a nearby TV station.''

As this demonstration illustrates, bugs that transmit continuously have a serious weakness: they're relatively easy to detect. Several ingenious schemes have been developed to minimize that possibility. For example, bugs can be built to collect information and transmit it in practically undetectable short bursts. One source speculates that such a bug could collect information in digital form for perhaps 15 seconds, then send out the whole package in one microsecond. Such a device would be practically impossible to find with a scanner.

A tiny electret microphone—just 3/16 of an inch at its largest diameter—fits into a pinhead-sized hole.

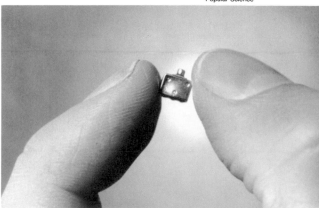

Others come with voice-actuated circuits that turn them on when there are sounds of voices in the room, off when not. Some have remote switches by which they can be turned on and off. ''I can put a bug someplace and turn it on and off remotely,'' says Charles Miller of Law Enforcement Associates, Inc., of Medford, New Jersey. ''I hear you come into the room, and if I have any idea that you're going to start checking for bugs, click, it's off.'' All these methods help prevent detection by scanners that look for signals being radiated.

Snuggled Bugs

Yet other bugs use a technique known as ''snuggling'' to avoid detection. The bug transmits at a frequency just barely different from a local TV station's, for example. Because its signal tends to be lost in the much more powerful TV signal, the bug may go undetected. Other bugs are frequency switchers: they transmit at one frequency for a few thousandths of a second, then change to another, and then another.

Active bugs can often be detected by nonlinear junction detectors or scanners. These methods, however, will not detect microphones, which neither contain semiconductors nor put out an RF signal. ''You can find them,'' says Frank Mason, ''by X-raying the walls inch by inch, but that's time-consuming, expensive, and hazardous to your health. The only other defense is physical inspection, such as looking for pinholes in walls.''

An even more difficult-to-detect setup can be created by using a hairlike optical fiber to transmit the signal out of the room and perhaps out of the building. Because the signal is in the form of light, it creates no electromagnetic signal that can be detected, nor is it detectable by normal sweeping methods.

Bugs of many types—both transmitters and microphones—are widely used and, according to the Microlab textbook, easily placed. The book says that Microlab never identifies its clients, what it did for them, or what it found. However, it says, the company knows of actual cases of bugging detected by others. In one case, it says, one company wanted to find out what progress a competitor was making in research. So while a member of the bugging company visited the office of the director of research at the rival company, he noted the title of a book in the office. He then bought an identical book and had it fitted with a 520-kilohertz bug. The bug, made into a thin strip and sealed in epoxy, was glued into the binding of the book. Then a maintenance worker was persuaded to substitute the bugged book for the original one. The sneaky competitors parked in a car nearby and tuned in on conversations in the research director's office.

Sometimes planting a bug turns out to be a really inside job. In February 1982, the manager of the Soviet airline in Indonesia was arrested for running a spy ring. While he was in custody, authorities became suspicious about a scar on

UPI/Bettmann Newsphotos

Cold War espionage: in 1952, Henry Cabot Lodge, the American ambassador to the United Nations, pointed out where an electronic bug was located at the U.S. embassy in Moscow.

his chest, which he said was from an operation. But a closer look showed that a bug had been planted in the man's chest so KGB agents nearby could hear all conversation around him.

Computer Bugging

Bugs have gotten most of the headlines recently, but sleuths use a lot of other high-tech tricks. One active area: eavesdropping on the sensitive information in somebody else's computer. Computer users were recently shocked to learn that it isn't even necessary for someone to have access to their premises. He can tune in to a computer from down the street. It isn't even difficult or expensive.

The words, numbers, and even graphic images appearing on a computer screen are formed by a beam sweeping across the screen in a TV-like raster. The beam is off where the screen is supposed to be dark, and on as it crosses an area that is supposed to light up. This switching of the beam on and off generates a digital signal that can be picked up some distance away. If another display unit at the receiving location has a beam sweeping across it in perfect synchronization with the one at the computer being tapped, and if the received signal is used to switch on the electron beam in this display, then a display identical to the one at the original computer will be formed. This signal that switches the beam on and off is easy to pick up because it is amplified to several hundred volts, unlike other signals in the computer or display. Thus, it radiates strongly.

The only real trick is synchronizing the beam sweeping back and forth across the eavesdropping display with the one on the computer being bugged. A television broadcast contains synchronization signals that are used by the receiver to keep its beam in sync with the beam at the originating station. A computer transmits no such sync signal. Instead, a spy must use a special circuit to discover the original sync mode and generate a new signal to synchronize the receiver.

Computers involved in national security—especially those in such places as embassies in foreign countries—are presumably shielded to prevent such eavesdropping. For 20 years the U.S. Government has had a series of standards called TEMPEST, designed to cut down on the radiation allowed to escape from a computer. (TEMPEST was originally an acronym for Transient Electromagnetic Pulse Emanation Standard.) Although no one will comment officially, we learned informally that the standards require that the potential signal be attenuated (reduced in magnitude) by about 70 decibels—a large amount. But one source estimates that it may double the cost of a computer to build in this kind of protection. A spokesman for Wang Laboratories Inc., which builds TEMPEST-protected computers, said it adds 20 to 50 percent to the cost.

UPI/Bettmann Newsphotos

In 1987 the Soviet Union accused U.S. spies of planting this bug in the car of a Soviet reporter.

At the new U.S. embassy in Moscow, thousands of tiny diodes are mixed in among the bugs to confuse sweeping efforts. The only solution may be to tear down the structure and build a new embassy from scratch.

© M. Deville/Gamma Liaison

The Cold (Bugging) War

Bugging devices obviously were used in the new U.S. embassy in Moscow. But it's been hard to tell what types; in their outrage, U.S. officials shed a lot of heat, but little light, over exactly what they had discovered. They charged that the building might have to be demolished, since the spy devices packed in it can probably never all be found and destroyed. Yet, putting together the background information, it's possible to deduce what must have happened.

According to news reports, bugging is such a fact of life that U.S. officials simply weren't too concerned about it. They counted, the reports said, on sweeping the premises after they took over the building to get rid of the bugs. "Our assumption was that we could rectify whatever the Soviets had done once we took control of the building," said a senior State Department official. "That may have been too optimistic."

Official statements make it clear that sweeping teams found huge numbers of bugs, microphones, and other suspicious devices. They were stunned by the complexity of the bugging. What could the Soviets have put in the building that could have produced such a reaction? Practically everything: There were cables apparently connected to nothing, and reinforcing rods arranged in peculiar ways, possibly to form antennas. There were cavities of wire

mesh, and small, empty metal cones. All of these may well be passive units queried by microwave.

An elaborate network apparently covered the most sensitive area of the chancellery, a windowless floor obviously intended for secret operations. Hundreds of tiny microphones were cleverly hidden everywhere. "Normally, they could spot the wires leading to microphones," says Microlab/FXR's Augenblick. "But what the Russians appear to have done is to put the wires inside steel reinforcing bars and other metallic objects that X rays don't penetrate."

That wasn't the end. Charles Taylor, an expert on countersurveillance, says one thing the Soviets probably did that threw such consternation into the U.S. security forces was to bury thousands of tiny diodes in the concrete used for the building. Such diodes, which could be pinhead-sized and cheap in addition, could be mixed in the concrete by the thousands or even tens of thousands. Then a sweep with a nonlinear junction detector would get back thousands of signals from everyplace—completely masking the real bugs that undoubtedly lay hidden behind this electronic camouflage.

The future of the embassy? One security man said we'd have to "destructively search" the building to find all the bugs. That's a euphemistic way of saying we'd have to tear it apart brick by brick.

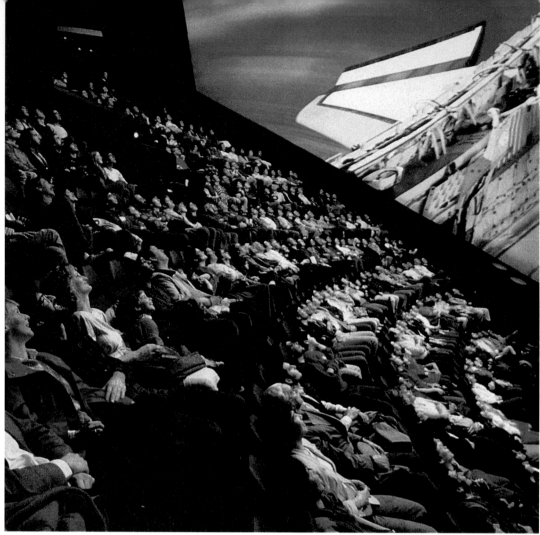

Raytheon

BEYOND THE BIJOU

by Jim Pettigrew, Jr.

In a world that at times seems defined by incompatibility, there is one interest that most of us have in common—a passion for the movies. And this love of the cinematic fantasy world shows no signs of dissipating. Different trends may appear, such as the VCR explosion, but upon examining the world of contemporary cinema, one fact becomes readily apparent—the movies are not going away. Nei-

ther, according to industry leaders, are those esteemed hideouts of escapism—the theaters.

Though movie theaters are here to stay, there is a great deal of debate currently going on inside the showcase, or exhibition end, of the film world. Some of it concerns topics such as changing image, and a considerable amount of the debate relates directly to technology.

The path of events that set the stage for this situation contains a number of key elements.

Beginning in the early 1970s, the movie-theater industry in the U.S. slowly slipped into what may be called a technical rut. Despite the tremendous advances in home-audio technology, the exhibition business did not really keep up at the same pace.

State-of-the-art theater: films projected by a fish-eye lens onto a vast domed screen tilted toward the audience create a wraparound effect that spellbinds patrons.

There was also a trend toward "multiplex" cinema facilities—not an inherently weak marketing idea—but their early manifestation didn't prove terribly successful. The first multi-cinemas were cramped, had very small screens, and ambient sound many times bled over from the theater next door.

Technological Blockbuster

In the spring of 1977, George Lucas produced a film that would have a revolutionary impact on the exhibition industry. It was released to theaters carefully picked for certain technical standards. Besides the well-known special effects and cinematography, *Star Wars* boasted a sound track in Dolby stereo. It was played over an advanced audio system filled with new designs, including a "subwoofer" that generated sound you could feel as well as hear.

The film also brought fresh attention to the large-frame 70-millimeter (mm) format. This expensive but vastly superior process had been used in earlier landmark movies *(Lawrence of Arabia, Patton)*, but had fallen out of favor in Hollywood.

With a new audio standard established by the Lucas blockbuster, the cinema industry moved into the 1980s—and a whole new set of business realities, coupled with a feverishly expanding foreground of technological developments.

Clearly, the industry had to adapt and change. The situation was brought to a head by the growth of home video, but that trend was only a part of the whole arena. Faced with this challenge, the theater industry began what is now a recognizable set of changes to "remain-stream" itself. (The latest studies, incidentally, show a kind of reverse effect from the home-movie phenomenon; it's actually sending patrons back to theaters, seeking favorite titles in full-blown film environments.)

Revitalizing the "Theater Experience"

Today the theater repositioning process takes a number of poses, including better sound, more sensible design, cleaner halls, and an overall push to reenergize the "experience" vital to moviegoing. "Theater companies are building at record numbers, by the way," notes Glenn Berggren, vice president of Optical Radiation Corporation of Azusa, California, one of the world's largest suppliers of theater equipment. "They want to make them better, not only as operations are concerned—breakdowns, etc.—they'd also like to have an effective theater that lets the public know they're modern, better than the ones built five, ten years ago."

Theaters are now utilizing computerized ticketing and central-data systems, such as those developed by Pacer Corporation of Bothell, Washington. The integrated Pacer system in-

At present, computerized box-office technology monitors cash flow and theater patronage, and feeds the information to central data-bases. Soon, however, these innovative systems will open up opportunities for credit-card as well as off-site purchasing of tickets.

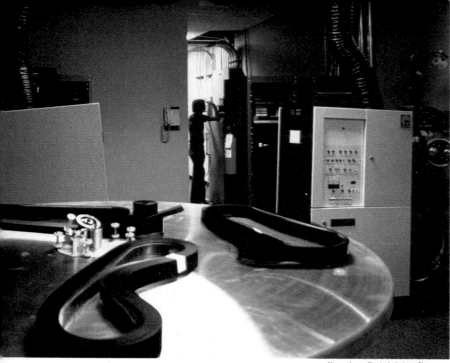

Even the projection booth has felt the wave of new theater technology. At left, the film in the foreground rests on a platter and feeds through a projector without the projectionist having to change reels. Below: conventional 35-millimeter, 24-frame-per-second film (left) versus the innovative new 70-millimeter film. At 60 frames per second, the 70-millimeter film approximates the speed at which the eye itself perceives reality. The result: a powerful perception of three dimensions, extreme clarity, dynamic motion, and brilliant color reproduction.

Above: Lucasfilm Ltd.; below: Showscan

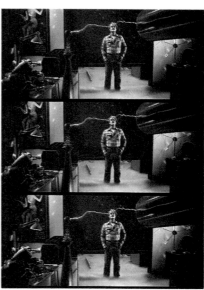

stantaneously gathers all sales data for the cash-intensive business, compiles it, and the information is uploaded nightly by automatic modem to central offices. ''Our system opens up the possibilities of credit-card and off-site ticket purchasing,'' notes Keith Myers, Pacer's marketing vice president. ''This may reach a whole different segment of affluent consumers—and even influence the kind of movies that are made.''

This trend is well characterized by numerous showcases across the country. One example is the General Cinema complex inside Merchants Walk, a north Atlanta mall. There, Cinema One features an advanced audio design from THX Sound Systems, a division of Lucasfilm Ltd. in San Rafael, California. ''Patrons don't really articulate it,'' explains theater manager Steve Crisp, showing off the loudspeaker system and heavily insulated walls, ''but they know what they want in a film experience today, and sound is very important.''

One healthy sign that experts point to is the influence exerted by firms such as THX Sound Systems and the Theatre Alignment Program (TAP), both components of Lucasfilm Ltd. All THX-installed systems undergo rigid certification and are then tested every six months to ensure quality adherence. TAP vigorously encourages high standards and dialogue between suppliers and theaters.

''We are targeting theater managers and personnel with seminars,'' says Kimberly Strub, marketing director of the Theater Operations division at Lucasfilm. ''These will help them answer questions about film presentation—sound tracks, how they're made.'' Strub cites a typical example: ''Lots of times, people will have questions about how films are made, and the only people that they have to turn to are the theater personnel. We're trying to make sure they are informed and can answer public questions—and also realize how important their roles are in the film chain.''

Roller-coaster rides (above) and car chases can be simulated with amazing realism by computer-synchronizing the motion of hydraulically actuated theater seats with the film's action sequences. The seats are programmed to move vertically, roll, pitch, and yaw (right), just as they would during an actual roller coaster ride.

Both photos: Showscan

The Push to Modernize

Currently, amid the film exhibitors' concerted push to modernize, there is an accelerating debate in both the equipment and showcase fields about what technical form the near future will take. The issues must be set in context within a growing array of spectacular new technology, film formats, and even new approaches to the filmic experience.

Two of the central topics now being debated with increasing fervor in the industry include film speed, expressed in frames per second (fps), and film format (frame size, coupled with larger screens). A third topic is the increasing impact of high-grade video and its eventual manifestation—high-definition television (HDTV)—and how the two industries will affect each other.

For decades the standard film speed in the theater industry has been 24 fps. At this speed a relatively low projection-light level must be maintained (10 to 16 footcandles) to prevent an annoying sensation called "flicker." There are now several proponents who are urging that film speeds be raised, so that higher light levels may be possible. Faster fps rates, they point out, also make for richer imagery, better color, and heightened special-effects possibilities—as well as decreasing industry headaches such as "comet-tailing" and blurring.

The 35mm film format has also been the industry standard for decades. Industry leaders are quick to point out its obvious obsolescence. The 70mm film size, they note, offers much more than a vast improvement in cinematographic possibilities. "Most people, including large film manufacturers, do not really understand how much detailed information can be put on 70mm film," asserts Optical Radiation's Berggren "and shown back on the screen."

New Theater Formats

A central point, in an overall sense, that brings these debates into focus is an already-existing arsenal of new cinema systems. Each camp points inarguably to the future, and each system is now offering spectacular movie experiences.

Some of the new formats first debuted in what the industry calls "special-venue" theaters—noncommercial, museum, and other educational halls. Currently, the granddaddy of these is the IMAX/OMNIMAX system, now amazing audiences at Washington, D.C.'s Smithsonian, Boston's Mugar OMNI Theater at the Museum of Science, Chicago's OMNIMAX Theater (located in the Henry Crown Space Center at the Museum of Science and Industry), the OMNI Theater at the Fort Worth Museum of Science and History, and the Science Museum of Minnesota in St. Paul, among others. Several of these "space" theaters were designed by the architectural firm of Hammel-Green and Abrahamson of Minneapolis, which estimated that 20 million people attended OMNIMAX theaters around the world in 1985.

The heart of the IMAX system is a unique projection approach: the large-format images are projected through a fish-eye lens onto a 76-foot (23-meter) dome, which washes the screen with an enormous picture. The screen is tilted toward the audience at a 30-degree angle, which creates a stunning wraparound effect.

Showscan® is another radically new film system with breathtaking sensory experiences. Developed by special-effects wizard Douglas Trumbull (*Star Wars, Star Trek;* director of *Silent Running* and *Brainstorm*), Showscan has amazed audiences at Expos '85, '86, and '87; the Vancouver theater in Canada remained open after the fair, and 50,000 people saw the Showscan presentation in January 1987. The corporation is currently opening special-venue theaters in Los Angeles and several other cities in the U.S. and throughout the world.

Showscan utilizes 70mm film, a very large screen, an extremely fast film speed at 60 fps, and sound on film. While developing the process, Trumbull ran extensive tests at various film speeds, using participants at California universities. For several years in the 1970s, Trumbull was also head of Future General, an experimental department at Paramount Studios.

Even though Showscan is at present confined to special-venue theaters and corporate presentations, the company clearly has plans to move into the box-office market. In April 1988, an agreement-in-principle was reached with Aaron Russo Films, Inc., for a three-picture feature deal. According to marketing director Cindy Aylward, a feature film will be out soon.

Currently, the leader in the race to bring stunning new technology into the first-run film market is FuturVision 360, a division of FuturCinema Inc. in New York City. The brainchild of former Kodak executive Eric Knutsen, this process utilizes large-screen (wall-to-wall, floor-to-ceiling) 70 mm, a sophisticated digital audio system, and runs at 30 fps.

Independent filmmakers lead the pack in producing movies that exploit new theater technology to the fullest.

VanDerKloot Film & Television

Moviegoers will continue to line up as long as the theater experience promises more excitement than the home video.

Audiovisual Sorcery

For some time, Knutsen and FuturVision have had ties with Loews, a major theater chain (his system is now being showcased at Loews Tower East, a Manhattan screening room). Additional theater chains will be acquired to form a "showcase" network covering the major metropolitan areas in North America and abroad.

Besides its audiovisual sorcery, one of FuturVision's big selling points to first-run theaters is comparative ease of compatibility and cost-effectiveness. Working with Optical Radiation Corporation, Knutsen has developed his system so that it can be integrated into existing theater hardware—and still offer the dazzling filmic experiences that all aggressive chains are now scrutinizing.

One aspect of FuturVision is digital audio, said to be comparable to compact disk (CD) quality (actual CD/movie presentations are still in the future). With this process the digitally recorded audio is taken from the film and fed to a Knutsen-designed processor, which sends audio signals to an upgraded house system.

"Now," Knutsen says, "the projectionist can walk into the booth and flip two switches. One automatically changes screen brightness from low level to a much higher level for our film, and at the same time changes film speed from 24 to 30. The second switch automatically bypasses house audio and goes to our processing equipment. So, there's virtually no setup time."

Fascinating and Fantastic

Until recently, the film-production community and the exhibitor/theater equipment industries have viewed each other as barely tolerable neighbors, forced to get along, but with little meaningful dialogue between the two camps. Now, though, in the face of this star burst of new technology, the two industries are working together, insiders point out, to achieve the common goal of a truly realistic cinematic experience, and the subsequent fiscal rewards.

Bill VanDerKloot, owner of VanDerKloot Film and Television in Atlanta, one of the premier independent filmmakers in the South, has a keen eye on these and other developments. His firm extensively utilizes computers and high-grade video in production work. "Today," he points out, "stereo sound tracks are mandatory, even for low-budget films, not the case just ten years ago. People have become very sophisticated in their technical tastes for film.

"I am just incredibly excited about what the future has to offer," VanDerKloot concludes. "The more like reality we can make the dreams that we create on film, the more fascinating and fantastic films will be."

WILDLIFE

Rescuers wrestle with a pilot whale in the shallow waters off Cape Cod, Massachusetts, as they attempt to steer it back to sea. Some zoologists believe that whales beach themselves when land obstacles such as Cape Cod peninsula obstruct their travel down the coast. Other scientists think that parasites interfere with the whales' sense of direction. Whatever the reason, the natural herd instinct of whales compounds the problem: once one whale beaches itself, its herd (or pod) mates invariably do the same.

AP/Wide World

REVIEW OF THE YEAR

WILDLIFE

Drama marked the wildlife scene in 1987, with some events promising to be the curtain raisers for decades of debate. As always, powerful forces both helpful and harmful continued to reshape wildlife's living space.

SAVING THE CONDORS

The last California condor living in the wild was captured as part of a program to rehabilitate the critically endangered species (see page 348). In April 1988, zoologists were thrilled when the first condor chick bred in captivity successfully hatched. Named Molloko, the baby condor is thriving on a diet of minced mice and egg yolks.

CARIBOU TRANSPLANTED TO MAINE

Reintroducing wildlife species to former ranges is often successful, but it has seldom been attempted with creatures as large as caribou. However, a small herd of several dozen caribou was brought 1,200 miles (1,930 kilometers) from Newfoundland to Maine, where the species died out early this century because of habitat change. The transplanted caribou started a new generation when a dozen calves were born last spring. These animals will probably be released to the wild in 1989. The goal of the project is to have a self-sustaining herd within 10 years.

THE WONDER OF WHALES

In the past decade, many people have come to view whales as the noblest of wildlife, almost humanlike in their communication and care of young. Part of this phenomenon may be a reaction to the well-documented killing by humans of these largest-of-all mammals during the past centuries. In the Northeast last fall, hundreds of volunteers were trained to rescue whales that become stranded on beaches after being driven ashore by ocean storms. Whale-watching tours are thriving off U.S. coasts, and watchers in New England thrilled to the sight of the largest animals that ever lived—blue whales—the first seen in those waters for 50 years. Four nations continued their defiance of a global moratorium on whaling: South Korea, Japan, Norway, and Iceland. When the United States threatened Iceland with an embargo on its fish exports unless it stopped whaling, Iceland retaliated by saying it would evict U.S. military forces from a key military base if the embargo were imposed. The U.S. backed off, and Iceland is continuing to kill whales under the guise of "research whaling."

SEA OTTERS MOVED TO NEW HOME

Since a remnant population of 300 southern sea otters was discovered on a remote island off the U.S. West Coast in 1938, the soft, furry creatures have steadily increased their numbers to about 1,650. Last year, to protect the species from the possibility of extermination by a large oil spill, which could mat their thick fur and allow them to freeze in cold ocean waters, the U.S. Fish and Wildlife Service carried out a plan to relocate part of the population. Dozens of otters were netted out of the water and released on San Nicolas Island to the south. If these individuals survive, plans are to relocate more otters until the transplanted population totals 250.

HABITAT LOSSES AND GAINS

Chesapeake Bay, the world's largest estuary, is under siege from urban, industrial, and agricultural runoff pollution. Wetlands are being drained and filled. Nearly pristine forestlands are being crisscrossed with logging roads. Toxic chemicals infest even National Wildlife Refuges. In short, wildlife's living space is being crowded and soiled at an ever-increasing rate as modern America reshapes its landscape to suit human whims and needs. Even where laws and policies purport to protect wildlife habitat, major damage occurs. For instance, in southeastern Alaska, clear-cutting and road building on steep land have caused major landslides into rivers with large salmon runs, and stripped protective vegetation from alongside shallow streams, raising water temperatures to levels lethal to fish. Though the state is charged with protecting soil and water affected by timber harvests, it lacks the authority necessary to protect against fish kills caused by landslides or overheated water. Although soil practices are deficient on much of U.S. farmland, the nation's farmers used conservation tillage on a record one-third of all planted land in 1986. In Minnesota, farmers have enrolled 661,000 acres (268,000 hectares) in the federal soil-conservation reserve, and a state program has converted 22,000 acres (8,900 hectares) of erodible, marginal cropland to wildlife habitat and outdoor recreation use.

SPECIES MAKE COMEBACKS

The number of bald eagles sighted on the St. Lawrence River between Ontario and New York State has risen from four a decade ago to 23 in 1987. Reduction of chemical pollution is thought

California biologists captured dozens of sea otters and relocated them to a new home in an attempt to establish a colony out of the range of oil spills.

to be the main factor. In June 1987, a pair of captive black-footed ferrets produced six healthy kits, bringing the population of the endangered species to 24. A century after the reclusive lynx disappeared from New York State, authorities are making final plans to reintroduce the shy animal into logging areas where reforestation is crowding out deer and its predator, the bobcat, and opening a niche for lynx. (The more aggressive bobcat drove lynx from the state in the 1800s.) In Vineyard Haven, Massachusetts, osprey poles are all the rage in front yards. Nesting platforms atop the 30-foot (9-meter) poles have had remarkable success in attracting nesting ospreys. The area's last large trees were knocked down by gales in 1970. Peregrine falcons nesting atop a tall office building in downtown Minneapolis successfully hatched two chicks last summer. Two pairs of peregrines have nested on New York City's Verrazano and Throgs Neck bridges since 1981. In the past five years, the world's only wild flock of whooping cranes, one of America's most endangered species, has almost doubled in size to 130 birds. This represents a tenfold increase from the 1930s, when only a few breeding pairs existed.

MANY SPECIES IN CRITICAL TROUBLE

In a major report, the Office of Technology Assessment (OTA), Congress' research arm, called for an integrated effort to halt the decline in animal, plant, and insect species. OTA said continued loss of wildlife species poses a direct threat to the economic future of major industries, including the pharmaceutical sector. Its report said that species are now disappearing at a rate greater than any since the dinosaurs vanished 65 million years ago. Grizzly bear populations in the lower 48 states are down to an estimated 750 individuals. Grizzlies are among the most difficult species to manage; an individual may travel over a 1,000-square-mile (2,600-square-kilometer) range that includes timberland, mining land, and oil fields.

Populations of many woodland songbirds are declining throughout North America, victims of urbanization and competition from more adaptable species. As suburban developers hack forests into smaller blocks, the numbers of warblers, vireos, and thrushes decrease while the numbers of jays, cardinals, cowbirds, and grackles increase. Another problem is the loss of tropical forests, where many North American songbirds winter. Even national parks are losing wildlife species, especially mammals, because the parks are too small to provide all the necessary habitat. Species most affected are grizzlies, wolves, lynx, gray foxes, bighorn sheep, wolverines, otters, mink, and pronghorns.

BOB STROHM

Last Chance for the CONDOR

by John Nielsen

He's lying in wait beside the trap, staring at the carcass of a stillborn calf, talking to trackers on the radio, reading magazines. Then it happens. Peter Bloom always feels a chill at the arrival of a California condor. From 100 yards (90 meters), he hears a whistle of air, a sound that slowly builds to a roar. Next comes a heavy thud-thud and the clatter of enormous wings folding as the bird touches ground. Bloom hears its deep, even breath. It sounds a bit like a winded child.

Eventually he sees the condor through a tiny opening in the dirt-covered foxhole somewhere in south central California. It is a monster of a bird, the largest land bird in North America, with a wingspan almost 4 feet (1.2 meters) longer than 5-foot, 9-inch (175-centimeter) Bloom is tall. It is jet black except for a fleshy, reddish head; a vivid halo of red in the eyes; and a pennant of long white feathers on the underside of each wing. This particular bird is the last free-flying member of a species with roots in the Pleistocene epoch. It is known to condor-watchers as Adult Condor-9.

"You get the feeling he knows something is up," says Bloom, a member of the five-man team that has stalked AC-9 for several months. "You can sense him looking around. He looks at every little detail, at the grass, at the bait carcass, at the eagles. He's very methodical. You get the impression he's listening."

He should be. This time AC-9 didn't come close enough for Bloom to grab him, but someday soon Bloom or some other team member will rise out of a hole and grab AC-9 from behind, or fire a net that will trap the bird. The last wild condor will then be caged and driven to an isolated corner of the San Diego Zoo.

The capture of AC-9 might save the species, which has been on the brink of extinction for at least half a century, and it might not. All that's certain is that shortly after the bird is snared, it will pass into a scientific twilight zone of computerized gene-tracking, puppet-mothering, and behavior modification.

California condor AC-9, the last to live in the wild, soars high above the mountains just prior to its capture. AC-9 has since joined 27 other condors in a program to rehabilitate the nearly extinct species.

Life in Captivity

Twenty-eight California condors are now living in that world, hidden away at the Los Angeles and the San Diego zoos. Most of them arrived as eggs. The rest were trapped and delivered in fiberglass containers. And finally, in April 1988, the first condor bred in captivity hatched successfully. All are supposed to be released, though no one is sure when. No one is happy that these birds are in captivity, including the zoos and, least of all, Bloom. A relic of the Ice Age, the California condor can cover 150 miles (240 kilometers) in a day. It can ride a thermal wind for miles, seemingly without moving its wings. At other times it appears to hang in flight before suddenly diving to earth for a meal.

"Seeing a condor in the wild is unlike anything you can imagine," says Michael Wallace, the curator of birds at the Los Angeles Zoo. "It's eerie." What's also eerie is that after thousands of years in the wild, the California condor will soon be visible to only a handful of scientists, its guardians in a last-ditch effort to save the species.

Only a few species have come this close to extinction and survived, among them the whooping crane, the red wolf in North Carolina, the Arabian oryx in the Middle East, the Mauritius kestrel, and the Puerto Rican parrot. "It's an ecological crapshoot, but we've got to go through with it," says Whitney Tilt, an endangered-species specialist employed by the National Audubon Society, and a grudging supporter of captive-breeding proposals. "It's what you do when you just don't know, but you've got to do something fast."

At one time the condor ranged over most of western North America. Many of its contemporaries—such as mammoths and saber-toothed cats—disappeared centuries ago. By this decade the condor's habitat had become limited to the foothills and mountains of the Sierra Madre and the Tehachapi, and to the coastal ranges of central and Southern California. It is a total area of around 11 million acres (4.5 million hectares), nearly 20 percent of which is officially designated rangeland, including three condor sanctuaries.

In the late 1930s, when the Audubon Society first studied the condor, probably no more than 100 condors were extant. Since then the bird has fallen victim to a variety of natural and unnatural threats. Besides loss of habitat, these include witting and unwitting hunters, collectors of exotic eggs, power lines and oil sumps,

Bruce Coleman Inc.

Like its fellow vultures, the California condor has a distinctive S-shaped neck and a nearly naked head.

lead-shot-filled carcasses and pesticides. In the 1950s, oilmen seeking drilling rights in the midst of the condor's habitat went so far as to describe the bird's protected lands as a threat to U.S. forces in Korea. During the 1960s, backers of a plan to construct a dam and reservoir near one of the sanctuaries dismissed the carrion-feeding California condors as "flying garbage cans."

Infighting among Environmentalists

Battles over how to save the condor have raised difficult questions of conservation ethics and left scars at many wildlife organizations, including the Los Angeles and San Diego zoos, the Audubon Society, the Sierra Club, and the Friends of the Earth. Historically, the principals involved in the controversy have fallen into two camps. The hands-off forces until recently opposed almost all human intervention, besides that of protection of the bird's habitat. Otherwise, argued this group, this solitary scavenger would become domesticated to the point where it would be no more than a "feathered pig."

The hands-on camp maintained that the species would disappear unless it was forced to

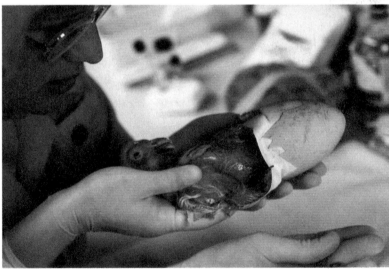

The future of California condors seemed brighter when a pair in captivity displayed characteristic courtship behavior (above). In April 1988, zoologists at the San Diego Zoo became even more hopeful when a condor chick hatched from an egg conceived in captivity. Previously, only condor eggs taken from nests in the wild had been incubated successfully in the laboratory (left).

thrive, and that it could not thrive until it was better understood. Although condors are thought to be hardy, their scarcity and solitary life-style have made them a biological mystery. For instance, scientists now realize that the bird lays eggs on the average of only once every two years.

For 50 years these two opposing factions fought tooth and nail at public hearings, in newspapers, and in rumor campaigns. In the early 1950s, the San Diego Zoo secured a captive-breeding permit, only to see it revoked at the insistence of the Audubon Society and local

conservationists. Hands-on people believe those permits might have helped immeasurably in the bird's fight for survival by providing a sufficient number of mature birds to prompt captive breeding. The opponents disagreed, noting among other things that there was no recorded instance of the bird breeding successfully in captivity. This circular argument assured that the acrimony would continue until one side caved in completely.

In 1980 the National Audubon Society, which at that point favored a hands-on approach, joined with the U.S. Fish and Wildlife

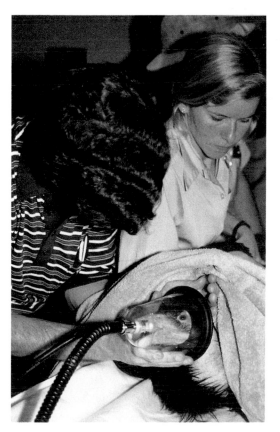

Meticulous care: the condor chick above is fed by means of a surrogate parent—a hand-held "condor" puppet. A team worked around the clock for 15 days to save condor AC-3 (below) from lead poisoning. Its ultimate death spurred efforts to halt the condor's alarming decline.

Service to set up the Condor Research Center (CRC) to coordinate efforts to save the endangered bird. The hands-off forces complained that they had been excluded from this scheme, which gathered information on condors by tagging the birds, equipping them with tracking devices, and visiting their nests.

The CRC's program also endured more than its share of public relations fiascoes. In 1980 a condor chick died in its nest while being measured, apparently of fright and rough handling. News that some of the human visitors had lacked the required permits to attempt such measurements provoked general outrage and a two-year freeze on any contact with the remaining wild condors. But the CRC eventually won approval to tag more condors in 1982, and the tagged birds soon were described as an invaluable source of breeding and nesting information. For example, scientists learned that condors are apparently capable of "double" and "triple clutchings" to replace eggs that have fallen from or been taken from nests.

"Blood on Their Hands"

Such new information has not eliminated the angst and antagonism. In particular, David Brower, the founder and former chairman of Friends of the Earth, says that "the condor was destroyed in order to save it." He has challenged hands-on proposals at almost every turn, accusing the opposition of incompetence and shortsightedness. On occasion he has implied that zoos are interested in capturing condors so that they can eventually put the birds on display. However, no zoo has displayed a condor in at least 20 years, and both the San Diego and Los Angeles zoos, the two that are involved in the CRC project, deny such intentions.

What finally ended the argument was the fact that from the fall of 1984 to the end of 1985, one condor died of lead poisoning (after feeding on a buckshot-filled carcass), and five more disappeared from unknown causes. At the end of 1985, with only six birds still thought to exist in the wild, the U.S. Fish and Wildlife Service announced plans to capture the remaining birds. The Audubon Society sued to prevent the cap-

With the capture of condor AC-9 on April 19, 1987, all of the surviving California condors live in captivity.

ture effort, effectively halting the work of the CRC, the agency it helped to create.

While the case was in the courts, condor AC-3 was found lying in a field, dying. The bird had been hit by a shotgun blast and was suffering from lead poisoning caused by the pellets. In addition, while feeding on a carcass, the bird had swallowed a bullet, which had paralyzed its digestive tract. The condor died on an operating table at the San Diego Zoo.

Marcia Hobbs, a fund-raiser for the Los Angeles Zoo, was enraged by the bird's death. The lawsuit and subsequent restraining order may have hampered attempts to save AC-3. According to Hobbs, the hands-off forces now had "blood on their hands," even though it wasn't clear that the bird had ever had a chance. The death of AC-3 was particularly chilling because her fertility had long given the bird special status among scientists. She was known to have produced five hatchlings.

Raised by Puppets

The hands-on case has been further strengthened by recent developments that give at least faint hope of successful captive breeding. First, eggs have been taken from nests to zoos, and their hatchlings successfully raised with the help of birdlike puppets. Adult condors have been trapped and tagged with electronic beepers to track their range and nesting habits. Advances have been reported in genetic studies and in raising the birds in captivity. Most encouraging is the news that seven Andean condors, the California birds' closest relatives, reared in captivity have been successfully restored to a flock of the birds living in the Peruvian wilds.

On the political front, Brower left Friends of the Earth for reasons unrelated to the condor controversy. In his absence the organization has given captive breeding qualified support. The Audubon Society also announced that it had resolved its differences with the CRC, which greatly reduces the chances of further legal action.

The last of the trapping permits was issued in September 1986. A condor-recovery team immediately began tracking the remaining three wild California condors with planes and trucks and by waiting for them in foxholes. In December 1986, Bloom caught the condor known as AC-2, grabbing the bird when it landed to eat in front of one of the traps. The two other condors eluded the team for the next two months. At times they confined themselves to canyons inac-

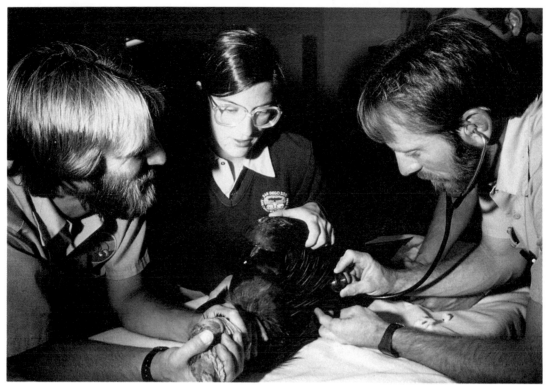

Upon arrival at its new home in San Diego, condor AC-9 underwent a thorough health evaluation.

cessible to the trappers. At other times they were too skittish to catch when they approached the bait.

Catching the Last Two

These two remaining wild condors, AC-5 and AC-9, had little in common except for a mate, which has since been captured and placed in the San Diego Zoo. AC-5, known to some as Old Smudgepits, was an old and aloof bird. For years, and possibly decades, Old Smudgepits roamed the hills near Santa Barbara, nesting in sequoia trees and keeping his distance from any signs of human life.

AC-9 was young and gregarious, and he has been known to condor-watchers since his hatching in 1980. AC-9 was the last condor to fledge in the wild and the first to be tagged with lithium-powered beepers. He seemed friendlier than the rest of his breed. Bloom says AC-9 was fascinated by condor-watchers, sometimes even seeming to buzz them.

A February snowstorm left both birds hungry. Their only potential meal was one near the trap. Both birds circled the site before noon, and they eventually landed in oak trees near the bait.

AC-9 approached the carcass first, only to be chased away by AC-5. Old Smudgepits then rousted young AC-9 out of several oak trees before landing by the carcass. After shoving his way through a group of eagles also anticipating a free meal, Old Smudgepits began to feed on the carrion.

From inside his foxhole, Bloom detonated the net and then rushed out and held AC-5 until the rest of the team arrived. The tracking beeper was removed, AC-5 was loaded into a truck, and the net was gathered and folded.

As Old Smudgepits began his trip toward benevolent captivity, AC-9 watched from his perch in an oak 40 yards (36 meters) away. Bloom had never seen a condor so inquisitive. "The truck was parked underneath him, but he never moved," said Bloom. "He never took his eyes off us. He might have been hungry, or curious. We left him sitting there, watching us drive away."

The trappers came back a week later, to dig new foxholes and wait. On April 19, 1987, AC-9 was netted. Thus, after millennia soaring above North America, no California condors remain in the wild.

Pinniped pastime: sea lions bask on the rocks of a protected promontory in large groups called rookeries.

A *PLETHORA* *of* *PINNIPEDS*

by Downs Matthews

When good fortune next finds you driving along the California coast, accept the highway department's invitation to turn off the road at one of the scenic vistas that provide a look at the sea. Aim your binoculars beyond the breakers, out to the edge of the kelp beds. Notice the sleek black heads that rise and fall with the incoming swells, the glossy, streamlined bodies that now and then roll and toss. You are looking at marine mammals known as pinnipeds, the fin-footed clan of seals and sea lions.

The entire length of the California coast is home to these "brine-bred children of the sea," to use Homer's lyrical phrase from *The Odyssey*. From prehistoric times, seals and sea lions have frolicked in this surf, hunted their fishy foods, and basked on sunbaked rocks.

Most of us have come to know seals and sea lions by watching them swim effortlessly in zoo ponds or marine aquariums. Or perhaps you recall the sea lion in the circus act that balanced a ball on its nose and played *America* ("My country 'tis of thee . . .") on a set of horns.

But to know seals and sea lions as they really are, you must be prepared to say hello in person. So follow the coastal highway to Ventura and board a tour boat bound for Channel Islands National Park. Altogether, California's eight islands support a larger and more diverse number of seals and sea lions than any other site near to a major population center. So this is a good place to begin.

California Sea Lions

Allow a couple of hours to cover about 16 miles (25 kilometers) of indigo ocean, and Anacapa Island's blond bluffs rise up to meet you. The skipper eases our vessel near wave-washed cliffs. Our arrival is heralded by the whooping of hundreds of California sea lions, known to science as *Zalophus californianus*. These are just a few of the 125,000 animals of this species that populate the Pacific coastal waters of North America.

We're amazed at their size. From the circus bleachers, they seemed so small. But some of these males are 8 feet (2.5 meters) long and weigh up to 800 pounds (360 kilograms). The females, much smaller, still reach 6 feet (2 meters) in length and weigh a respectable 200 pounds (90 kilograms).

Ashore, they are the most agile of the pinnipeds, although "least awkward" might be a more appropriate description. With large, muscular front flippers, they can walk, after a fashion. In the water, they are more at home. A male puts his head down and launches himself from a boulder, entering with scarcely a splash. He propels himself with powerful strokes of his broad front flippers, using them like airfoils to twist and turn as gracefully as a bird on the wing. His shorthaired coat is a dark chestnut brown, his flippers black-skinned. From the back of his long, narrow head, small earflaps protrude. He is a member of the pinniped family known as the Otariidae, or the eared seals.

They seem unafraid and curious. Small groups of six or eight rest together in the water, floating on their sides with one flipper held aloft like small sailboats all on the same tack. They're saving energy, our guide explains. As a body will lose heat 25 times more rapidly in water than in air, the sea lion holds one flipper out of the water when he has no other use for it. This conserves body heat and gathers warmth from the sun.

Lolling about seems to be what sea lions do best. They spend most of their time sprawled out on sandy beaches or floating lazily in their watery cradle. A layer of blubber keeps them warm and gives them buoyancy. Many take advantage of the 20 steel platforms erected in the Santa Barbara Channel for the production of oil and gas from huge fields beneath the ocean's floor. Sea lions by the score relax on the structural crosspieces or on anchor buoys nearby. A converted tanker placed by Exxon near its Hondo platform to process and store oil became home for hundreds of sea lions, providing both a place to rest and proximity to a smorgasbord of seafood around the platform's huge legs. While California sea lions may be seen occasionally on all of the Channel Islands, they favor San Miguel and San Nicolas as rookeries.

The life cycle begins when a California sea lion male stakes out his territory on a section of beach. He defends it against incursions by other males, with whom he engages in shouting matches and vigorous scuffling. Some males sustain serious injuries. But as a rule, the larger guy gets the girls.

From May to September, sea lion females will choose a beach on which to give birth. The newly born pup, weighing 11 to 13 pounds (5 to 6 kilograms), stays onshore for the first few weeks or so, after which it begins to enter the water to learn the sea lion trade.

Within about a month after delivering her pup, a female will mate again. She may select

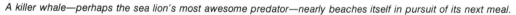

A killer whale—perhaps the sea lion's most awesome predator—nearly beaches itself in pursuit of its next meal.

Now that many of the natural gathering places for pinnipeds have fallen under human development, seals have had to improvise, making do with such artificial environments as the oil rig at left. Habitat encroachment particularly endangered elephant seals, whose population at the turn of the century dropped to about 100. Their numbers have rebounded dramatically, reaching over 100,000 according to recent estimates. On some offshore California islands, bull elephant seals even can be seen battling over harem rights (below).

the bull in charge of the beach where she has given birth, or move to another beach and a different mate. Male sea lions don't gather harems, as fur seals do. Nature delays the implantation of her fertilized egg until the time is right for her to begin her pregnancy, an ability she shares with other pinnipeds.

Shallow feeders, sea lions work the top 600 feet (183 meters) of the water column for hake, rockfish, herring, sardines, anchovies, Pacific whitings, and squid, but opportunistically capture anything that happens by. Sometimes they rob fishing nets and lines, with unhappy consequences. Caught in a gill net or on a hook and line, a sea lion may drown or suffer fatal injury. If caught in the net by a commercial fisherman, the sea lion legally may be killed under a special permit.

While they may live to be 30 years old in captivity, sea lions rarely reach such an advanced age in nature. Lethal parasitic diseases await those sea lions that escape their predators, the great white shark and the killer whale. Most, in time, will succumb to illness or injury.

Despite such fates, California's sea lions become more numerous each year. With the exception of a temporary slump in birthrates in 1983 (when, scientists say, the El Niño climate phenomenon contributed to a sharply reduced food supply), more pups are born every year than the year before. So far, there's no reason to suppose that the sea lion population is anything but healthy, wildlife zoologists believe.

Elephant Seals

The same promising future applies to California's elephant seal population as well. And that is truly remarkable.

For elephant seals, it was a near thing. Early in the 19th century, tens of thousands of these huge, homely creatures are thought to have populated California and Mexico beaches. But with demand for whale oil high and the supply of whales diminishing, whalers began looking for substitutes. The Elefante marino, as Spanish-speaking Californians called him, wore a 6-inch (15-centimeter)-thick coat of fat, which could be rendered into some 150 gallons (570 liters) of high-quality oil. Slow and clumsy on land, he was easily captured and killed. By 1870 island rookeries were bare of elephant seals. Many thought poor *Mirounga angustirostris* to be extinct. But in 1892 a small colony of about 100 animals was discovered on Guadalupe Island off the Baja Peninsula.

By now the youthful petroleum industry had created better, cheaper products such as kerosene and lubricating oils that soon drove expensive whale and seal oil out of the market. For elephant seals, this salvation came barely in time. From the turn of the century, their numbers have increased steadily, as they prospered and returned to their traditional rookeries and beaches. The world population of elephant seals now exceeds 100,000.

You may consort with elephant seals from Alaska to Baja. But the Farallon Islands, some 28 miles (45 kilometers) offshore from San Francisco, shelter a thriving colony that likes to be around on their leeward beaches. Ashore, they sleep side by side or piled one on another like giant pink and brown sausages. Elephant seal females can grow to be 10 feet (3 meters) long and weigh 2,000 pounds (900 kilograms); males reach 20 feet (6 meters) in length and 6,000 pounds (2,700 kilograms).

With a long, droopy nose like an elephant's trunk, a bull elephant seal presents a visage only a mother could love. The snout amplifies his roars so that he can be heard for miles. Lacking earflaps, elephant seals belong to the Phocidae family of pinnipeds.

On a sandy beach, elephant seals are content to drowse away the day. But let an ambi-

When on land, elephant seals help to maintain a stable body temperature by flipping sand over themselves.

tious bull challenge another dominant bull, and a fight is inevitable. Rising on their foreflippers, the two waddle ponderously together, grunting threats and maledictions. With open jaws, they spar for an opening, each trying to bite the other's neck or head. Gashed and bloody, one or the other will retreat, leaving the field of battle and nuptial couch to the victor.

Females come and go as they please, choosing a beach on which to give birth. The older, wiser mothers select the best birth sites, well beyond the high-tide line. Pups arrive from December to February. Their mothers nurse them with milk said to be one of the richest of any mammal, designed to put fat on the baby as quickly as possible. Born weighing 65 to 75 pounds (30 to 34 kilograms), an elephant seal pup will gain an amazing 200 to 300 pounds (90 to 135 kilograms) by the time it is weaned a month later.

Their blubber layer is vital to elephant seal survival, as the animals feed in deep, cold water, descending more than 2,500 feet (760 meters) to take ratfish, skates, rays, and squid. Elephant seals are prey to sharks and orcas. But elephant seal pups are more in danger from their own fathers, who will step on and crush youngsters that get in their way.

Like other pinniped populations along the California coast, elephant seal numbers have risen dramatically over the past 20 years. But the herds may be approaching an optimum number, scientists suggest, as birthrates seem to be leveling off. As they establish new colonies on beaches frequented in past centuries, elephant seals may become commonplace along the Pacific coastline.

Harbor Seals

Already commonplace, but seldom noticed, are the little harbor seals, whose colonies range along the Pacific coast. Easily identified, harbor seals wear spotted coats in colors ranging from tan through silver-gray to black. They, too, belong to the earless Phocidae family of pinnipeds and have the Latin name of *Phoca vitulina*. Males get to be nearly 6 feet (2 meters) long and weigh up to 300 pounds (135 kilograms), while females are a little shorter and lighter. Unlike their cousins, harbor seals are difficult to distinguish sexually, although he can tell, and so can she.

Resembling animated footballs, harbor seals spend two-thirds of their lives bobbing about in the surf alongside beaches. Wary of people and dogs likely to be encountered ashore, they often emerge only at night, although a colony that has lived for decades beside an oil company pier serving offshore oil activity has become accustomed to humans.

With their small foreflippers and round, tubby bodies, harbor seals seem clumsy on land. They move inchworm fashion, and rarely travel far from the water's edge. In their element, they are swift, competent swimmers, propelling themselves with a sculling motion of their hind flippers.

In pursuit of food, harbor seals hunt the middle water depths, down to 1,200 feet (365 meters). Their huge, luminous eyes enable them to see their prey in the darkness of the depths, and also to spot intruders on the beach a mile away. Safe in the restless swells, harbor seals sometimes smack the water's surface with a flipper to make a loud pop. Scientists aren't sure why they do it, but, as they are almost silent, it may serve as a warning to other seals.

Aggression is not the harbor seal's forte. Even during the mating season, which takes place after pups are born in March, April, and May, male harbor seals don't do a lot of fighting. Not much is known of their behavior, because so much of it takes place in the water. But competition seems to consist mostly of hard stares, flipper shaking, and subdued snorting. Occasionally a harbor seal male may bite a rival on the neck or hindflippers.

Because of their wary nature, harbor seals are difficult to count, but they are abundant along the entire Pacific Coast. Their world population is estimated at more than 380,000.

Sanctuary on the Beach

Along with the three most numerous species, California biologists also see a few northern fur seals and Steller's sea lions, for whom the North Pacific is home, and a few Guadalupe fur seals, which in recent years have ventured up from Mexico. They appear interested in starting a colony. For the past seven years, a solitary Guadalupe fur seal male has staked out a mating territory on the south side of San Nicolas Island, while a single female has hauled out nearby. Object: matrimony. Baffled zoologists wish there were some kind of lonely hearts club for pinnipeds. But so far, neither seems to be aware of the other.

Growing pinniped populations have understandably captured the attention of California shore dwellers. The beach is the zone where

© Jeff Foott

Harbor seal and pup. These shy pinnipeds, only rarely seen on land, spend most of their time bobbing in the surf.

seals and people come in contact. Seals and sea lions alike take their ease on the coastal shingle, retreating to the sea when approached.

Yet the beach is also the sanctuary of last resort for pinnipeds in trouble from injury or disease. Without some kind of human help, most would die.

To extend a measure of help to marine mammals in distress, close to 1,000 volunteers work through a score of nonprofit organizations covering the entire California coastline. Trained and licensed in the rescue and rehabilitation of marine mammals, they save hundreds of animals, mostly seals and sea lions, from almost certain death every year.

Rescuing a Pinniped

The Marine Mammal Center (MMC) in Santa Barbara demonstrates how a network of volunteers cooperates in a seal rescue. Founded in 1976 by Peter Howorth, who operates vessels used by marine scientists for research, the MMC maintains a rehabilitation facility on a barge in Santa Barbara Harbor where animals are held until they can be returned to the sea. Supported entirely by donations, the MMC has a membership of close to 100 persons, of whom perhaps 10 actually take part in rescue and rehabilitation work.

At Howorth's home the hot line rings. Someone strolling along the beach has spotted a stranded seal. Howorth folds his tall body into a pickup truck and goes to have a look.

Searching the rocks at the base of the coastal bluff, he finds a small patch of dried blood and hair. "A harbor seal mother gave birth here," he explains. The pupping season has started. A mile down the beach, Howorth spots a small form draped over a boulder at the water's edge. It's a harbor seal pup, born within the past three days, and so weak it cannot raise its head. Its stomach is empty, and its big, soulful eyes have sunk into its head.

Howorth searches the surf for a mother seal who might be waiting for a chance to come in and get her pup. But she is not to be seen. Finally, Howorth grasps the infant by the scruff of its neck and brings it ashore to the dry sand, where the sun will dry and warm it. It proves to be a female. She protests feebly, opening her mouth and threatening to bite with teeth that are still just pink buds in her gums. "It's all bluff," Howorth smiles.

"We had a severe storm three days ago," Howorth explains. "This newborn pup was separated from her mother and carried down here by the shore current." Every year, severe weather claims many seals and sea lion pups, washing them away from rookeries before they can fend for themselves.

Pinniped mothers will look for lost pups where they were last seen, it seems, but will not venture any distance away. A pup carried off by storm waves is a dead pup, unless a human comes to its aid.

An hour passes, and Howorth concludes

that no mother is coming for "little Gertrude." If she is to survive the next 12 hours, emergency measures must be taken. Howorth takes Gertrude to the MMC. She needs food immediately. He mixes an anchovy milkshake, emulsifying small fresh fish, cod-liver oil, whipping cream, vitamins, and minerals in a blender. The food is poured into a modified stomach pump, and a tube inserted into Gertrude's empty stomach. With a few strokes of the pump, the nourishing slurry is injected directly into Gertrude's stomach. The little animal's body swells, and her eyes return to their normal place. She gives a grateful sigh and goes to sleep.

Every four hours for the next 30 days, Howorth and a group of volunteers will take turns feeding and cleaning Gertrude as they would a human infant. As she recovers and grows, she'll learn about swimming and fishing. In about three months, Gertrude will be large enough and sufficiently skilled to fend for herself. Howorth will take her to a harbor seal colony and release her into the sea. Other seals will accept her readily, and she will become a member of their colony.

"They are intelligent animals," Howorth points out, "and very adaptable. She has a good chance of making it in the wild." He and his

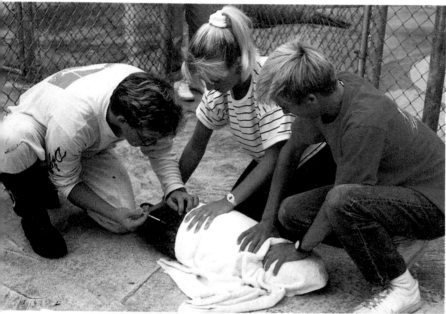

Friends of the Sea Lion

An injured or ill pinniped has little chance for survival without human intervention. At left, volunteers at Friends of the Sea Lion in Laguna Beach, California, nurse a sick sea lion back to health with special injections of medicine. Before healed pinnipeds are returned to the sea, they are tagged (below) so that zoologists can better monitor their behavior in their natural habitat.

© Jeff Foott

volunteers enjoy an 86 percent success rate in returning to health the seals and sea lions that they rescue.

Pinniped Perils

Not all marine mammals are so fortunate, however. The parasites that infest all seals and sea lions sometimes get the upper hand, and some animals suffer injury at the hands of people.

Dr. Charles D. Woodhouse, deputy director and curator of vertebrate zoology at the Santa Barbara Museum of Natural History, has been doing necropsies (postmortem examinations) of marine mammals found dead along this section of coast paralleling the Santa Barbara Channel. Since his studies began in 1975, he has determined the causes of death of several hundred seals and sea lions.

Half of the animals he has examined died as the result of some man-inflicted injury, having crushed skulls, knife or gunshot wounds, gill-net strangulation, or hook wounds. The other 50 percent died as the result of disease, usually induced by parasitic infection. Victims are usually the very young or the very old. "I see few animals in the prime of life," Woodhouse reports.

Concern for oil as a threat to seals and sea lions appears unwarranted, Woodhouse suggests. "Of what I have seen, there has been no reason to conclude that oil was involved in their deaths in any way." As natural seeps continually leak crude oil into the Santa Barbara Channel, seals and sea lions are sometimes found with oil on their fur, but, as Woodhouse puts it, "there is no database for oil as a cause of pinniped mortality."

Biologists with other marine mammal centers report much the same ratios in pinniped mortality. Bill Ford, who serves as administrative manager for Friends of the Sea Lion (FSL), a Laguna Beach–based group, notes the same 50–50 split between man-created injuries and natural causes. Since its founding in 1971, FSL has handled several thousand marine mammals suffering debilities ranging from shark bites to gill-net strangulation, but petroleum is not one of the problems.

"Fishermen kill as many animals as we save each year," he says. "But the oil companies here are very sensitive to environmental issues. They show us every kind of cooperation and courtesy."

At the California Marine Mammal Center (CMMC) near San Francisco, the state's largest rescue and rehabilitation operation, biologists find that parasitic and viral diseases are the major problems for seals and sea lions. Jan Roletto, CMMC's curator, reports that of the approximately 100 seals and sea lions treated there during an average year, 4 to 6 percent have run afoul of boats and fishermen and have been injured by gunshots, gaff wounds, or net entanglement; 3 to 4 percent have been bitten by sharks; 2 to 3 percent exhibit broken bones from unknown causes; and almost all the rest, up to 90 percent, come in with natural problems. Few of them come in with oil on their fur.

With its extensive facilities and enthusiastic public support, CMMC is a leader in marine mammal rescue and rehabilitation. Its research programs have contributed significantly to greater understanding of marine mammal diseases and how to treat them successfully.

"We are able to save 66 percent of our patients," reports CMMC's executive director, Peigin Barrett. Without help, almost none would survive.

Why save seals and sea lions?

"Wild animals have a value unto themselves," Barrett says. "If we lose them, we lose those values. If that happens, we lose much of what it means to be alive and human. I think we should respect the mystery of each individual species and its right to be here. Without animals, it would be a sad world."

Therefore, apply to seals and sea lions this advice posted by the San Diego Zoo: "Please do not annoy, torment, pester, plague, molest, worry, badger, harry, harass, heckle, persecute, irk, bullyrag, disquiet, grate, beset, bother, tease, nettle, tantalize or ruffle the animals."

© Tom & Pat Leeson

The bobcat, a relatively common though rarely seen relative of the lynx, is named for its short, stubby tail.

THE SHY BOBCAT SURVIVES

by Gary Turbak

A driver near Olema, California, saw in her headlights the sudden image of a bobcat crossing the road. Before she could stop, her car smashed into the cat, and two tires rolled over it.

Not wanting to leave the dead animal on the road, the woman loaded it into the rear of her hatchback and drove off. A few miles farther on, however, she heard a low growl. The bobcat in the back of her car was not dead, and apparently it was not happy.

The terrified woman raced to the home of Ray Deiter, a local veterinarian known for patching up injured wildlife. Deiter cautiously removed the bobcat from the car and took it to his animal hospital. He and a colleague spent eight hours in the operating room, rebuilding the cat's broken bones. In the months that followed, Deiter nursed the animal back to health. And finally, four months later, he released it at the appropriately named Wildcat Beach in Point Reyes National Seashore.

True Survivors

Bobcats are indeed survivors, individually and as a species. While many North American predators have been pushed toward extinction or exist only in wilderness enclaves, bobcats can still be found from Nova Scotia to Central America and from the Pacific coast to the Atlantic.

''The bobcat is a resilient, very successful species,'' says Doug Miller, a biologist who has studied bobcats and is the National Wildlife Federation's vice-president for wildlife research and education. ''It lives in a variety of habitats, eats a wide array of foods and has the ability to go virtually unnoticed.'' These attributes, plus the cat's predatory skills and sometimes feisty personality have helped it endure.

Only in the last decade have wildlife managers even begun to manage bobcats. For centuries the cats were ignored or perfunctorily bountied—not regarded as valuable enough to be managed as game animals nor destructive enough to be seriously persecuted.

How has the bobcat borne up under our lack of attention? Very well. In fact, says Richard Mitchell, a zoologist with the U.S. Fish and Wildlife Service, ''There are probably more bobcats in this country today than during colonial times.''

Barely twice the size of a housecat, the average bobcat weighs about 20 pounds (9 kilograms) and stands perhaps 22 inches (56 centimeters) at the shoulder. Its reddish-to-yellowish brown fur is streaked and spotted with black, and a ruff of fur surrounds its face. Pointed tufts of hair, which may serve as sound-amplifying antennae, rise from the tips of its ears. A stubby 6-inch (15-centimeter) tail and bobbing gait on the run give the cat its name.

With the exception of Indiana, where the felines are believed to have vanished, bobcats probably inhabit at least part of every state in the continental United States. (They have never ranged in Alaska or Hawaii.) The secret of their success? Partly, it's a matter of being the feline equivalent of a jack-of-all-trades.

Never Misses a Meal

Like most wild cats, the bobcat is a highly adaptable eater, concentrating on whatever food happens to be most abundant and most vulnerable at a given time. If cottontail rabbits suddenly become scarce, the bobcat will—without missing a meal—switch to chasing squirrels or rats. Researchers in New York once sifted through the contents of 169 bobcat stomachs and found the remains of 24 prey species. Rodents and birds are everyday bobcat fare, but snakes, lizards, and even insects also get on the menu.

Relying on its keen vision and hearing, the cat usually stalks to within a few feet of a prospective meal, then attacks in a rush. Like most felines, the bobcat lacks endurance and must catch its prey in a few strides. Sometimes it lies in ambush along a game trail, where it can nail dinner in a single pounce.

Surprisingly, bobcats are able to kill deer and bighorn sheep, both of which may far outweigh the cat. The little hunter usually attacks a sleeping deer; the terrified prey may end up fleeing with the cat clutching to its back. "The bobcat kills an adult deer by biting into its throat while clawing furiously with all four feet for a good hold," explains Dave Hamilton, who is a research biologist with the Missouri Department of Conservation. The deer probably dies from suffocation.

Despite such killing instincts, many biologists believe that bobcats get the majority of their venison from deer that have already died of other causes. Thus, the felines pose little threat to deer herds. "Most bobcats are quite happy to eat nothing but small animals," says Gary Koehler, an Idaho biologist who has just completed a four-year study of bobcats. "Deer will almost never be the bobcat's preferred prey, because the cat puts itself at great risk in attacking so large an animal." The cat's claws and teeth are no protection against stabbing antlers, kicking hooves, or a head-on collision with a tree limb when the predator rides the neck of a running deer.

Though their reputation as killers of livestock is exaggerated, bobcats do raid barnyards. In February 1987, Oscar Slaven, a farmer near Cedarville, Ohio, lost 35 domestic rabbits, 23 ducks, several chickens, and one lamb to a sly nighttime slayer. Traps failed to catch the intruder, so late one night Slaven visited his barn with shotgun in hand. In the dim glow from a flashlight, he spied and shot a small bobcat. It was only the fifth representative of its species to be documented in Ohio since the early 1970s.

Like its fellow felines, the bobcat sometimes will "play" with captured prey before consuming it.

Bobcat mother and young. The mother keeps her mate away from the litter until after the kittens are weaned.

© Ernest Wilkinson/Animals Animals

Habitats for Hiding

Open-minded on the subject of prey, bobcats are equally easygoing about where they decide to live. The adaptable cats thrive in virtually any terrain—from swamp to mountain to desert—at almost any elevation. "In the lower 48 states, about the only habitat that doesn't support bobcats is fencerow-to-fencerow cropland," says Missouri's Dave Hamilton. "Intensive agriculture just doesn't give the cat many places to hide."

Bobcats have always needed at least a few places to hide. European colonists to the New World regarded the bobcat as a petty thief of poultry and young farm animals, and the little feline had a price on its head even before the days of the American Revolution. But unlike other bountied wildlife, the bobcat held its own against the human tide that rolled across the continent. Where the wolf, cougar, and grizzly retreated, the bobcat dug in and emerged, in the 20th century, as a solid survivor.

Today, in rural regions, the cats sometimes behave as if they are oblivious to people. One night in Arkansas, biologist Richard Rucker was certain that a notoriously ornery farmer had killed a radio-collared bobcat Rucker was tracking for a population study. The scientist had a strong signal from the cat, but it was coming from the farmer's barnyard. Over the course of the night, Rucker rechecked the reading from different locations, but it never varied. He assumed that his study cat now hung dead on the wall of a shed. Returning in the morning to confront the farmer, Rucker checked one more time; he now found that the cat was broadcasting from the woods some distance away. Apparently, the unconcerned cat had passed the entire night near the farmer's barnyard, probably hunting mice.

Rodent Hunters

Relations between people and bobcats are often mutually advantageous. Humans inadvertently increase bobcat habitats by breaking up forests into fields and woodlots: by growing grain, they ensure a steady supply of rodent prey. The cats return the favor by keeping rodent numbers in check. In Alabama, for example, farmers have learned from Doug Miller's research that the quail-eating felines so reviled by southern bird-hunters are actually an asset. Bobcats do consume some valuable gamebirds, but they also eat cotton rats, which are even more voracious

The bobcat tends to hunt at night, even though its neutral coloration makes it nearly invisible among the surroundings (above). Like other wild cats, the bobcat is a highly adaptable eater. If small rodents and birds are not available, the bobcat will even substitute fish (right). More frequently, however, the bobcat stalks such small game as hares (below) and mice. Typically, it relies on its keen vision and extraordinary hearing as it silently approaches within a few feet of a prospective meal. Then, in a split second, it pounces on its prey, often bringing it down within a few strides.

consumers of quail eggs, quail food, and young fledgling birds.

While the cats can take down animals larger than themselves, they usually avoid other predators. "It's not in the bobcat's nature to stand and fight unless it's cornered," says Michael O'Brien, a wildlife researcher with Nova Scotia's Department of Land and Forests. "But when it does, a 30-pound (13-kilogram) bobcat can make mincemeat out of a 90-pound (40-kilogram) hound."

Some experts believe that it is the bobcat's "irascible" nature that prevents the lynx from expanding its range south from Canada. As for old-time frontiersmen who boasted they could "lick their weight in wildcats," they almost certainly would have been shredded had they ever attempted it.

These days, the little wildcats are getting a boost from humans. Until recently, for example, bobcats were extremely rare, perhaps extinct, in New Jersey. But with 1,000 square miles (2,590 square kilometers) of excellent cat habitat on their hands, New Jersey wildlife managers decided to bring the animal back. Between 1978 and 1982, two dozen bobcats were imported from Maine and released into the ridge country of northwestern New Jersey, an hour's drive from New York City. The reintroduction, believed to be the first of its kind, appears successful. "The cats are still there, they're reproducing, and they're even expanding their range," says Patricia McConnell, a project biologist.

Conservation Programs

Only recently have wildlife officials in the United States attempted such a project. It came about as a result of what appeared to be a bobcat crisis. In the early 1970s, conservationists pressed hard for measures to end the slaughter of the rarest spotted cats—the cheetah, leopard, and jaguar. Prohibitions against killing those animals led European fur buyers to cast their eyes upon the American bobcat. Almost overnight a tremendous market sprang up for its fur. In 1974 an average bobcat pelt had sold for $12, and few trappers tried to catch the animals. By the end of the decade, however, prime pelts were netting about $600 each, and, of course, cat trappers were out in droves.

In the meantime, the bobcat was listed (under the Convention on International Trade in Endangered Species) as an animal that could become extinct if the skin trade was not strictly regulated. While many states believed they had healthy populations of the animals, they now had to document that fact before bobcat pelts could be exported.

The result has been a flood of new research data and some relief from the panic over possibly declining bobcat numbers. The Fish and Wildlife Service now estimates that the overall U.S. bobcat population ranges between 700,000 and 1,500,000 adult animals. Each year about 90,000 cats are killed in the 38 states that permit bobcat trapping or hunting (40 percent of that annual harvest occurs in two states, California and Texas). Last season, top-grade bobcat pelts were selling for $300 in some parts of the United States.

Wildlife managers are continuing to keep an eye on the status of bobcats. But because the felines are nocturnal and generally shy, they are difficult to count. "Bobcat management is never going to be precise," says Doug Miller. Among other things, he notes that bobcat watchers would like to know more about the assimilation of young cats into the adult population and about the effects that the fur harvest and habitat destruction are having on the species.

Those concerns notwithstanding, the bobcat remains an extremely successful predator, among the world's most abundant species of wild feline. That, however, does not mean that you are apt to see one in your headlights or crossing a forest path. Even biologists who study bobcats may get only infrequent glimpses of the shy, elusive creatures.

Carrying an antenna and radio receiver, researcher Richard Rucker regularly traveled the Arkansas backcountry at night, homing in on the bobcats to which he had fastened radio collars. Several times, Rucker's telemetry equipment told him that the curious felines, although utterly invisible in the night, had crept to within a few feet of him.

Most human-bobcat encounters resemble the otherworldly experience of Massachusetts biologist Chet McCord. Creeping along a rocky ledge, McCord glanced up and was startled to see a bobcat sunning itself a few feet away. For a long minute, McCord stared at the cat and the cat stared at McCord.

Finally, eager to squeeze just a bit closer, McCord glanced away long enough to check his footing on the ledge. When he looked back, the bobcat was gone. There had been no sound, no sense of movement. To the scientist, it was as if the shy survivor had never been there at all.

Snakes under Pressure

by Harvey B. Lillywhite

On the first Thursday of May, the townspeople of Cucullo, Italy, walk in processions behind a wooden statue of Saint Dominic, which they have adorned for the occasion with harmless rat snakes belonging to the genus *Elaphe*. These snakes have a natural inclination to climb, so when they are released at the base of the statue, they grip it and move upward, ultimately ornamenting Saint Dominic's head. The organizers of the procession know their native snakes well, for they avoid using ground-dwelling species, which would not grip the statue and climb.

Many snakes are adept at climbing. A familiar North American species is the red rat, or corn, snake, well known for its ability to mount the vertical trunks of pine trees and search for birds' nests in the lofty canopy. Held against the tree as if by magnetic attraction, the snake glides upward by following depressions in the bark. The use of skin and muscle to secure a limbless body as it crawls against gravity evokes awe and curiosity. Equally amazing is the snake's ability to maintain blood circulation when its long body is extended vertically, as when climbing up and down trees.

Gravity and Blood Pressure

Gravity affects all organisms, but terrestrial animals that are long or large are especially subject to disturbance of their body fluids. The giraffe

The green python preys on small animals in the rain forests of New Guinea and northern Australia. Like other climbing snakes, its cardiovascular system is adapted to accommodate vertical ascents and descents.

When the corn snake moves in a head-down position, its heart rate slows to prevent excessive blood pressure from building in its head. When the snake moves upward, its cardiovascular adjustments reverse.

© Zig Leszczynski/Animals Animals

has intrigued biologists for many years because its height requires high levels of blood pressure to maintain blood flow above the heart to its head, as well as rapid adjustments of pressure when the head moves up or down. Medical doctors concerned with high blood pressure in human beings began studying giraffes in the 1950s. Other investigations followed, and the giraffe became a textbook example of adaptation in the cardiovascular system.

Studies of blood circulation in snakes are now complementing studies of giraffes. For the past 20 million years, snakes have undergone an impressive adaptive radiation, attaining a wide diversity in terms of habitat and behavior. Today approximately 300 genera, comprising some 2,700 species, live in nearly every available habitat except for polar regions, higher mountaintops, and deep oceans. To take just the extremes, four families of snakes successfully inhabit the seas, where gravity problems are almost nonexistent, while numerous other lineages live in trees, where coping with gravity is a major challenge.

When a long animal assumes an upright, or vertical, position, blood pressure falls in the higher blood vessels and rises in the lower vessels. This gravitational pressure, which is caused solely by the weight of the blood, increases with depth so long as the blood column is continuous and regardless of whether the liquid is in motion. A 17-foot (5-meter)-long python that is fully vertical has a gravitational pressure in its tail of about 16 inches (400 millimeters) mercury (abbreviated hereafter as Hg), which is equivalent to the pressure of a column of mercury 16 inches (400 millimeters) high. When this pressure is added to the snake's normal arterial blood pressure, which in a horizontal posture is probably about 2 inches (50 mm) Hg, the blood pressure in the tail is roughly three times greater than the blood pressure measured in a hypertensive human being.

Because of gravitational pressure, the walls of the lowermost blood vessels stretch, and blood tends to collect in them like water in the bottom of a water-filled balloon. Most of this pooling occurs in the veins, which are far more elastic than arteries. As a result, a considerable proportion of the blood may shift to the lower veins during upright posture. Unless automatic physiological reflexes or a change in the animal's behavior opposes this shift of fluid, less and less venous blood will return to the heart, decreasing the heart's output and jeopardizing blood flow to the brain. The magnitude of the problem depends on the angle of posture, the length of the animal, and the characteristics of the blood vessels.

Arboreal Snakes

Pumping hearts must overcome both frictional resistance to the movement of blood and the gravitational pressure of a blood column that might depart from horizontal. A little more than a decade ago, on a research expedition to the Visayan Sea (in the Philippines), Roger Seymour discovered adaptive trends in blood pressures in several species of snakes. Subsequently, he and I published a series of papers in which we reported that arboreal (tree-dwelling) species maintain relatively high arterial pressures, averaging 2 to 3.5 inches (50 to 90 mm) Hg, sometimes overlapping values that are measured in mammals. On the other hand, fully aquatic species such as sea snakes have low blood pressures, typically between 0.6 to 1.2 inches (15 to 30 mm) Hg. Intermediate pressures are found in semiaquatic and nonclimbing terrestrial species.

The greater pressures in tree-dwelling snakes allow them to assume a head-up posture with little danger that a passive fall in arterial pressure will impair blood flow to the brain. Moreover, physiological reflexes that control blood pressure are well developed in these snakes and tend to compensate for gravitational disturbance. As in mammals, this control is exerted both by the pumping action of the heart and by the resistance to blood flow in the blood vessels. The latter is regulated by the smooth muscles that alter the diameters of the smaller arteries.

Studies of rat snakes have shown that when the head is elevated, the fall in gravitational pressure in the head arteries is rapidly compensated for by accelerated pumping of the heart and increased vascular resistance, particularly in the lower body. The changes of resistance distribute the blood upward so that it reaches critical organs such as the heart and brain. These responses vary in different species of snakes, but probably are present in all terrestrial ones, which faint or quickly die if blood flow to the brain is stopped. (When snakes assume a head-down posture, the cardiovascular adjustments are generally the reverse: the heart rate tends to slow, vascular resistance tends to relax, and pressures at the head are prevented from reaching excessive levels.)

Aquatic Snakes

An aquatic snake has very different demands on its circulatory system because the gravitational pressure within its blood vessels is matched by the water pressure on its body. Since the water pressure similarly increases with depth, the distribution of blood is largely the same regardless of body position in the water. When in a vertical position, therefore, an aquatic snake does not require high blood pressures to support a blood

In an aquatic snake, the gravitational pressure within its blood vessels matches the water pressure on its body.

Much like snakes, the giraffe's cardiovascular system is adapted to maintaining an appropriate blood supply to the brain whether the animal stands erect or stoops to drink water.

© M. P. Kahl/Bruce Coleman Inc.

column above its heart, nor does it need to regulate blood pressure as it changes posture. When a sea snake is taken out of the water, however, and held head up for more than a few minutes, arterial pressures at the head fall toward zero as blood pools in the lower body, and the vessels near the head presumably collapse.

The Lofty Giraffe

The "adaptive hypertension" of arboreal snakes is similarly found in other long terrestrial animals, such as the giraffe. The giraffe has the highest measured blood pressure of any animal. When erect, an average adult stands between 15 to 18 feet (4.5 to 5.5 meters) tall, with the neck making up about half this height. Giraffes are almost always in an upright posture, even when

dozing. From their lofty vantage point, giraffes can detect predators; they can also disperse widely while feeding and still maintain visual contact as a herd. Heat dissipates quickly from their lean bodies, an adaptation similarly thought to help the tall Watusi and Masai peoples of Africa endure a hot climate. The giraffe's greatest advantage is that it can browse on leaves up to a height of about 20 feet (6 meters), whereas no other terrestrial mammal except the elephant can reach much above 10 feet (3 meters).

To ensure adequate circulation to the brain, the giraffe's arterial blood pressures are as high as 10 inches (260 mm) Hg at the heart level. The pressure decreases with height above the heart, averaging about 4 inches (100 mm) Hg in the carotid artery at the base of the skull, approximately the blood pressure at heart level in human beings. Cardiovascular adjustments and the muscular carotid and vertebral arteries (the main arteries of the neck) evidently protect the brain from excessive pressure when the head is lowered, for example, during drinking.

The idea that hearts must pump blood more forcefully in order to overcome gravity has been challenged recently by Henry Badeer of Creighton University School of Medicine in Omaha, Nebraska. He suggests that blood supply to the brain of an animal like the giraffe operates on the principle of a siphon, with the action of blood descending in the veins toward the heart helping to lift blood in the arteries. Badeer proposes that the high arterial pressures of giraffes are necessary only to overcome vascular resistance and prevent the collapse of head arteries.

Others point out, however, that the operation of a siphon depends on the flow of liquid in a rigid tube. Unless the veins from the brain to the heart are kept open by the reinforcement of surrounding structures (as occurs in the skull bones), they are subject to collapse, and this prevents a siphon effect. While the siphon principle could work, no animal is known to possess externally reinforced veins to exploit it.

Giraffes are the tallest animals whose blood circulation is accessible for direct study. These great mammals are dwarfed, however, by the giant dinosaurs that once roamed the earth. The circulation of aquatic dinosaurs probably was not disturbed by gravity, as is the case among contemporary sea snakes. Many of the larger dinosaurs, however, were terrestrial. Paleontologist Robert Bakker argues in his recent book *The Dinosaur Heresies* that the gigantic Late Jurassic sauropods were plant eaters that, like giraffes, browsed on high vegetation, sometimes rearing up on their hind legs and tail.

Heart Location

This has significant implications for cardiovascular problems, inasmuch as a number of long-necked brontosaurs could have reached upward 35 to 45 feet (11 to 14 meters). In the extreme case of *Barosaurus,* the heart would have had to pump out blood at a pressure in excess of 26 inches (650 mm) Hg just to support the blood column above the heart to the elevated head. If this dinosaur held its head erect most of the time, the stress on its heart would have demanded tremendous heart muscles. Hearts of

giraffes are massive in comparison with those of other mammals. Although we do not know the actual sizes of dinosaur hearts, we do know that sauropods had very large chest cavities.

Because of their skeletal features, all quadripedal mammals and dinosaurs have hearts more or less in the same part of the body. As a result, a long neck inevitably means longer blood vessels leading from the heart to the head. Among mammals, the greater this distance, the greater the arterial pressure. In snakes, however, the heart position can vary considerably in relation to the total length of the limbless body. This anatomical freedom provides another weapon in the arsenal of adaptations that help these animals cope with gravity.

In aquatic snakes the heart is close to the body center, while in semiaquatic snakes the heart is located farther forward. Terrestrial and arboreal snakes have hearts still farther forward, from 15 to 25 percent of the body length from the head. The forward heart reduces the distance to the brain, so that when the snake is in an upright position, the weight of the blood column above the heart is less of a challenge. In water, where gravity is not a problem, a more centrally located heart is favored because it does less work in moving blood to both ends of the body. When snake species are compared within one category of habitat, however, the absolute distance from heart to head increases with body length, and so does blood pressure, just as in mammals.

The forward heart necessitates a very long venous flow to return blood to the heart from the tail; this becomes a problem when the animal is vertical or erect. In giraffes, compression as a result of skeletal muscle contractions helps the blood return to the heart, assisted by valves that prevent excessive backflow. The veins of snakes seem to lack valves, but recently I reported a type of behavior in some arboreal species that may compensate for this. When these snakes are upright or have been climbing for a while, they pause momentarily and, while stationary, wiggle the body so that laterally undulating waves advance from the lower torso toward the head. The advancing undulations squeeze the blood forward in the veins. Ultimately, the effect is to increase the output of blood from the heart and thereby increase arterial pressures. The behavior is not seen in aquatic species of snakes, and presumably evolved specifically to assist the blood circulation in arboreal environments. Normal crawling movements also help, but they are less effective than this special wiggling.

Despite the various adaptations that maintain cerebral blood flow in an upright snake, there remains a serious problem at the other end of the body. Not only does blood tend to collect in stretched vessels, especially the veins, but (since the cardiovascular system is not itself a closed system) plasma tends to filter out of capillaries into tissues, causing edema, or swelling. The amount of blood that is displaced to lower tissues depends both on how permeable, or leaky, the capillaries are and on how much the vessels and their surrounding tissues can distend. In climbing snakes the capillaries appear less permeable than those of sea snakes. When the lower arteries constrict to distribute blood upward, their increased resistance reduces the flow of blood into the lower capillaries.

Animal Body Structure

The general build of the animal affects the tendency of blood vessels and tissue to become distended with fluid. Tree snakes usually have slender bodies with firm muscles and tightly attached skin. This combination resists stretching caused by accumulating fluid better than that of a larger-circumference body with looser tissue. In other words, the body covering behaves like the G-suit worn by pilots during maneuvers in jet aircraft. A research team led by Alan Hargens of the University of California at San Diego recently showed that the very tight skin on the legs of giraffes similarly functions to limit the swelling of their lower tissue.

Many aquatic and nonclimbing snakes have more flaccid bodies and looser skin than their arboreal counterparts. Terrestrial, nonclimbing vipers, for example, often have a large girth and sedentary habits. In the upright posture, a terrestrial rattlesnake is seven times more susceptible to blood pooling in the tail than arboreal pit vipers, which are short and slender. Of course, a heavy-bodied viper is less suited than a thin one to negotiating a maze of tree branches even if blood circulation is not a problem. A thin body may also have other advantages, such as camouflage. Nevertheless, the trait of slenderness may well be a physiological prerequisite for active life in trees.

In aquatic snakes, pulmonary vessels (those which circulate blood to the lung) extend nearly the entire length of the lung. In arboreal (tree-dwelling) species, the shorter pulmonary vessels minimize blood flow into lung tissue during climbing. The heart is also further forward in climbing species.

Joe LeMonnier/Natural History Magazine

Lung Anatomy of Snakes from Different Habitats

Heart   Lung

Aquatic

Semiaquatic

Terrestrial, nonclimbing

Terrestrial, semiarboreal

Concentration of Pulmonary Blood Vessels

Above: © Gary Braasch/Wheeler Pictures; below: © Zig Leszczynski/Animals Animals

Snakes depend on more than cardiovascular adaptations to thrive in their habitats. A tree snake of the Central American rain forest (above), like most arboreal snakes, has a slender body. Its even narrower neck enables it to slide its head out through the tips of branches and leaves without startling prey. An Indian cobra (right) spreads its neck into a hood as part of a threatening posture that precedes attack.

Lung tissues are especially apt to become swollen with fluid, in part because the capillaries in the lung must be highly permeable to enable the blood to acquire oxygen and give off carbon dioxide. Moreover, the inner lining of the lung is exposed to the air in the lung, and so is not protected from distension by the body's covering of skin and muscle. Theoretically, the longer and more stretched out the pulmonary vessels (those that circulate blood to the lung for oxygenation and return it to the heart to be pumped to the rest of the body), the greater the risk of edema during upright posture.

Once again, examination of different snake species shows that natural selection has produced the form appropriate for the corresponding gravitational environment. The pulmonary vessels extend almost the entire length of the body cavity in aquatic snakes, but occupy as little as one-tenth the body length in arboreal species—not even the full length of the lung. Semiaquatic and nonclimbing terrestrial species fall somewhere in between these two extremes.

In arboreal snakes, pulmonary blood pressures are kept constantly low, with small gravitational effects during vertical movements. In contrast, if a sea snake is removed from water and tilted vertically in the air, pulmonary blood pressure at the lower end of the lung increases so much that serious edema ensues and the lung capillaries sometimes rupture. These conditions impair respiration and can kill a snake within a relatively short time. Normally, when the snake is in water, the pressure of the water surrounding its body causes the lower portions of the lung to collapse and increases pressure in any air spaces, thus counteracting the forces that promote edema.

Snake Adaptations

Many sea snakes go to depths of 100 to 160 feet (30 to 50 meters), and some species are thought to dive as deep as 325 feet (100 meters). Since the pressure of seawater increases approximately 1 atmosphere (normal atmospheric pressure) for every 33 feet (10 meters) of depth, such deep-diving snakes experience high overall pressures of gases within their compressed lungs. Although the high gas pressures in the lung help to prevent edema, they also cause large quantities of nitrogen to dissolve into pulmonary blood. Under similar conditions, human divers risk decompression sickness (the bends) when they resurface. If the pressure is reduced too quickly, tiny bubbles form that can block blood vessels. Because sea snakes have more compressible bodies than humans, their lungs collapse more when they dive, reducing the amount of blood that comes into actual contact with the lung gas. The blood also loses excess nitrogen to the seawater through the skin, which is a permeable organ important to respiration. Roger Seymour has demonstrated that both of these factors—collapse of the lung and nitrogen loss through skin—protect diving snakes from getting the bends.

Does gravity constrain the overall length of snakes, as it does the length of their pulmonary vessels? The answer seems to be a qualified "yes." The largest snakes include Asian and African pythons and South American anacondas and boa constrictors. Contrary to popular belief, these giant serpents, which reach lengths of from 15 to nearly 33 feet (4.5 to 10 meters), are mainly terrestrial or semiaquatic, and none are primarily arboreal. The image of giant pythons dropping onto people from trees is simply a myth created by Hollywood moviemakers. Truly arboreal constrictors belong to a group of snakes called tree boas, whose maximum length averages 6 or 7 feet (1.5 or 2 meters). These snakes are slender and possess prehensile tails.

Similarly, tree vipers are generally shorter, as well as much thinner, than the terrestrial members of the Viperidae family, which includes some of the stoutest of snakes. The longest vipers are the fer-de-lance and the bushmaster, which inhabit forested areas of tropical Central and South America and approach lengths of 8 and 13 feet (2.5 and 4 meters), respectively. Although juvenile fer-de-lance snakes of both species are arboreal and hunt prey in trees, the adults become terrestrial and seek prey on the forest floor. In the families Colubridae and Elapidae, however, some of the longer species (including the mambas, vine snakes, and various tree snakes) are, in fact, arboreal. These snakes, some of which may be 10 or 12 feet (3 or 3.5 meters) long, are the slenderest of snakes and possess the shortest pulmonary vessels.

Apart from their physiological and anatomical adaptations, all snakes can combat gravity stress through behavioral adjustments. While climbing, they can form their flexible bodies into loops, as well as alter the angle of posture. In this respect, limbless snakes have more control over blood circulation than do such habitually erect animals as the giraffe.

RECALL
of the
WILD WOLF

by Diane D. Edwards

For thousands of years the wolf has been admired, hated, and feared in a conflict over the predator's rightful place in human society. Continuing that drama is the slow return of the wolf, with helping human hands, to remnants of its native habitat in the United States.

Once, 24 subspecies of the gray wolf, or *Canis lupus,* roamed North America, making the wolf and its howling a common sight and

Photos: © Jim Brandenburg

Wolves are a gregarious species. They frequently hunt in pairs or packs (above), often running down their prey in relays. Once having made the kill, the entire pack shares in the bounty (below).

sound through the past century. But wolves and humans clashed, and the animal lost. By the time the first werewolf movie was filmed in 1935, there were essentially no wolves left in the United States, except for Alaska territory. With bullets and poison, bounty hunters hired by ranchers and the federal government had exterminated wolves until only a few notoriously evasive individuals like Three Toes and Old Snowdrift remained in the early 1900s.

Today in the lower 48 states, fewer than 1,300 have regrouped in pockets of wilderness, and those are thought to be Canadian natives that headed south, or their offspring. Now some humans are calling for more wild wolves, while others are trying to keep the predator from their back doors.

Current and planned wolf-protection programs—anchored on federal laws that protect species in danger of extinction—have a unified goal of increasing the number of wild wolves. But pursuing each program are packs of conflicting opinions, legal maneuvering, and economic factors that are complicating such protection efforts.

Endangered Status

"Clearly, the wolf . . . epitomizes, and suffers from, the dichotomy of man's emotions [about wild animals]," says Gilbert M. Grosvenor, National Geographic Society president and one of a cross-sectional group attending a wolf symposium recently in Washington, D.C. The meeting, sponsored by the Washington, D.C.–based Defenders of Wildlife, focused on so-called "wolf-recovery projects." Mandated under the Endangered Species Act of 1973 (which requires recovery plans for any animals listed as endangered), the controversial programs are the overall responsibility of the U.S. Fish and Wildlife Service. The agency's administrators, according to several symposium speakers, have been criticized by environmentalists, ranchers, and biologists alike for their wolf-recovery efforts.

As it now stands, the federal recovery program for one gray-wolf subspecies, the eastern timber wolf, has three objectives: save the two wolf populations in northern Minnesota and on Lake Superior's Isle Royale, plus establish a stable population of about 100 wolves at a third location (most likely in Wisconsin or Michigan). Another recovery plan is being compiled for the northern Rocky Mountain subspecies. Not all planning for the various wolf-recovery

projects is complete, but there are several programs either under way or being considered.

Most established is the program in Minnesota, the only state other than Alaska where the wolf, because of a stable population, is not considered "endangered." Instead, Minnesota wolves (there are an estimated 1,200 of them) are listed as "threatened"—they cannot be hunted for sport, but livestock-eating wolves can be eliminated under very strict rules.

The state's wolf-control program—which is not under Fish and Wildlife Service purview—is considered a model project by many, but the road to recovery has been rough. An estimated 250 to 400 wolves are killed illegally each year in the state. And decisions on how to control "bad" wolves came only after eight years of litigation, culminating in a U.S. District Court decision in 1984.

According to lawyer Brian O'Neill of Minneapolis, "the political experience in Minnesota

Baying at the moon: most Americans have never heard the distinctive howling of wolves.

© Jim Brandenburg

A timber wolf and pups. Wolf litters, averaging seven, are usually born in May. Like other members of the dog family, wolves make devoted parents.

© Jim Brandenburg

. . . centered around the courtroom." But, he adds, "the courtroom served as a forum for getting all the groups [with different opinions] together." Helping swing public attitudes in favor of the wild wolf in Minnesota are plans for the International Wolf Center being built in economically depressed Ely, where tourists will be shown both the predatory and family-loving sides of the eastern timber wolf.

Public opinion in Minnesota regarding recovery programs has had more time to settle than that in other proposed recovery sites. But Stephen R. Kellert of Yale University, who conducted surveys of public attitudes toward wolves and other wildlife in Minnesota and elsewhere, concludes that "a deep-grained bias against predators"—found mostly among ranchers, farmers, and hunters in all potential recovery areas—must be accommodated before recovery programs will be successful.

Protecting Livestock

There is no doubt that the wolf is a predator, and likely to remain so. A major question is: How many wolf kills are acceptable? Another is whether they can be stopped without hindering recovery. There are 12,000 farms within the Minnesota wolves' range, says Fish and Wildlife ecologist Steven Fritts, who recently completed a five-year study of wolf depredation on livestock. On those farms are an estimated 230,000 cattle and 90,000 sheep, as well as thousands of turkeys raised in outdoor pens.

Fritts told those at the symposium that Minnesota wolf kills inexplicably peaked in 1981, with about 100 cows and calves and 240 sheep killed. Ordinarily, he says, about 10 animals are killed each year by wolf packs. Although owners of the animals are compensated by the government for their losses, the money doesn't soothe the savage feelings of those who have lost valuable stock animals. As Montana sheep grower Joe T. Helle of Dillon said, "We [ranchers] don't have to feed your wolves. . . . We like to market our own livestock at the proper time."

Despite the lessons learned from the Minnesota experience, a northern Rocky Mountain wolf-recovery project still in the planning stages has ignited an even larger bonfire of resistance from logging, hunting, and agriculture interests, as well as state politicians, say scientists and environmentalists. In the tri-state area of Wyoming, Montana, and Idaho, there are two sites considered by biologists at the symposium to be prime locations for recovering the wolf subspecies: Yellowstone National Park and nearby public lands in Montana and Wyoming, and Montana's Glacier National Park and Bob Marshall Wilderness Area.

Currently, there are no more wolves in Yellowstone Park, where poison and bounty hunters once were used to eliminate the animal. Biologists, who seek an "ecological wholeness" in the natural preserve by reintroducing the missing wolf, say they have set a goal of 10 breeding pairs (only one pair of wolves in a pack of three to 25 produces offspring). Where those wolves come from is a question debated between those who want wolves shipped in, and those—like Fish and Wildlife director Frank H. Dunkle—who support a slow, natural migration of wolves down the Continental Divide from Canada and Glacier Park in northwestern Montana. In 1979 scientists radio-tagged the first wolf in Montana near the Canadian border. By 1985 a pack of 12 had moved into Glacier Park from Canada, crisscrossing the mountains and covering a territory of over 2,000 square miles (5,200 square kilometers), according to biologist Robert Ream of the University of Montana in Missoula.

Experimental Populations

Just as the western landscape differs from that of the eastern timber wolf's territory, so do some of the local factors impinging on wolf recovery. Larger herds of livestock, for example, are less protected and allowed to range more freely in huge pastures, some of which are federally owned. (Wolves apparently killed two cattle May 8, 1987, near Glacier Park, the first such kills reported in the state in decades.)

With deer as the wolf's preferred meal, hunters in the area are equally concerned, fearful that a favorite source of sport and food may be depleted. "If the wolf is in the prey system, there will in the long run be fewer prey," says L. David Mech, a wolf expert with the Fish and Wildlife Service. "But the situation is nowhere near as dire as portrayed." Biologists also expect wolves to have minimal effect on the grizzly bear and on the 30,000 elk living in Yellowstone Park.

However, it isn't what the wolf does inside a park that worries nearby residents like Helle, who says it is the wolf's killer instinct, not its right to avoid extinction, that angers those opposed to current recovery plans. In Italy, where wolves live within a few miles of downtown Rome, local shepherds use watchful eyes and trained dogs to protect their relatively small flocks. But in the United States, research on guard dogs, tracking systems, and even fluttering plastic flags to frighten wolves has had mixed success in controlling predation.

Details of the Rocky Mountain wolf-recovery project will come after more meetings between federal and local officials, as well as a probable environmental-assessment report, says Dunkle. But out of the controversy may come an acceptable compromise allowable under the Endangered Species Act: a rarely used designation called "experimental population." Recently applied to a predator (a red-wolf population released in North Carolina), an experimental population is defined as one at a specific site that cannot be hunted—yet individual problem animals can be removed or destroyed.

Will the Genghis Khan image of a thrilling wolf hunt be replaced by an appreciation and tolerance of the wolf? While lawyers on both sides of the recovery issue hint at prolonged legal battles, biologists speak of a new "wolf fever" stirring romantic notions of the wild wolf. A Latin proverb warns, *Homo homini lupus:* Man is a wolf to man. Yet how human are we willing to be to the wolf?

A tranquilized red wolf is fitted with a radio collar that will enable scientists to follow its movement. The wolf was one of eight released in a North Carolina refuge, where wildlife experts hope to restore a viable population. Although three have since died, at least two red wolf cubs have now been born in the wild.

IN MEMORIAM

AARONSON, MARC ARNOLD (37), U.S. astronomer who shared (with Jeremy R. Mould) the 1984 Newton Lacy Pierce Prize for discovering that the universe is younger and smaller than was thought. He was killed in an accident at Kitt Peak Observatory, where he was crushed between a door and a 150-ton revolving telescope dome; d. Tucson, Ariz., April 30.

ARBIB, ROBERT S., JR. (72), U.S. author and ornithologist who wrote five books on nature and conservation. His *The Lord's Woods: The Passing of an American Woodland* won the John Burroughs Medal as the best U.S. nature book of 1972. Arbib, who had worked in advertising, edited the National Audubon Society's *American Birds* magazine and ran the society's annual Christmas bird count from 1970 to 1984; d. White Plains, N.Y., July 20.

BALICKI, MARIAN (79), Polish-born U.S. engineer who was research director of the Atomic Energy Commission's New York research division in the 1960s. He was educated in Poland, won the Andrew Carnegie Silver Medal in 1947 for his research into the hardening and recrystallization of iron, and taught at Brooklyn Polytechnic Institute in the 1950s; d. New York, N.Y., March 20.

BENDER, LAURETTA (88), U.S. child psychiatrist known for her role in developing the Bender-Gestault Visual Motor Test, now a standard neuropsychological examination. She devised the test in 1923, while obtaining a master's degree in pathology at the University of Chicago. Bender became a specialist in childhood schizophrenia and suicide and received the Adolf Meyer Memorial Award in 1955 for her work with schizophrenic children. For much of her career, she was associated with Bellevue Hospital and the New York State Mental Hygiene Department, and she later taught at the University of Maryland; d. Annapolis, Md., Jan. 4.

BERGMAN, JULES (57), U.S. journalist who was science editor at ABC News for more than 25 years. He was the first network correspondent assigned to cover science and space, and he reported on all 54 U.S. manned space flights, bringing the subject to life by acting out phases of astronaut training, recovery, and the like. Bergman also covered developments in medicine, technology, and environmental hazards. He won numerous awards, including an Emmy in 1974 for "Closeup on Fire"; d. New York, N.Y., Feb. 12.

BLISS, ELEANOR (88), U.S. medical researcher who conducted pioneering work in the use of sulfa drugs. In 1939, with Dr. Perrin H. Long, she published a study of the effects of sulfa compounds against bacterial infections. The increased knowledge of these "miracle drugs" that resulted was credited with saving thousands of lives in World War II and opened the era of antibiotic treatment. She was on the staff at Johns Hopkins University until 1952, when she joined the faculty at Bryn Mawr College as dean of the graduate school and professor of biology; d. Bryn Mawr, Pa., June 27.

BRATTAIN, WALTER H. (85), U.S. researcher who shared the 1956 Nobel Prize in Physics for the invention of the transistor. With Dr. John Bardeen and Dr. William B. Shockley, he developed the first transistor in 1947, while working at Bell Laboratories in Murray Hill, N.J. The invention revolutionized the electronics industry by permitting electronic circuits to be miniaturized. Brattain worked at Bell until 1967 and also taught at Harvard University, the University of Minnesota, and the University of Washington; d. Seattle, Wash., Oct. 13.

BRENTANO, SISTER MARY THERESA (84), U.S. educator who developed one of the first electronic teaching systems. A

Benedictine nun, she designed a system for teaching children through tape recordings in 1957, while she was principal of St. Scholastica Academy in Covington, La.; d. Atchison, Kans., June 14.

BROGLIE, LOUIS DE (94), French physicist whose work in wave mechanics was important to the development of quantum theory and won him the 1929 Nobel Prize in Physics. He demonstrated mathematically a link between the behavior of particles and waves, an idea that was later confirmed in experiments. A member of a French noble family that included many political and military leaders, he carried the honorary title Prince until the death of his older brother Maurice in 1960, when he inherited the family title of Duke. De Broglie founded the Center of Studies in Applied Mathematics at the Poincaré Institute in 1943, taught throughout his career, and wrote more than 20 books, including *The Revolution in Physics* and *Matter and Light;* d. Paris, March 19.

BROWN, GEORGE H. (79), U.S. engineer who was a leader in the development of color television. He worked for RCA for 40 years, becoming executive vice president for research and engineering, and held more than 80 patents. Among them was one for a drying device that shortened the production time of penicillin from 24 hours to just 30 minutes; d. Princeton, N.J., Dec. 11.

CARR, ARCHIE FAIRLY, JR. (77), U.S. zoologist widely known for his studies of giant sea turtles. He tracked the migration habits of green turtles and helped reestablish populations of turtles in the Caribbean, where they had been nearly wiped out by humans. Carr, who in 1937 earned the University of Florida's first doctorate in biology, also wrote 11 books on turtles and other nature subjects, including *Handbook for Turtles, High Jungles and Low,* and *The Windward Road;* d. Micanopy, Fla., May 21.

CASTROVIEJO, RAMON (82), Spanish-born U.S. physician who developed an early technique of corneal transplant surgery in the 1930s. He also developed a method of gilding corneas to improve vision, and he urged people to will their eyes to science, an idea that led to the founding of present-day eye banks. Educated in Spain, Castroviejo worked in the United States throughout his career and was associated with Columbia-Presbyterian Medical Center, St. Vincent's Hospital, and other institutions. He returned to Spain on his retirement in 1972; d. Madrid, Jan. 1.

COGGESHALL, LOWELL T. (86), U.S. physician who was an authority on malaria and other tropical diseases. During World War II, he won the Gorgas Medal of the Association of Military Surgeons for his work in preventing and treating tropical diseases among servicemen, and he later served as a special assistant for medical affairs in the Eisenhower administration. Coggeshall combined his work in tropical diseases with a career as an educator and academic administrator at the University of Chicago, where he rose to become a vice president and trustee in the 1960s; d. Foley, Ala., Nov. 11.

COX, ALLAN V. (60), U.S. geologist who helped solve several puzzles in the fields of plate tectonics and paleomagnetism. In the 1970s and early 1980s, studies by Cox and several colleagues helped track the past movements of the continents (continental drift), demonstrated that the earth's magnetic field had reversed several times, and led to the development of a new geologic time scale. Cox taught at Stanford University and became dean of earth sciences in 1979. He received the Vetlesen Prize in 1971 and the Arthur Day Prize in 1984; d. Woodside, Calif., Jan. 27.

CURTIS, WILBUR DARBY (82), U.S. inventor who devised the glass coffeepot. After working as a stockbroker and as a salesman for the Silex Company, he developed his first all-glass pot in 1940 and formed his own company a year later. Darby held 16 patents for tea- and coffee-brewing devices and also invented a fiberglass-bodied car, the Shamrock; d. Calabasas, Calif., Oct. 24.

EISELE, DONN (57), U.S. astronaut who was navigator on the first manned Apollo spaceflight. A former Navy test pilot, Eisele orbited the earth with Walter M. Schirra, Jr., and R. Walter Cunningham to test the reliability of the craft in 1968. It was his only spaceflight. He later served as a Peace Corps director in Thailand and worked for a financial-services company in Florida. He was abroad on a business trip at the time of his death; d. Tokyo, Dec. 2.

EVENSEN, RICHARD H. (57), U.S. librarian who was an expert in Braille transcription. Evensen, who was blind, headed the Braille research and development section at the Library of Congress from 1984 until his death, and directed volunteers who transcribed literature, music, and mathematics by hand. He also worked on the development of machines that could read Braille. He was killed when he and his wife, Lorraine, were struck by a car while crossing a busy street with their guide dog; d. Washington, D.C., Jan. 12.

FINLAND, MAXWELL (85), Russian-born U.S. physician who was an international expert on infectious diseases. In a career that spanned more than 50 years at Harvard University and Boston City Hospital, where he was head of the department of medicine, he made important contributions to the treatment of pneumonia, antibiotic therapy, and the problem of bacterial resistance to antibiotics. He wrote or cowrote some 800 scientific papers; d. Boston, Mass., Oct. 25.

FULLER, LEONARD F., SR. (96), U.S. electrical engineer known for his inventions in the field of communications. He designed transoceanic radio telegraph stations for the Army and Navy in World War I and, after the war, developed the first carrier current telephone system on power lines over 50,000 volts. Fuller taught at the University of California and Stanford University and held 24 patents; d. Palo Alto, Calif., April 23.

GOLDBERG, LEO (74), U.S. astronomer who directed the Kitt Peak National Observatory from 1971 to 1977. Goldberg, who was a consultant to a number of federal agencies, had previously taught at the University of Michigan and Harvard University, where he chaired the astronomy department and was director of the observatory (1966–71). He received the Distinguished Service Medal of the National Aeronautics and Space Administration in 1973; d. Tucson, Ariz., Nov. 1.

GREENWALD, HARRY (75), U.S. inventor who developed the coin meters used on washing machines and clothes dryers in coin laundries. He cofounded and was president of Greenwald Industries, which marketed the meters; d. Queens, N.Y., Nov. 13.

GRZIMEK, BERNHARD KLEMENS MARIA (77), West German veterinarian known around the world for his books and films on wildlife. He worked his way through school by operating a poultry and vegetable farm and served as a veterinary officer in World War II. After the war he was responsible for rebuilding the Frankfurt Zoo, which had been reduced to a burned ruin with 12 surviving animals. Grzimek began a television series on wildlife in 1959, and three years later made a documentary, *Serengeti Must Not Die,* that won an Academy Award. He was the recipient of honorary awards from numerous groups, including the World Wildlife Fund; d. Frankfurt, West Germany, March 13.

HAAS, NICU (60), Israeli scientist who was involved in the discovery, in 1968, of the only known remains of a person crucified at the start of the 1st century A.D. The remains were found in a stone vault near the Church of the Holy Sepulcher in Jerusalem, and were believed to be those of a man named Jehohanan, who might have been a rebel at the time of the anti-Roman census revolt in A.D. 7. Haas, who was born in Rumania, was an anthropologist and a senior lecturer in anatomy at the Hadassah-Hebrew University Medical Center. At his death he

had been in a coma since 1975, when he slipped and fell on ice; d. Jerusalem, early December.

HANSON, WESLEY TURNELL, JR. (74), U.S. chemist who developed a color-film-manufacturing process now used worldwide to increase purity in color prints. As a researcher with the Eastman Kodak Company, he invented the process (known as the color coupler masking system) in 1943, a year after Kodak introduced the first color print film. He later became director of Kodak's research laboratories; d. Rochester, N.Y., May 22.

HAUROWITZ, FELIX (91), U.S. chemist who made important contributions to the understanding of human immunology and hemoglobin in blood. In 1930 he proposed the template theory of immunology, which explained how the body forms specific antibodies against foreign organisms. He later discovered that blood hemoglobin takes a different form in the human fetus than in the adult. Haurowitz taught at Indiana University; d. Bloomington, Ind., Dec. 2.

HENLE, WERNER (76), German-born U.S. virologist who (with his wife, Dr. Gertrude Henle) identified the link between Burkitt's lymphoma, infectious mononucleosis, and the Epstein-Barr virus, the first virus to be associated with cancer. The Henles also developed a diagnostic test for mumps and evaluated vaccines against mumps and influenza. Henle taught at the University of Pennsylvania School of Medicine and was emeritus director of the Virus Diagnostic Laboratory of the Children's Hospital of Philadelphia; d. Bryn Mawr, Pa., July 6.

HIRSCH, JAMES G. (64), U.S. physician known primarily for his research into the immune response. He worked at Rockefeller University and the Josiah Macy, Jr., Foundation, where he developed medical education programs and became president in 1981. Hirsch's special interest was in the role of phagocytes, white blood cells that kill invading organisms, but he also conducted research into other aspects of immunology and into tuberculosis treatment. He was the author of over 100 scientific papers and edited several journals and books; d. New York, N.Y., May 25.

HUFF, VAN ELLIS (93), U.S. inventor of the jalousie window. An engineer, he developed the glass-and-aluminum window after seeing wooden slat windows in houses in the Bahamas. In 1956 he sold his share of the company formed to manufacture the windows; d. Miami, Fla., Dec. 10.

KINZEL, AUGUST B. (87), U.S. metallurgist who helped develop low-alloy structural steels and methods to prevent metals from oxidizing. He worked for most of his career at Union Carbide, where he headed the research and development of titanium-manufacturing processes and rose to become president of the company's research laboratories (1931) and vice president for research (1955); d. La Jolla, Calif., Oct. 16.

KOLMOGOROV, ANDREI N. (84), Soviet mathematician who was the founder of modern probability theory. Considered by many to be among the most important mathematicians of the century, he developed a way to use probability to predict apparently random events. He also helped create the Kolmogorov-Arnold-Moser (KAM) theorem, a method of analyzing the stability of physical systems; pioneered in the concept of entropy as a mathematical measure of disorder; and worked out an early theory on the flow of energy in turbulent fluids. Many of his ideas found application in physics. Kolmogorov was also instrumental in developing successful methods of teaching mathematics in the Soviet Union; d. Moscow, Oct. 20.

LELOIR, LUIS FEDERICO (81), Argentine chemist who won the 1970 Nobel Prize in Chemistry. The award stemmed from his discovery of nucleotide-sugars and their role in the biosynthesis of carbohydrates. Leloir headed several research foundations and was honorary president of the Argentine National Council for Scientific and Technological Investigations; d. Buenos Aires, Dec. 2.

LEVINE, PHILIP (87), Soviet-born U.S. physician who discovered the Rh factor and other important components of human blood. His work led to the successful treatment of Rh hemolytic disease (in which a fetus' blood is Rh positive and its mother's blood is Rh negative, causing antibodies from the mother to attack the fetal red blood cells) and improvements in the safety of transfusions. He headed the Ortho Research Foundation for much of his career and was a member of the National Academy of Sciences; d. New York, N.Y., Oct. 18.

LI, CHOH HAO (74), Chinese-born U.S. biochemist who in 1971 isolated and synthesized the human pituitary growth hormone, opening new avenues in many areas of medical treatment. He also isolated other pituitary hormones and in 1978 discovered beta-endorphin, a painkilling substance produced by the brain. Li taught at the University of California at San Francisco, edited several journals, and won dozens of awards for his work; d. Berkeley, Calif., Nov. 28.

MALLAKH, KAMAL EL- (69), Egyptian archaeologist who discovered the boat of Pharoah Cheops, the oldest wooden relic of the Egyptian Old Kingdom. He uncovered the boat, which is 4,600 years old, in a pit just south of the Great Pyramid in 1954. It has since been restored and placed on display. Mallakh was also an associate editor of the newspaper *Al Ahram,* the author of several novels, and the founder and a chairman of the Egyptian Society for Movie Writers and Critics; d. Cairo, Oct. 29.

McCLUSKEY, HAROLD R. (75), U.S. chemical technician who in 1976 suffered the largest dose of radiation ever recorded in an accidental nuclear contamination. While processing nuclear waste at the Hanford Nuclear Reservation near Richland, Washington, he was contaminated with the radioactive metallic element americium 241 when a sealed compartment exploded in his face. McCluskey received more than 500 times the safe lifetime dose of radiation and spent five months in a steel and concrete isolation tank while the americium was flushed from his system. Although the accident damaged his eyes and weakened his health, he was not known to have developed cancer; d. Puyallup, Wash., Aug. 17.

MEDAWAR, PETER B. (72), British physician who shared the 1960 Nobel Prize in Medicine for his work in tissue transplants. He confirmed the theory of Australian physician Macfarlane Burnet (with whom he shared the prize) that burn victims rejected skin grafts through an immunological reaction, and that tolerance to foreign tissues could be built up during the embryonic stage. The work helped lead to transplant surgery and to advances in immunology. Medawar, who was knighted in 1965 and received the Order of Merit in 1981, also discovered a substance that helped reunite several nerves. He taught at the University of Birmingham and University College in London and was director of the National Institute of Medical Research (1962–71); d. London, Oct. 2.

MINDLIN, RAYMOND D. (81), U.S. engineer who was known for his work in the mathematical theory of elasticity and received the National Medal of Science in 1979. Mindlin, who taught at Columbia University for 43 years, also received the Medal for Merit in 1946 for his work on the radio proximity fuse, a weapons detonator; d. Hanover, N.H., Nov. 22.

NORTHROP, JOHN H. (95), U.S. chemist who shared the 1946 Nobel Prize in Chemistry for his work in the purification and crystallization of enzymes. Northrop, who was associated with Rockefeller University for much of his career, shared the prize with Wendell M. Stanley and James B. Sumner. He also taught at the University of California at Berkeley and was the author of *Crystalline Enzymes;* d. Wickenburg, Ariz., May 27.

ODEKIRK, GLENN (81), U.S. aircraft manufacturer who designed and built the *Spruce Goose,* Howard Hughes's flying cargo boat. The *Spruce Goose,* made of wood and weighing 200 tons, was conceived as a way of evading German submarines during World War II. It flew only once (piloted by Hughes in 1947), and now serves as a museum in Long Beach, Calif. Odekirk was Hughes's friend and copilot and served as superintendent of the Hughes Aircraft Company; d. Las Vegas, Nev., Jan. 12.

PIRET, EDGAR LAMBERT (77), U.S. chemical engineer who held patents that led to the development of K rations issued to troops in World War II, reflective materials for highway signs, and methods of measuring pollution in air and water. A professor at the University of Minnesota and a consultant to Minne-

sota Mining and Manufacturing (3M), he was among the first scientists to be posted to a U.S. embassy, spending eight years in Paris in the 1960s to coordinate international scientific programs; d. Lexington, Mass., Sept. 24.

QUASTEL, JUDA H. (88), British-born Canadian biochemist who was among the discoverers of 2,4-D, a widely used herbicide that now is suspected of causing health problems. Quastel and two colleagues discovered the compound in 1941 while working for the British Agricultural Research Council. Besides its use in agriculture, it was a component of the defoliant Agent Orange used in Vietnam. Quastel also conducted research in chemical origins of mental disorders. In 1947 he moved to Canada, where he taught at McGill University and the University of British Columbia; d. Vancouver, B.C., Oct. 15.

RITTLER, M. CATHERINE (82), U.S. optic researcher who helped develop the ruby laser to treat eye disorders. She taught physiological optics at the Edward S. Harkness Eye Institute of Columbia University College of Physicians and Surgeons from 1936 to 1971; d. New York, N.Y., Sept. 17.

ROGERS, CARL R. (85), U.S. psychotherapist whose client-centered and humanistic approaches, presented in popular books, had a profound impact on psychotherapy. Rogers' theory of humanistic psychology held that therapy should emphasize a person's potential for growth rather than events of the past; his client-centered approach allowed the client, or patient, to direct the course of therapy. He was among the first to develop encounter groups, and he conducted such groups with Protestants and Roman Catholics in Northern Ireland and with blacks and whites in South Africa. Rogers taught at Ohio State University and the universities of Chicago and Wisconsin before founding the Center for Studies of the Person in La Jolla, Calif., in 1963. Among his popular books were *On Becoming a Person, Freedom to Learn, Personal Power,* and *A Way of Being;* d. La Jolla, Calif., Feb. 4.

SEVERNY, ANDREI B. (73), Soviet astronomer who was a pioneer in the setting up of observatories on earth-orbiting artificial satellites. He was the director of the Crimean Astrophysical Observatory and conducted extensive research on solar flares, particularly their relation to solar magnetic fields. Severny headed the International Astronomical Union from 1964 to 1970 and received the title Hero of Socialist Labor, the highest Soviet civilian award, in 1973; d. April 4.

SINCLAIR, DAVID (85), U.S. physicist who was an expert in aerosols. He helped develop an aerosol generator that was used to produce protective smoke screens for Allied troops in the Normandy invasion, and he later devised a way of measuring submicron aerosols for the detection of radon and other pollutants. Sinclair, who worked for Johns-Manville and the Department of Energy, was the son of the writer Upton Sinclair; d. New York, N.Y., Oct. 24.

STROHM, JOHN (75), U.S. journalist who was a founding editor of *National Wildlife* magazine. Before starting the magazine in 1962, he was a newspaper and magazine publisher in Woodstock, Ill., and was twice nominated for the Pulitzer Prize for articles about his travels to the Soviet Union (where he was the first U.S. journalist to travel unescorted after World War II) and China. He was also an adviser to the Department of Agriculture and a speechwriter on agricultural issues for President Dwight D. Eisenhower; d. Woodstock, Ill., Dec. 5.

WEI, H. R. (87), Chinese nuclear physicist who was an adviser to the Republic of China's mission to the United Nations from 1946 to 1963 and represented his country at conferences on the peaceful uses of nuclear energy and outer space. He later headed the department of physics at Bethany College in West Virginia; d. Honolulu, Hawaii, Jan. 2.

ZUELZER, WOLFGANG W. (77), German-born U.S. physician who was an expert on blood diseases and the first to treat childhood leukemia with chemotherapy. He worked for much of his career at the Child Research Center and Children's Hospital in Detroit, and in 1975 he became director of the division of blood diseases at the National Heart, Lung, and Blood Institute; d. Washington, D.C., March 20.

INDEX